microwave transmission design data

By Theodore Moreno

DOVER PUBLICATIONS INC. NEW YORK · NEW YORK

Manufactured in United States of America.

PREFACE

The purpose of this volume is to provide a reference handbook for radio engineers whose work is related to microwave systems or components. The subject matter deals with microwave transmission lines and associated components. No attempt is made to deal with related topics such as generation and reception, propagation, or measurement techniques.

The first three chapters deal with general transmission-line theory, which may be applied to all types of microwave transmission lines. These chapters are not intended to develop a thorough treatment of the theory, but are intended rather to deal with those aspects of the theory which are most useful at ultrahigh frequencies, and which may be inadequately covered in the average engineer's education.

The next three chapters cover the topics of coaxial lines and flexible cables, but again only from the ultrahigh-frequency point of view. An attempt has been made here, as in other parts of the book, to include the material which will prove most useful to the engineer whose work brings him in contact with these types of transmission lines.

Chapters 7 through 11 cover the subject of wave guides. The basic theory of wave guides is treated in a number of excellent texts which have appeared in recent years. This volume is intended to supplement these texts by providing information on practical structures and components; the type of information an engineer must have to design a transmission system employing wave guides.

Finally, Chap. 12 is a discussion of dielectric materials and their properties at microwave frequencies, and Chap. 13 deals with cavity resonators, which find extensive use at these frequencies.

This volume had its origins in 1943, in the Measurement Development Laboratory of the Sperry Gyroscope Co. At that time, the subject of microwave transmission lines had assumed considerable importance in connection with the wartime development of radar, and a great many engineers in a great many places were obtaining information of engineering importance. It was felt that a worth-while service would be performed by compiling these data and making them generally available.　This project grew in scope once it was under way, and culminated in the publication by Sperry in 1944 of a "Confidential" volume (subsequently declassified) titled "Microwave Transmission Design Data," which had wide distribution in the armed services, government laboratories, and private organizations.

The present volume is in a sense a revision of that earlier volume, although it has been almost completely rewritten and much new material has been added.　Four complete new chapters have been added, those dealing with transmission-line theory and flexible cables; and the material in the other chapters has been greatly revised and extended.　This has been done for two reasons: to take advantage of material which became available subsequent to the publication of the original volume, and because the present volume was designed from its inception to be a book, in contrast to the Sperry publication which was originally intended to take the form of loose-leaf notes.

The material in this volume has been drawn from a large number of sources, including publications, wartime reports of the M. I. T. Radiation Laboratory and other organizations, and the work of the author and many of his colleagues at Sperry.　Particular acknowledgment is made to W. W. Hansen, from whose unpublished notes much information was gleaned; to E. L. Ginzton, who inspired this work; and to H. E. Webber and W. T. Cooke, under whose direction the author worked while the present volume was in preparation.

THEODORE MORENO

CAMBRIDGE, MASS.
March, 1948

CONTENTS

CHAPTER 1

GENERAL CONSIDERATIONS
FOR MICROWAVE TRANSMISSION LINES

1. Microwaves

It is difficult to define precisely the portion of the electromagnetic spectrum termed "microwaves," but the low-frequency boundary is somewhere between 300 and 3,000 mc, and the high-frequency boundary somewhere in the millimeter region, where radio and infrared techniques begin to overlap. It is a portion of the spectrum where nearly all circuit components have dimensions that are an appreciable fraction of a wavelength or greater. For this reason transmission-line theory, particularly "long-line" theory, is well adapted to handling many engineering problems that arise at these frequencies.

2. The Nature of Transmission Lines

Definition.—A transmission line is a system of material boundaries forming a continuous path from one place to another and capable of directing the transmission of electromagnetic energy along this path. If the geometrical dimensions and constants of the materials are identical in all transverse sections, the line is said to be uniform. Any changes in the physical configuration of the transmission line are termed "nonuniformities" or "discontinuities" in the system.

Nature of Traveling Waves.—Electromagnetic energy is carried along a transmission line in the form of guided electromagnetic waves. These waves are composed of electric and magnetic fields that interact while varying periodically with time and that adjust their configurations to fit the material boundaries in a manner that satisfies Maxwell's equations. In general, the variation with time of the various electric and magnetic field components will be considered here as sinusoidal.

If the material boundaries of the transmission line are composed wholly or in part of conducting material, currents will in general flow in these conductors. At low frequencies, the transmission line is usually formed of two or more separated conductors, and the char acteristics of an electromagnetic wave being carried along the line are specified in terms of the voltage existing between the conductors

1

and the currents carried by them. Concepts arrived at in this manner are generally useful when extended to microwave frequencies but are often insufficient for complete understanding of the behavior of transmission lines at these frequencies. This is particularly true for hollow-pipe and dielectric wave guides, for in the former a single conductor is sufficient to guide electromagnetic waves, and in the latter no conducting boundaries whatsoever are required.

To obtain a more complete understanding of these systems, it is necessary to consider instead the fundamental nature and behavior of electromagnetic waves and the electric and magnetic fields that compose them. This does not mean that ordinary transmission-line theory should not be used with these systems. On the contrary, most engineers find that practical application of high-frequency transmission lines is most easily done in terms of this theory and is facilitated when the behavior of various components is expressed in terms of their equivalent lower frequency circuits.

Whenever analogues of this sort are used, it must be done with due consideration of the restrictions that have been imposed. Many of these restrictions can be pointed out, but others become apparent only as one gains familiarity with the microwave lines. For example, a narrow crack in a metallic shield that is unimportant at low frequencies may radiate large amounts of energy at microwave frequencies.

The following discussion will concern ordinary transmission-line theory. The validity of this theory when extended to microwaves will then be pointed out, and it will be shown how microwave components and structures can often be dealt with in terms of this theory.

3. Ordinary Transmission-line Theory

Consider a uniform transmission line that is composed of two separated conductors. If an electromagnetic wave is carried along the line (in the principal mode), a voltage V will exist between the conductors and a current I will flow in the conductors at all points in the line. The current I will encounter

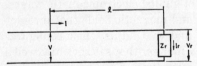

Fig. 1-1.—A uniform transmission line, illustrating the notation used in transmission-line equations.

an impedance Z per unit length, given by

$$Z = R + j\omega L$$

where R is the equivalent series resistance per unit length, taking into account all series loss elements, and L is the series inductance per unit length. The voltage V between the conductors appears across a shunt admittance Y per unit length, given by

$$Y = G + j\omega C$$

where G is the equivalent conductance per unit length, taking into account all shunt loss elements, and C is the shunt capacitance per unit length.

The four parameters R, L, G, and C will usually change slowly if at all with frequency.

The distribution of voltage and current along the line is best expressed in terms of two derived parameters. The first of these is the propagation constant γ, defined by

$$\gamma = \sqrt{ZY} = \sqrt{(R + j\omega L)(G + j\omega C)} \tag{1-1}$$

The propagation constant is in general a complex quantity and may, therefore, be divided into real and imaginary parts

$$\gamma = \alpha + j\beta$$

where α is the attenuation constant and β is the phase constant.

The physical significance of these quantities will be discussed later in further detail. For most high-frequency transmission lines, the phase angle of γ will be close to 90 deg, and γ will become a pure imaginary when R and G are zero, which occurs when there are no power-absorbing elements in the transmission line.

The second derived parameter that is important is the characteristic impedance Z_0, defined by

$$Z_0 = \sqrt{\frac{Z}{Y}} = \sqrt{\frac{R + j\omega L}{G + j\omega C}} \tag{1-2}$$

or its reciprocal, the characteristic admittance Y_0, defined by

$$Y_0 = \frac{1}{Z_0}$$

This is also a complex quantity, but in general it will be very nearly a pure real quantity.

At high frequencies, the resistance and conductance of the line are frequently neglected for purposes of calculation. When losses are small,

$$Z_0 \cong \sqrt{\frac{L}{C}}$$

The voltage V_r appears across the load impedance Z_r, and the current flowing through the load impedance is $I_r = V_r/Z_r$. At a distance l from the load, the voltage V across the transmission line and the current I flowing in the line are given by

$$V = V_r \cosh \gamma l + I_r Z_0 \sinh \gamma l \tag{1-3}$$

$$I = I_r \cosh \gamma l + \frac{V_r}{Z_0} \sinh \gamma l \tag{1-4}$$

These equations may be rewritten as

$$V = V_1 e^{\gamma l} + V_2 e^{-\gamma l} \tag{1-5}$$
$$I = I_1 e^{\gamma l} - I_2 e^{-\gamma l}$$

$$= \frac{V_1}{Z_0} e^{\gamma l} - \frac{V_2}{Z_0} e^{-\gamma l} \tag{1-6}$$

V_1 and V_2 are voltages, and I_1 and I_2 are currents the significance of which becomes apparent in the following discussion. The values of these various coefficients may be obtained from the following equations:

$$\frac{V_r}{I_r} = Z_r \tag{1-7}$$

$$V_r = V_1 + V_2 \tag{1-8}$$

$$I_r = I_1 - I_2 = \frac{V_1}{Z_0} - \frac{V_2}{Z_0} \tag{1-9}$$

It should be kept in mind that all voltages and currents are quantities that vary periodically with time. Consider, for example, the first term on the right-hand side of Eq. (1-5). The alternating voltage V_1 may be written

$$V_1 = V_{10} e^{j\omega t}$$

where V_{10} is defined as the peak amplitude of V_1. The first term then becomes

$$V_{10} e^{j\omega t} e^{\gamma l} = V_{10} e^{j\omega t} e^{(\alpha + j\beta)l}$$
$$= V_{10} e^{\alpha l} e^{j(\beta l + \omega t)}$$

The physical nature of this term is now apparent. It represents a wave train of voltage traveling along the transmission line toward the load (in the direction of decreasing l). The second term in Eq. (1-5) represents a wave train of voltage traveling in the opposite direction, away from the load. The corresponding two terms in Eq. (1-6) represent current waves traveling to and from the load. The amplitude and phase of each voltage wave are related to the values of the corresponding current wave by the characteristic impedance of the line Z_0, *i.e.*,

$$\frac{V_1}{I_1} = \frac{V_2}{I_2} = Z_0$$

A physical interpretation of the conditions that exist on a transmission line is now possible. The voltage and current that are measured at any point on the line may be said to result from the vector addition of two wave trains of voltage and current that are traveling along the line. The voltage and current of each wave train are related by the factor Z_0, the characteristic impedance of the line. One wave train is traveling toward the load and is referred to as the *incident* wave. The other wave train is traveling in the opposite direction along the line, away from the load and toward the generator, and is termed the *reflected* wave.

The relative amplitude of the incident and reflected waves is established at the load, where Eqs. (1-7), (1-8), and (1-9) must be satisfied. These equations may be solved to give

$$\frac{V_2}{V_1} = \frac{Z_r - Z_0}{Z_r + Z_0} \tag{1-10}$$

A very important conclusion to be drawn from Eq. (1-10) is that the *relative* amplitude and phase of the incident and reflected waves at any point on the line is affected only by impedance conditions on the *load* side of the point of measurement and is unaffected by impedances on the generator side of the point in question. The absolute magnitude of the incident and reflected waves will, of course, be determined in part by impedances on the generator side.

4. Validity of Ordinary Line Theory

If the transmission-line problem had been approached from the point of view of electromagnetic-field theory, it would have yielded a similar result. The answers would be in terms of electric field E and magnetic field H rather than in terms of voltage and current, but would have yielded the same concepts of traveling waves and characteristic impedance. The more rigorous approach of field theory would have given additional information, however, which greatly complicates the problem in some ways. But at the same time this additional information leads to a more thorough understanding of the behavior of all kinds of transmission lines.

It is found that there can exist on the transmission line not one traveling wave of a given frequency, but rather an infinite number of types of waves, or *modes*. Each of these possible modes of transmission has its own distinctive configuration of electric and magnetic fields, and all these configurations satisfy Maxwell's equations and fit the boundary conditions imposed by the transmission line. The infinite number of modes may be separated into three classes. If there are not more than two separated conductors, the first class consists of a single mode, termed the "principal" mode. The other two classes are both infinite in number and are commonly termed "transverse electric" and "transverse magnetic" modes.

The principal mode is distinguished from the infinite number of other (higher) modes in a number of ways. The following statements apply to uniform lines, assumed lossless except where otherwise noted:

1. Only the principal mode of transmission consists solely of electric and magnetic fields that are transverse to the direction of energy flow. It is a purely transverse wave. All other modes have field components in the direction of energy flow. For this reason, the principal mode is sometimes referred to as the transverse electromagnetic (TEM) wave. The higher modes will have components of either electric or magnetic field that are in the direction of energy flow. This leads to a means commonly used to distinguish the two families of higher modes. If the magnetic field has a component in the direction of energy transmission, the electric field will be everywhere transverse, and the waves having this characteristic are referred to as H waves or transverse electric (TE) waves. Modes of the other family have electric field components that are in the direction of transmission, the magnetic field is everywhere transverse, and the modes are termed E waves or transverse magnetic (TM) waves.

2. The transverse electromagnetic waves will transmit energy at all frequencies down to and including zero cycles per second (direct current). All the higher modes have low-frequency limits or cutoff frequencies below which energy will not be transmitted along the line. These cutoff frequencies are in general different for different modes. If the line is excited in one of these higher modes at a frequency below its cutoff frequency, there will be no real transmission of energy along the line and the fields will diminish very rapidly with increasing distance from the point of excitation.

3. To be capable of supporting a transverse electromagnetic wave, a transmission line must consist of two or more separated conductors. Coaxial lines are the most common examples of this type of transmission line at microwave frequencies. The higher modes of transmission can exist on such a line, but they can also be supported by a transmission line that has only a single conducting boundary, or none at

all, and is not capable of supporting the principal mode of transmission. Hollow-pipe wave guides will therefore support the higher modes, but not the principal mode.

4. When field penetration into the conductors is neglected, which is permissible at high frequencies, the instantaneous electric-field configuration of the principal mode at any point on the line is always the same as would exist if only a static charge properly distributed were present on the line.

5. By neglecting the effect of losses in the conductors, and assuming a uniform dielectric medium separating the conductors, the velocity of propagation of the principal mode is the same as the velocity of propagation of an unguided plane wave traveling in the medium that separates the conductors. All the higher modes, at frequencies higher than their cutoff frequencies, will have phase velocities in excess of this amount which approach infinity as the frequency approaches their respective cutoff frequencies. The group velocities of these higher modes will always be less than the velocity of the unguided plane wave and will approach zero as the frequency approaches cutoff for the respective modes.

6. For a high-frequency line with finite losses, assuming that the properties of the dielectric and conductors remain constant, the attenuation of the principal mode will always decrease with decreasing frequency. With the higher modes, however, the attenuation will increase rapidly with decreasing frequency as the cutoff frequency is approached.

7. In the high-frequency region, assuming that losses are zero and that the dielectric properties remain constant, the characteristic impedance of the line for the principal mode will be independent of frequency. The characteristic impedances of the higher modes will in general differ from each other and from the impedance of the principal wave and will depend upon the ratio of the operating frequency to the cutoff frequency of the respective modes.

5. The Effects of Below-cutoff Modes on a Transmission Line

Higher Order Modes (Local Waves) at Launching Elements and Discontinuities.—A practical transmission line is nearly always designed so that it is able to carry energy in only one mode of transmission. For this reason, the line is restricted in size so that only the principal mode (or only the dominant mode in the case of wave guides) can transmit energy, and the line is then below cutoff for all the infinity of higher modes. This does not mean that these higher modes can be neglected in the determination of operating characteristics of a transmission line.

Any physical structure that launches a traveling wave in a line will generally excite a large number of modes at the point of excitation. Only the modes that are above cutoff, usually only one mode, are able to carry energy down the line, and the other modes that are below cutoff are unable to carry any real energy down the line. They attenuate rapidly with distance from the point of excitation and are

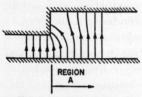

usually negligible at a distance roughly equal to the transverse dimensions of the line. The attenuation is reactive rather than dissipative, and there is no energy consumption in these below-cutoff waves. Nevertheless, they may be of large amplitude in the immediate vicinity of the launching structure, and contribute greatly to the reactive component of its impedance. At sufficiently low frequencies, when all the higher order waves are a long way from

FIG. 1-2.—Fringing electric fields at a discontinuity in a parallel-plane transmission line, resulting from higher order modes excited at the discontinuity.

cutoff, they add to give the fringing fields that are predicted by static-field theory.

The higher order modes may also be set up by a discontinuity in the line. If there is an abrupt change in cross section, and it is not possible to meet the boundary conditions at the discontinuity by addition of components of the principal and above-cutoff modes only, below-cutoff modes will be excited at the discontinuity. Consider for example a step in a parallel-plane transmission line, as illustrated in Fig. 1-2. The line may be restricted in size so that only the principal mode of transmission can carry energy down the line. But this principal wave alone is unable to satisfy the boundary conditions imposed by the step discontinuity. The distortion and fringing fields, which exist principally in the region A, result from higher modes that are excited at the discontinuity, but which attenuate rapidly with distance.

This is a reactive attenuation, and energy is not dissipated in these higher modes. Nevertheless, there is energy storage in these fringing fields similar to the energy storage in a reactive circuit element. It is possible to show that there is a net energy storage in the electric fields if the higher order modes that are excited are of the transverse magnetic (TM) type. If the higher order modes are of the transverse electric (TE) type, the net energy storage will be in the magnetic fields.

Equivalent Circuits of Discontinuities.—We shall consider here transmission lines which are above cutoff for only a single mode of transmission. If there is a plane discontinuity at the junction of two such transmission lines at which additional below-cutoff waves are excited, the effect of this discontinuity may be taken into account by replacing it with an equivalent reactive network for purposes of calculation.[1] This equivalent circuit is valid only at a distance from the discontinuity where the below-cutoff waves are of negligible amplitude. In the general case, an unsymmetrical tee network is required to account for the discontinuity.

A convenient approximation, which is rigorously correct in many problems of practical interest, leads to an equivalent circuit of an ideal transformer shunted by a simple reactance. Where the discontinuity consists of a thin obstacle with no change of cross section of the line, the equivalent circuit may be reduced to a simple shunt reactance.

If *TM* waves are excited by a thin obstacle, the discontinuity will be equivalent to a simple shunt capacity, and if *TE* waves are excited, the equivalent circuit is a shunt inductance. In general, both types of higher order waves are excited. Resonance effects are then possible, and both series and parallel resonance effects may be expected from different kinds of discontinuities.

One effect of these shunt admittances set up by discontinuities is that the current flowing down the line is divided and part of the current flows through the discontinuity reactance. The voltage is still continuous when the discontinuity is equivalent to a reactive element in parallel with the line.

Effect of Changing Frequency.—If the higher order modes are far from cutoff, the equivalent circuit of a simple discontinuity is a shunt capacity or inductance the magnitude of which is nearly independent of frequency. But as the frequency increases so that the line approaches cutoff for the higher modes, the magnitude of the equivalent circuit elements will change, and resonance effects can be expected as the higher modes reach cutoff.[2]

Interaction between Multiple Discontinuities.—In a simple step discontinuity, as shown in Fig. 1-2, the fringing fields are principally

[1] See, for example, SCHELKUNOFF, S. A., "Electromagnetic Waves," pp. 490–494, D. Van Nostrand Company, Inc., New York, 1943; WHINNERY, J. R., and H. W. JAMIESON, Equivalent Circuits for Discontinuities in Transmission Lines, *Proc. Inst. Radio Engrs.*, **32** (No. 2), pp. 98–114 (1944); MILES, J. W., The Equivalent Circuit for a Plane Discontinuity in a Cylindrical Wave Guide, *Proc. Inst. Radio Engrs.*, **34** (No. 10), pp. 728–742 (1946).

[2] See, for example, WHINNERY and JAMIESON, *loc. cit.*

in the region A, if the higher modes are far from cutoff, and only extend on one side of the step.   When two steps are placed close together, they may be treated as separate circuit elements if the fringing fields set up by each step are in separate regions and, therefore, do not interact with each other.   But if the fringing fields tend to occupy the same region, they will interact with each other and the equivalent susceptance of each discontinuity will be modified by the presence of the other.[3]   Examples of some double discontinuities that do not

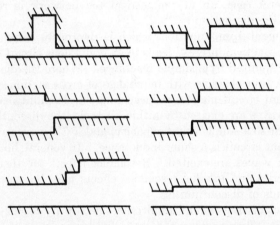

DOUBLE DISCONTINUITIES   **DOUBLE DISCONTINUITIES**
THAT INTERACT   **THAT DO NOT INTERACT**

Fig. 1-3.—Multiple discontinuities in a parallel-plane transmission line.

interact to a first approximation and some that do interact are shown in Fig. 1-3.   The required modification of the equivalent circuits of the individual steps will increase with increasing interaction of the fringing fields and will, therefore, increase as the steps are moved closer together.   The presence of a short circuit in the region occupied by the fringing fields of a discontinuity will also modify the equivalent circuit.   In fact, any structure that is close enough to a discontinuity to affect the higher order fields will have a corresponding effect upon the equivalent circuit that accounts for these fields.

[3] See, for example, WHINNERY and JAMIESON, *loc. cit.*

CHAPTER 2

ATTENUATION, IMPEDANCE MATCHING, AND REFLECTIONS ON TRANSMISSION LINES

1. Attenuation in Transmission Lines

General Relationships.—An electromagnetic wave being carried by a transmission line is continuously attenuated or weakened by lossy elements in the line. This is apparent from the traveling-wave terms that appear in Eqs. (1-5) and (1-6), *e.g.*, the incident voltage wave $V_1 e^{\gamma l}$. If the propagation constant γ is split into its real and imaginary parts

$$\gamma = \sqrt{(R + j\omega L)(G + j\omega C)} \qquad (2\text{-}1)$$
$$= \alpha + j\beta$$

then this term for incident voltage becomes

$$V_1 e^{\alpha l} e^{j\beta l}$$

The rate at which the wave attenuates with decreasing l is given by the factor $e^{\alpha l}$. The quantity α is therefore called the "attenuation constant." When α is used as above to measure the decrease in intensity of a traveling wave, it will be in units of nepers per unit length. To express the attenuation in the more common units of decibels per unit length, α in nepers should be multiplied by the constant 8.69.

$$\alpha \ (\text{db/unit length}) = 8.69\alpha \ (\text{nepers/unit length})$$

When the attenuation is small, it may be expressed by the approximate formula

$$\alpha = \frac{R}{2Z_0} + \frac{G}{2Y_0} \qquad \text{nepers/unit length} \qquad (2\text{-}2)$$

where R is the resistance per unit length, G is the conductance per unit length, Z_0 is the characteristic impedance, and Y_0 is the characteristic admittance of the transmission line.

Special Cases Where One or the Other Parameter Is Supplying Losses. CASE 1: The series resistance per unit length R only is not zero. $R \neq 0$. $G = 0$.

Defining $Q = \omega L/R$, the following formulas hold approximately:

11

1. The loss per wave length is small (R is small):

$$\alpha = \frac{\beta}{2Q} = \frac{R}{2Z_0} \tag{2-3}$$

2. The loss per wave length is large (R is large):

$$\alpha = \frac{\omega \sqrt{LC}}{\sqrt{2Q}} \left(1 - \frac{Q}{2}\right) \cong \frac{\omega \sqrt{LC}}{\sqrt{2Q}} \tag{2-4}$$

Assumption (1) is generally valid for microwave transmission, but assumption (2) is useful for attenuators.

CASE 2: The shunt losses only are not zero. $G \neq 0$, $R = 0$.

This is infrequently true in practice, but in most solid dielectric lines the shunt losses exceed the series losses at microwave frequencies. Q is defined here as $Q = \omega C/G$.

1. The shunt losses are small (G is small):

$$\alpha = \frac{\beta}{2Q} = \frac{G}{2Y_0} \tag{2-5}$$

2. The shunt losses are large (G is large):

$$\alpha = \frac{\omega \sqrt{LC}}{\sqrt{2Q}} \left(1 - \frac{Q}{2}\right) \cong \frac{\omega \sqrt{LC}}{\sqrt{2Q}} \tag{2-6}$$

Causes of Attenuation and Numerical Formulas.—There are five possible causes of energy loss in microwave transmission lines: (1) ohmic losses resulting from currents flowing in conductors of finite resistivity, (2) hysteresis losses in ferromagnetic conductors, (3) dielectric losses resulting from imperfections in the dielectric medium through which the electromagnetic fields travel, (4) radiation of energy from the line, (5) reflections caused by impedance mismatches.   Microwave transmission lines are usually shielded well enough so that the radiation does not contribute appreciably to the attenuation.   The problem of reflections is dealt with in Sec. 2-2.

Conductor Losses.—At microwave frequencies, the conduction current flowing in the conductors is concentrated in the surface layer. The current density is a maximum at the surface and decreases exponentially with depth into the conductors.   The depth at which the current density has fallen to $1/e$ of its surface value is known as the "skin depth δ."   This skin depth is a function of frequency and also of the conductor material.   It is given by the formula

$$\delta = \frac{1}{2\pi} \sqrt{\frac{\lambda \rho}{30\mu}} \tag{2-7}$$

where ρ is the resistivity of the conductor in ohm-centimeters, μ is the permeability of the conductor, λ is the free-space wavelength, and δ is the skin depth in centimeters. For copper the permeability is unity, the resistivity is $\rho = 1.72 \times 10^{-6}$ ohm-cm, and the skin depth is $\delta = 1.2 \times 10^{-4}$ cm for $\lambda = 10$ cm.

The losses that result from the current being concentrated near the surface are the same as if the total current were of uniform density to

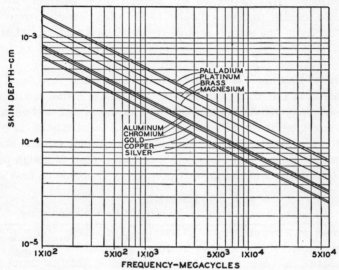

FIG. 2-1.—Skin depth as a function of frequency for a number of different metals.

a depth δ. Because of this the conductor losses in a transmission line operating in the principal mode increase as the square root of increasing frequency.

The skin depth δ is plotted as a function of frequency in Fig. 2-1 for a number of different metals. These are ideal values which are derived from handbook values of conductivity. Because of skin effect, the attenuation resulting from conductor losses in high-frequency transmission lines will vary as the square root of the resistivity of the metals and will also increase as the square root of increasing permeability. Table 2-1 gives the resistivity of a number of metals and also their high-frequency attenuation as compared with the attenuation of copper.

Effect of Machining.—The values in Table 2-1 are again standard handbook values of resistivity and represent minimum limits of experimental results at microwave frequencies. Because of the surface concentration of the current, the condition of the metal surface has considerable effect upon the attenuation, which is nearly always higher than that predicted by theory. The difference will generally be small at the low-frequency end of the microwave spectrum; but at the higher frequencies, any surface roughness will tend to increase the losses. At 25,000 mc, a well-machined surface will frequently have only two-thirds the theoretical conductivity of an ideal surface. This difference will depend upon whether the toolmarks are parallel or perpendicular to the direction of current flow, as well as upon the smoothness of the machined surface. Attenuation will be less if the current flow is parallel to the toolmarks, but for most applications this can be ignored.

Effect of Plating.—The skin depth in most metals is so small that, if one metal is plated on another to a thickness of a thousandth of an inch, essentially all the current will flow in the plated surface metal. But a variety of factors will cause the effective resistivity of the plated metal to be somewhat higher than its low-frequency value. For one thing, plated surfaces are porous to a certain extent, although polishing or burnishing will reduce this porosity. The type of base metal

TABLE 2-1
RELATIVE ATTENUATION IN METALS AT HIGH FREQUENCIES

Metal	Resistivity (ohm-cm)	Attenuation relative to copper
Aluminum	2.828×10^{-6}	1.28
Brass	6.4–8.4	2
Cadmium	7.54	2.09
Chromium	2.6	1.23
Copper	1.724	1.00
Gold	2.44	1.19
Lead	22	3.57
Magnesium	4.6	1.63
Manganin	44	5.05
Palladium	11	2.52
Phosphor bronze	10.5	2.47
Platinum	10	2.41
Rhodium	5	1.71
Silver	1.629	0.97
Tin	11.5	2.58
Zinc	6.1	1.89

upon which the surface metal is plated will affect the electrical qualities of the surface, as well as its adhesion and corrosion resistance.

The losses in the plated metal will be affected by aging, tarnishing, and corrosion and may vary somewhat in a random manner from day to day. The surface finish of the base metal will also have an effect. The plating technique will have considerable effect, but even samples of plating made in the same bath at the same time upon the same base metal will usually have losses that are not identical. Accurate measurements are difficult to make. For these reasons, exceptions can be drawn to almost any general statements that are made about losses in plated surfaces, but the following remarks are usually applicable.

The difference between theoretical and measured losses will usually increase with increasing frequency. But at even the highest frequencies, the losses in a high-quality plated surface, especially when polished, will be approximately equal to the losses in a well-machined surface of solid metal. Frequently a plating with the best electrical characteristics does not have the best mechanical characteristics. The effective resistivity of a plated surface at 10,000 or 20,000 mc will frequently be twice again as large as the theoretical value, but it seldom exceeds five times the theoretical value unless the plating is of poor quality or has corroded. For best results, the thickness of a plated surface should be several times the skin depth (*e.g.*, 0.5 mil minimum is recommended for silver plate at 9,000 mc).

Effect of Insulating Coatings.—If the surface is coated with a thin protective layer of high-resistance material, the conduction current will flow under this layer in the base metal, and the attenuation will not be greatly affected by the presence of the insulating layer. For example, if aluminum wave guide is anodized, the losses will not be greatly different, and may even be less than in the unanodized guide (which, of course, still has a very thin layer of nonconducting aluminum oxide on the surface). Covering a conducting surface with a thin coating of lacquer will also usually have little effect upon the losses in the surface and may greatly improve its corrosion resistance.

Dielectric Losses.—Any dielectric or insulating medium other than a vacuum will absorb part of the energy from an electromagnetic wave passing through that medium. This loss may be taken into account by considering the dielectric constant ϵ as complex and of the form

$$\epsilon = \epsilon' - j\epsilon'' \tag{2-8}$$

where ϵ' is known as the real part and ϵ'' the complex part of the dielectric constant. The loss tangent of the dielectric is defined as

$$\tan \delta = \frac{\epsilon''}{\epsilon'} \tag{2-9}$$

Usually δ is small, and it can then be said that the loss tangent is approximately equal to the power factor of a condenser using the dielectric. The true power factor is defined as

$$\text{Power factor} = \cos\theta \qquad (2\text{-}10)$$

with

$$\theta = 90° - \delta$$

The dielectric constant and power factor of many materials may vary with frequency over the microwave spectrum. The properties of dielectric materials are discussed in further detail in Chap. 12.

If the dielectric constant and power factor of an insulator remain constant with changing frequency, the dielectric losses in a transmission line operating in the principal mode with the given insulator separating the conductors will increase linearly with frequency. It was noted above that conductor losses in such a line increase only as the square root of increasing frequency, and for this reason dielectric losses become increasingly important with respect to conductor losses at higher frequencies. Over most of the microwave frequency band, the dielectric losses in a solid dielectric line will be greater than the conductor losses for even the best dielectrics. For this reason, a solid dielectric is seldom used when low attenuation is desired—air dielectric is preferred.

Corrosion by Salt Spray.[1]—Experiments in which a section of wave guide is exposed to a salt spray for periods up to 200 hr indicate that the attenuation in the guide can usually be expected to increase as a result of this treatment. The amount of increase will, of course, depend greatly upon the material of the guide and upon the finish or plating. The increase in attenuation is usually small in unplated brass guide. If the brass guide is plated with any of the standard finishes, such as silver or gold, its attenuation will be less, but the relative increase of attenuation resulting from exposure to the salt spray will be greater. The attenuation in unprotected aluminum guide will increase enormously when the guide is subjected to a salt-spray test, but an anodizing coat will greatly increase the guide's resistance to corrosion. Various plated coatings have also been found beneficial in improving the resistance of aluminum guide to corrosion, but in general it will always be inferior to brass guide in this respect. Coatings of protective varnish or lacquer can be of great benefit to either aluminum or brass guide.

[1] WALKER, R. M., X-Band Waveguide Corrosion Proofing, M.I.T. Radiation Laboratory, Rept. S-29, Oct. 6, 1945.

Corrosion by Spark Discharge.[2]—A metal conductor will corrode when exposed to a spark discharge, such as might occur inside a wave guide or coaxial line carrying high power. The extent of the corrosion will depend upon the metal and upon the gaseous dielectric, and also

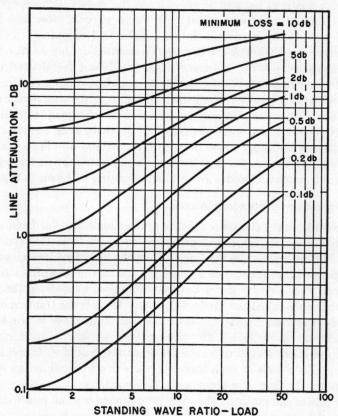

Fig. 2-2.—The increase in transmission-line attenuation caused by terminating the line in a mismatched load.

upon whether the gaseous dielectric is dry or moist. A compromise must be made between dielectric strength and corrosion resistance. Dry helium, which does not corrode any metal when activated by a spark discharge, has a relatively poor dielectric strength. Dry nitrogen has intermediate values of both dielectric strength and corrosion resistance. Freon No. 12, which has great dielectric strength, will

[2] PEARSALL, C. S., Report on Corrosion of Copper, Brass, and Aluminum by Gaseous Dielectrics, M.I.T. Radiation Laboratory, Rept. 53-17, Jan. 13, 1943.

cause serious corrosion when activated by a spark discharge, especially in aluminum lines.

The results of a number of tests of protective coatings for brass and aluminum lines indicate that, with the exception of paraffin, the protective coatings have little effect upon the resistance to spark corrosion. Plating the base metal with silver or gold does not help; because the plating is porous, the base metal still corrodes.

Increase in Attenuation When the Transmission Line Is Not Properly Terminated.—When a transmission line is not terminated in its characteristic impedance, there will be two traveling waves on the line, one carrying power toward the load and one carrying power away from the load. The net power delivered to the load will be the difference between the power contained in the two waves, but the transmission line will absorb power from both waves, and the effective attenuation will be increased. The increase in line attenuation for a given minimum attenuation and a given load mismatch is shown in Fig. 2-2.

2. Reflections and Standing Waves

The fields that exist on a uniform transmission line far from a discontinuity may in general be considered to result from two traveling waves that are present on the line.[3] One, the "incident wave," carries power toward the impedance at the load end of the transmission line. The other carries power in the opposite direction, away from the load, and is therefore called the "reflected wave," for it is the fraction of the incident wave that is reflected from the load impedance of the transmission line.

Both of these traveling waves are attenuated as they travel along the line. The phase of each traveling wave is a linear function of the position on the line, the more advanced portions of the wave being more retarded in phase. The relative amplitude and phase of the two traveling waves are established at the load impedance.

Characteristics of Standing Waves.—The presence of two traveling waves gives rise to standing waves along the line. The voltage and current (or electric and magnetic fields) vary periodically with distance. The points of maximum field strength are found where the two traveling waves add in phase, and the minimums are found where the two waves are in opposing phase. If the two traveling waves are equal in strength, the minima will fall to zero. If the reflected wave is smaller than the incident wave, the minima will be finite, and the ratio between

---

[3] This assumes that the size of the line and its excitation are so chosen that only one mode of propagation is carrying energy along the line.

maximum and minimum will decrease as the reflected wave becomes relatively weaker compared with the incident wave.

The successive maxima of these standing waves are spaced apart by a half wavelength. The maxima of the voltage standing waves coincide with the minima of the current standing waves; *i.e.*, the voltage standing waves are displaced one-quarter wavelength along the line from the current standing waves. Correspondingly,

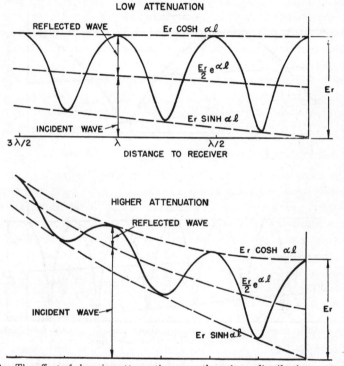

FIG. 2-3.—The effect of changing attenuation upon the voltage distribution on an open-circuited transmission line.

of course, the standing waves of electric field are displaced one-quarter wavelength along the line from the standing waves of magnetic field.

Effect of Line Attenuation and Phase Velocity.—The rate at which the individual wave trains decay is determined by the attenuation constant of the traveling waves. The effect of changing this attenuation constant is shown in Fig. 2-3. If the attenuation is zero, the standing-wave pattern is independent of position along the line. But if the attenuation is appreciable, the reflected wave attenuates with increasing distance from the load, while the incident wave is stronger.

The standing-wave pattern therefore becomes less pronounced with increasing distance from the receiver.

For high-frequency low-loss lines, the phase constant will be a linear function of frequency if the line is operating in the principal mode; otherwise it will be a more complex function. The effect of changing the phase constant while leaving the attenuation constant unchanged is shown in Fig. 2-4. The envelope of the standing-wave

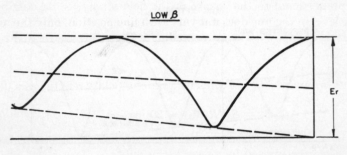

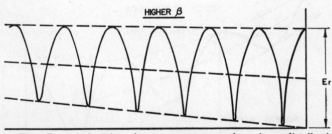

FIG. 2-4.—The effect of changing phase constant upon the voltage distribution on an open-circuited transmission line.

pattern remains unchanged, but the distance between successive maxima decreases with increasing phase constant.

Standing-wave Ratio (Definition of).—When the attenuation in the line is sufficiently low so that the standing-wave pattern is essentially independent of position along the line, the concept of standing-wave ratio is applicable. The standing-wave ratio (SWR) is defined as the ratio of maximum to minimum field strength as the position along the line is varied through a distance of at least a half wavelength. Several ways of expressing this ratio have been used. Sometimes the ratio of field strengths is taken as always less than unity. But usually the ratio of the field strengths is expressed directly as a ratio greater than unity and is called "voltage standing-wave ratio ($VSWR$ or σ)." This is the method in most common usage and will be adhered to in this book. Another method that is sometimes used arises from the fact that the detectors used in instruments that measure standing waves are frequently square law (*e.g.*, low-level crystal detectors and hot-wire detectors). The ratio of maximum to minimum meter reading is called "power standing-wave ratio ($PSWR$)," as the readings are then proportional to the square of the field strengths. Actually, the power level in the line does not vary with line position, only the impedance level changes. The two standing-wave ratios are related by

$$PSWR = \sigma^2 \tag{2-11}$$

A third method is to express the ratio of field strengths as a decibel ratio

$$SWR(\text{db}) = 20 \log_{10} \sigma \tag{2-12}$$

This is, of course, a technically improper use of the term decibel, which is correctly used for power ratios only.

The points of maximum field strength along the line $E_{\max}$ are found where the two traveling waves add in phase

$$E_{\max} = |E_1| + |E_2| \tag{2-13}$$

and the minima where they tend to cancel

$$E_{\min} = |E_1| - |E_2| \tag{2-14}$$

The standing-wave ratio σ is given by

$$\sigma = \frac{E_{\max}}{E_{\min}} = \frac{|E_1| + |E_2|}{|E_1| - |E_2|} = \frac{1 + \dfrac{|E_2|}{|E_1|}}{1 - \dfrac{|E_2|}{|E_1|}} \tag{2-15}$$

The ratio E_2/E_1 is commonly known as the "reflection coefficient (ρ)." Equation (2-15) may be rewritten to give ρ in terms of σ as follows:

$$|\rho| = \frac{\sigma - 1}{\sigma + 1} \tag{2-16}$$

Relation between Standing Waves and Impedance Matching.—An incident wave traveling down a uniform transmission line will be reflected in part at any point where it encounters an impedance other than the impedance of the line on which it travels, and standing waves will then be set up on the line on the input side of the reflecting impedance. The magnitude and phase of this reflection will depend upon the amplitude and phase of the reflecting impedance. If an arbitrary load of impedance Z_r is used to terminate a line of characteristic impedance Z_0, the ratio of the reflected to incident wave will be given by

$$\frac{E_2}{E_1} = \frac{Z_r - Z_0}{Z_r + Z_0} \tag{2-17}$$

This is an equation involving complex quantities, and the ratio E_2/E_1

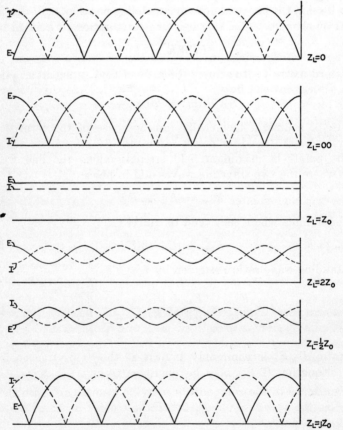

Fig. 2-5.—Standing waves of voltage and current on a lossless transmission line with various load impedances.

will give not only the relative magnitude but also the phase difference at the load of the electric fields associated with the incident and reflected waves. All the incident wave will be absorbed in the load impedance when $Z_r = Z_0$.

A number of typical standing-wave patterns that may be set up on uniform lossless transmission lines are illustrated in Fig. 2-5. It is seen that the standing-wave ratio is infinite when the load impedance is zero, infinite, or a pure reactance. None of these load impedances is capable of absorbing electromagnetic energy from the incident wave, and the two traveling waves are therefore equal in magnitude. It is apparent, however, that the standing-wave patterns are distinguished from one another by their phase with respect to the load impedance. When the load impedance is zero, no voltage can be developed across it, and the two traveling waves of voltage must cancel one another at the load, while the corresponding current waves will add. The standing waves of electric field are therefore a minimum at the load.

The converse is true for a load of infinite impedance, through which no current can flow. The current waves will therefore cancel at the load and the voltage waves add, giving a voltage maximum at the load. A capacitive load is equivalent to an additional length of open-circuited line, while an inductive load is equivalent to an additional length of short-circuited line.

Load impedances that have a resistive component will absorb some fraction of the incident load and reflect the rest. If the load impedance is real and greater than the characteristic impedance Z_0, the phase of the standing waves will be the same as for the open-circuited line. If the load impedance is real and less than Z_0, the phase of the standing waves will be the same as for the short-circuited line. For a load impedance equal to Z_0, there will be no standing waves on the line, as this load impedance absorbs all the energy of the incident wave.

Reasons for Impedance Matching.—An arbitrary microwave transmission system is composed of a number of component parts, and associated with these components will be lengths of low-loss transmission line that are likely to be electrically "long" although physically short. To know the power transfer between the component parts, the impedance of the components must be known, and also the laws governing the power transfer between these components as a function of their impedance.

In most microwave systems, the impedance of many component parts is made equal to the impedance of the transmission line between the components. When this is done, the component or "load" is said to be "matched" to the line. There are several reasons for matching components to the interconnecting transmission line. Some of these are as follows:

1. If the generator and load are both matched to the transmission line between them, the generator will always deliver maximum power to the load whatever the length of line. If the load and generator do not match the line, the power delivered to the load by the generator will then depend upon the length of line between them and, in general, will be less than the maximum power that the generator is capable of delivering. This does not take into account line losses.

2. If a generator and load whose impedances are not equal to that of a long interconnecting transmission line are matched to each other by the proper length of mismatched resonant line, this match will be good only at a single frequency, or over a narrow band of frequencies. But if both generator and load are matched to the interconnecting line, they will be matched to each other at all frequencies.

3. Having the load match the transmission line will minimize losses in the transmission line.

4. Having the load match the transmission line keeps the possibility of voltage breakdown in the line at a minimum.

Techniques of Impedance Matching.—Components of a microwave transmission system that are designed to absorb or transmit energy are usually matched to the interconnecting transmission lines by means of some kind of reactive impedance matching network. The components of these matching networks may in themselves be lengths of transmission line, or they may take the form of diaphragms, holes, rods, etc., whose behavior at microwave frequencies is equivalent to the action of more conventional radio components at lower frequencies. Sometimes the impedance-matching network is a structure in itself, usually tunable, which may be placed between the transmission line and the component that it is desired to match to the line. This sort of "impedance transformer" is especially valuable in laboratory or bench setups.

Frequently the elements of the impedance-matching network are built into the component, sometimes adjustable and sometimes not. In transmission systems that are designed for field service, the aim is usually to have each component fitted with fixed reactance elements where they are necessary to match the impedance of the component to that of the interconnecting lines.

Power Lost in the Reflected Wave.—The reflected wave on a transmission line may be considered as the fraction of the incident wave that is reflected from the load impedance and carrying that fraction of power not absorbed by the load impedance from the incident wave. Since the power associated with each of these traveling waves varies as the square of their field strengths, the per cent of power reflected from an arbitrary load impedance is given by

$$\text{Per cent of power reflected} = 100 \left| \frac{E_2}{E_1} \right|^2$$

where E_1 is the voltage associated with the incident wave and E_2 is the voltage associated with the reflected wave. The extent to which the line and load are mismatched is usually determined experi-

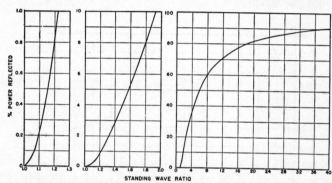

Fig. 2-6.—The per cent of the incident power reflected from a mismatched load as a function of the standing-wave ratio on the input transmission line.

mentally by measuring the standing-wave ratio in the input line. The relation between the percentage of power reflected and the standing-wave ratio is given by

$$\text{Percentage of power reflected} = 100 \left(\frac{\sigma - 1}{\sigma + 1} \right)^2 \qquad (2\text{-}18)$$

where σ is the voltage standing-wave ratio. The relationship expressed in this formula is plotted in Fig. 2-6.

Decrease on Power Transfer with Mismatch between Generator and Load.—Another way of looking at this problem is to consider the generator as having an internal impedance equal to the impedance of the line, and therefore delivering its maximum power output to a load whose impedance is that of the line. Terminating the line with a mismatched load will result in some impedance other than that of the line being presented to the generator, with a corresponding decrease in power output. (For a detailed discussion of impedance relationships on a transmission line, see Chap. 3.)

If the generator will deliver its maximum possible output to the impedance Z_0, the per cent of this maximum possible power that will be delivered to an arbitrary load Z_L is given by

Per cent of maximum possible power delivered

$$= 100 \; \frac{4RR_0}{(R_0 + R_L + jX_L)^2} \quad (2\text{-}19)$$

In this expression, Z_0 being a pure resistance is called R_0, and

$$Z_L = R_L + jX_L$$

This gives the same results for net power transfer as the equations of the previous paragraph.

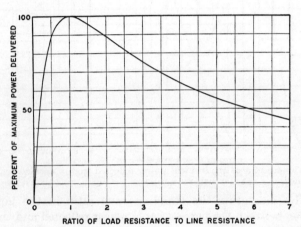

FIG. 2-7.—Variation of power transfer from transmission line to load impedance as a function of changing load resistance, with zero load reactance.

For a load that is purely resistive, the percentage of maximum possible power delivered to the load by a generator matched to the line is given by Fig. 2-7. For a load with resistance that is equal to the line impedance, but with reactance that is finite, the percentage of maximum possible power delivered to the load is given in Fig. 2-8. A reactance mismatch is seen to be more serious than a resistance mismatch of the same magnitude.

Power Delivered When Neither Generator Nor Load Is Matched to the Transmission Line.—A more general case than that considered previously is encountered when neither the generator nor the load is matched to the interconnecting transmission line. When this is true, the power delivered by the generator to the load will depend upon the length of line between the generator and load, as well as upon the impedance of the load and the internal impedance of the generator. If the generator may be considered as a source of voltage in series with a linear impedance,[4] it will deliver its maximum power output into a load impedance that is the complex conjugate of its own internal impedance. If it is required to deliver its maximum power output into a matched transmission line of different impedance, an impedance transformer must be placed between the generator and the transmission line in order to maximize the generator output.

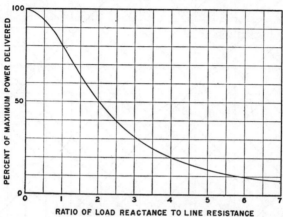

Fig. 2-8.—Decrease in power transfer from transmission line to load impedance as a function of load reactance. Resistance component of load maintained equal to characteristic impedance of transmission line.

This transformer may be avoided, and maximum power may be delivered to the terminal load (neglecting line losses) if the impedance of the load is tuned so that the impedance presented to the generator is the optimum load impedance of the generator. Of course, the load will no longer match the line, and there will be a reflected wave present, as indicated by standing waves on the line. But in spite of this reflected wave, the net power delivered to the load will be increased over the power that would be delivered to a load that matched the line, because of the increased generator output.

If the internal impedance of the generator is equal to that of the transmission line, the strength of the incident wave on the transmission line will remain constant as the load impedance is varied, and maximum power will be delivered to a load that matches the line. But if the generator impedance is not equal to the line impedance, the strength of the incident wave will depend upon the load impedance presented to the generator, and maximum power will be delivered into a mismatched load.

[4] Most microwave oscillators will not act as constant impedance generators unless followed by a lossy attenuator.

At microwave frequencies, the impedance of the load is usually found by measuring the standing-wave ratio in the line feeding the load, while the internal impedance of the generator may frequently be found by removing the source of power and measuring the standing-wave ratio in the line with a signal being fed into the generator from

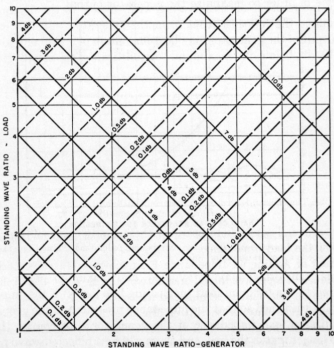

Fig. 2-9.—Possible loss in delivered power when neither generator nor load is matched to the interconnecting transmission line. Solid lines represent the worst possible loss, broken lines the least possible loss relative to maximum capabilities of generator.

the load end of the line.   Maximum power output from the generator will be found when the standing-wave ratios of the generator and load are properly phased and equal.   For arbitrary standing-wave ratios, the generator output will decrease by an amount depending upon the phase of the standing waves.   The range of decrease in power (below the maximum capabilities of the generator) that can be expected with loads of arbitrary phase is given in Fig. 2-9.   In this figure the ordinate is standing-wave ratio looking into the load, while the abscissa is standing-wave ratio looking into the generator.   The solid lines indicate the greatest decrease in power delivered from the generator that will be found with given standing-wave ratios, while the broken lines indicate the least possible decrease of power from the generator. The actual decrease in generator output will fall somewhere between these limits.

For example, if a standing-wave ratio $\sigma = 2$ was seen looking into the load, and $\sigma = 3$ was seen looking into the generator, the position of the intersection of these values with respect to the diagonal lines determines the loss in output from the generator. In this example, the output of the generator may be a maximum of 3.1 db or a minimum of 0.19 db below its maximum capabilities. The actual generator

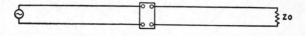

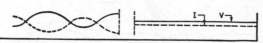

Fig. 2-10.—The effect upon voltage and current distribution of adding a discontinuity to a matched transmission line.

output will fall somewhere between these limits, depending upon the phase of the load impedance.

Effect of Adding an Impedance Element to a Matched Transmission Line.—If a passive impedance network is added at some point to a transmission line that is terminated at its far end by a matched load, standing waves may be set up on the line, as pictured in Fig. 2-10. Regardless of the character of the network, there will be no standing waves between the network and the matched load impedance. But in general there will be standing waves on the line between the network and the generator. To determine these standing waves, the input impedance to the network should be calculated with the characteristic impedance of the line (Z_0) considered as replacing the matched line feeding the load. The input impedance then serves as a load impedance for the section of line between the network and the generator.

Multiple Reflections on a Transmission Line.—A problem that frequently arises at microwave frequencies is the effect of the addition of a lossless reflecting network to a transmission line on which standing waves already exist (Fig. 2-11). If the network is capable of setting up a reflected wave on a matched line, how will this interact with a reflected wave already present? An analogous problem arises with a junction between two similar or dissimilar lines. The junction, although absorbing no power, may be imperfect in the sense that it sets up standing waves in the input line although the output line is matched. What will be the effect of this junction when standing waves are already present in the output line?

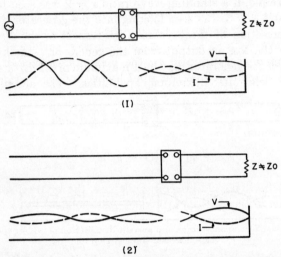

(I)

(2)

FIG. 2-11.—Possible effects upon voltage and current distribution of adding a discontinuity to an already mismatched transmission line. The mismatch may be made worse, or may be improved.

The reflected wave in the input line set up by the added junction or discontinuity will tend to add to or cancel on the input line any reflected wave that already exists on the output line. This addition or cancellation will depend upon the phase relationship between the two reflected waves. The problem is complicated by the fact that the reflected wave on the output line that is traveling toward the generator is again reflected in part at the added discontinuity. The following relationships are exact and take into account the infinite series of multiple reflections that occurs.

If the junction or discontinuity sets up a standing-wave ratio σ_1 on the input line when the output line is matched, and the output line is not matched, but has standing waves specified by σ_2, the maximum standing-wave ratio that can then exist on the input line is given by

$$\sigma_{max} = \sigma_1 \sigma_2 \qquad (2\text{-}20)$$

and the minimum standing-wave ratio by

$$\sigma_{min} = \frac{\sigma_1}{\sigma_2} \qquad (2\text{-}21)$$

if $\sigma_1 > \sigma_2$, or by

$$\sigma_{min} = \frac{\sigma_2}{\sigma_1} \qquad (2\text{-}22)$$

if $\sigma_1 < \sigma_2$.

These relationships may also be expressed in terms of reflection coefficients. If ρ_1 is the reflection coefficient associated with the standing-wave ratio σ_1 and ρ_2 is the reflection coefficient associated with the standing-wave ratio σ_2, the maximum reflection coefficient that will be encountered on the input line is

$$\rho_{max} = \rho_1 + \rho_2(1 - \rho_1{}^2) \frac{1}{1 + \rho_1\rho_2} \qquad (2\text{-}23)$$

and the minimum

$$\rho_{min} = \rho_1 - \rho_2(1 - \rho_1{}^2) \frac{1}{1 - \rho_1\rho_2} \qquad (2\text{-}24)$$

If the two reflections add in arbitrary phase, the total reflection coefficient is given in terms of an arbitrary phase angle ϕ by

$$\rho = \rho_1 + \rho_2(1 - \rho_1{}^2) \frac{e^{j\phi}}{1 + \rho_1\rho_2 e^{j\phi}} \qquad (2\text{-}25)$$

3. Power-carrying Capacity of Transmission Lines

Effect of Altitude.—The maximum power that can be carried by a transmission line is usually limited by the dielectric strength of the

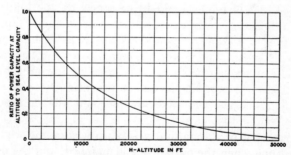

FIG. 2-12.—Variation of power-carrying capacity with altitude of unpressurized, air-dielectric transmission line.

medium carrying the electromagnetic waves. For air-dielectric lines, the maximum potential gradient at sea-level pressure is about 30,000 volts/cm. The potential gradient at which breakdown will occur decreases with altitude because of the change in atmospheric pressure, and the maximum power that can be transmitted along the line will decrease accordingly. In Fig. 2-12, the ratio P/P_0 is plotted against the altitude H, where P_0 is the maximum power that can be carried at sea-level pressure and P is the maximum power that can be carried in the same line at an altitude H. This is a theoretical curve which assumes that Paschen's law holds at ultrahigh frequencies and takes a seasonal average air density. That this curve is pessimistic was indicated by some laboratory tests[5] at about 9,000 mc, which showed that a reduction in pressure to an equivalent altitude of 41,500 ft. would reduce the power-carrying capacity of a wave guide to about 10 per cent of its sea-level value.

Effect of Standing Waves.—If a transmission line is not properly matched, and standing waves are present, the peak voltage will be increased over that of a matched line for the same net power delivered to the load. For a given net power flow down the line, the peak voltage will increase as the square root of the voltage standing-wave ratio. Stated differently, the maximum power that can be carried on a line for a given maximum voltage gradient is inversely proportional to the standing-wave ratio on the line.

[5] SAAD, T. S., X-Band Low Pressure Tests, M.I.T. Radiation Laboratory, Rept. 53-10, Dec. 10, 1942.

CHAPTER 3

IMPEDANCE RELATIONSHIPS ON TRANSMISSION LINES

1. Characteristic Impedance

The impedance at the input of a transmission line is usually defined as the ratio of applied voltage at the input to the resulting current that flows. The general equation that gives this impedance, derived from ordinary transmission-line theory, is

$$Z_s = Z_0 \left(\frac{Z_r + Z_0 \tanh \gamma l}{Z_0 + Z_r \tanh \gamma l} \right) \tag{3-1}$$

For ordinary low-frequency transmission lines, this equation is straightforward, and the input impedance is seen to depend upon four quantities: (1) l, the length of line; (2) γ, the propagation constant of the line; (3) Z_0, the characteristic impedance of the line; and (4) Z_r, the load impedance. For transmission lines operating at microwave frequencies, the first two of these quantities still have obvious physical significance, but the significance of the last two is not so obvious. This is particularly true of wave guides or other forms of transmission line that operate in modes of transmission other than the principal mode. The characteristic impedance of these transmission lines is a more obscure quantity than it is for a lower frequency line, and the absolute value of the load impedance is no less difficult to interpret. The situation is not helped by the fact that the voltage and current have become ambiguous quantities that may be defined in a number of ways.

To resolve these difficulties, it is well to consider the basic meaning of the term "characteristic impedance" of a transmission system.[1] Fundamentally, there are impedances associated with any traveling wave, no matter what its nature, whether electromagnetic, mechanical, acoustic, or otherwise. The "characteristic wave impedance" is the ratio of applied force to resulting response, when both force and response are periodic functions of time represented by complex exponentials. The characteristic wave impedance of a traveling electro-

---

[1] An excellent discussion of the impedance concept is contained in SCHELKUNOFF, S. A., Impedance Concept in Wave Guides, *Quart. Appl. Math.*, **2**, 1–15 (1944).

magnetic wave is therefore defined as the ratio of the electric and magnetic field components that are transverse to the direction of energy propagation. For a transmission system with two or more separated conductors operating in the principal mode of transmission, the characteristic wave impedance Z_w expressed in practical units is always

$$Z_w = 377 \sqrt{\frac{\mu}{\epsilon}} \quad \text{ohms} \tag{3-2}$$

where μ is the permeability and ϵ is the dielectric constant (both unity in free space) of the medium separating the conductors, through which the wave propagates.

For a wave guide or other transmission system operating in one of the other higher modes, and assuming that $\mu = 1$, the characteristic wave impedance is given as follows:

For TE waves

$$Z_w = 377 \left(\frac{\lambda_g}{\lambda}\right) \tag{3-3}$$

For TM waves

$$Z_w = 377 \left(\frac{\lambda}{\lambda_g}\right) \tag{3-4}$$

where λ_g is the wavelength on the wave guide or line and λ is the free-space wavelength. It is seen that a single transmission line will have values of wave impedance that depend upon both the frequency and the mode of transmission.

For wave guides below cutoff, the equations for wave length (see Sec. 7-4) will give answers that are imaginary, and the wave impedance then becomes a pure reactance.

The net power flow down any transmission line may be obtained at any cross section of the line by integrating Poynting's vector over the cross section. For low-frequency transmission lines operating in the principal mode, it is customary to integrate the field components and obtain the total voltage and current. This is an obvious and natural thing to do and leads to a simple interpretation of characteristic impedance as the voltage to current ratio associated with a traveling wave on the line. The characteristic impedance may also be specified in terms of power flow W and either voltage V or current I by the equations

$$Z_0 = \frac{V}{I} = \frac{V^2}{W} = \frac{W}{I^2} \tag{3-5}$$

Those who are accustomed to thinking in terms of voltage and current are often left in a state of uncertainty when dealing with high-frequency transmission lines, such as wave guides, operating in the higher modes of transmission. In these lines, there is no unique value of voltage or of current. Although the power flow is calculable, any number of values of characteristic impedance may be calculated, depending upon what voltage or current is chosen as reference.

Actually, this is of little importance. Consider what would happen if a set of measurements were made on a low-frequency transmission system and all measurements were made with a current meter that was in error by a constant factor. The data obtained would be completely self-consistent, and they would remain consistent so long as the meter readings had accuracy relative to each other. The error in the meter would be apparent only when the measurements were checked with a meter that gave the true values of current.

For a low-frequency line, the choice of total voltage and current is an obvious and natural one, but is still in a sense arbitrary. Any other choice would have led to an equally consistent set of results, different only in their relative values. For high-frequency lines, there is not always such an obvious and natural choice, but this should not lead to confusion.

All the foregoing problems that arise in attempting to define the characteristic impedance of a wave guide may be avoided by dealing with normalized impedances rather than by trying to specify their absolute values. The absolute value of the characteristic impedance of a high-frequency line may be an indeterminate quantity, but it is really unimportant. Results will still be complete and consistent if the impedances of all components are normalized with respect to the line impedance Z_0. Instead of the resistance R and the reactance X of a circuit element, the normalized resistance (R/Z_0) and normalized reactance X/Z_0 are used. When dealing with shunt elements, it is frequently more convenient to normalize conductances and susceptances with respect to the characteristic admittance Y_0 of the line (*i.e.*, G/Y_0 and B/Y_0). These normalized impedances and admittances may be determined experimentally from their effect upon the standing-wave pattern in a transmission line, and the question of absolute impedance values is completely circumvented.

2. Sending End Impedance of Transmission Lines

The normalized sending end impedance Z_s/Z_0 of a transmission line is related to the normalized load impedance Z_r/Z_0 and the propagation constant γ of the line by

$$\frac{Z_s}{Z_0} = \frac{\dfrac{Z_r}{Z_0} + \tanh \gamma l}{1 + \dfrac{Z_r}{Z_0} \tanh \gamma l} \tag{3-6}$$

For zero losses, this may be written

$$\frac{Z_s}{Z_0} = \frac{\dfrac{Z_r}{Z_0} + j \tan \beta l}{1 + j \dfrac{Z_r}{Z_0} \tan \beta l} \tag{3-7}$$

as γ is then equal to $j\beta$, where β is the phase constant (see Chap. 1).

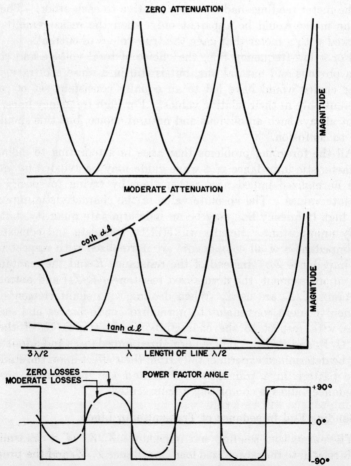

FIG. 3-1.—Variation of impedance with position on an open-circuited transmission line, with different values of attenuation.

When there are standing waves on the line, the impedance will reach a maximum value greater than Z_0 at the voltage maxima, and reach a minimum value less than Z_0 at the voltage minima.   At these points

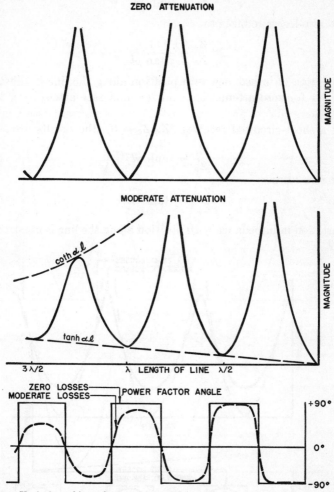

FIG. 3-2.—Variation of impedance with position on a short-circuited transmission line, with different values of attenuation.

the impedance will be a pure real, but at all other points on the line it will be a complex quantity, the phase angle changing from positive to negative at the voltage maximums and minimums.   The character of these impedance variations becomes apparent from the results of a few special cases, which follow.

For an open-circuited receiver $(Z_r/Z_0 = \infty)$, the input impedance becomes

$$\frac{Z_s}{Z_0} = \frac{1}{\tanh \gamma l} \tag{3-8}$$

and for zero losses reduces to

$$\frac{Z_s}{Z_0} = \frac{1}{j \tan \beta l} \tag{3-9}$$

The variation of impedance with position along the line is illustrated in Fig. 3-1 for zero attenuation and for moderate attenuation in the line.

For a short-circuited receiver $(Z_r/Z_0 = 0)$, the results are similar

$$\frac{Z_s}{Z_0} = \tanh \gamma l \tag{3-10}$$

and for zero loses

$$\frac{Z_s}{Z_0} = j \tanh \beta l \tag{3-11}$$

The variation in impedance with position along the line is illustrated in Fig. 3-2.

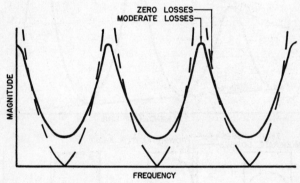

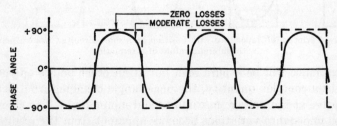

Fig. 3-3.—Variation of impedance with frequency of an open-circuited transmission line, with different values of attenuation. The attenuation is assumed to be independent of frequency.

For a matched or nonresonant line ($Z_r/Z_0 = 1$), the input impedance is constant and independent of position along the line.

$$\frac{Z_s}{Z_0} = \frac{Z_r}{Z_0} = 1 \qquad (3\text{-}12)$$

If the length of line is held constant, the variations of input impedance with frequency are similar in character to the results obtained when the frequency is unchanged and the length varied. In Fig. 3-3 are shown the variations with frequency of input impedance for an open-circuited receiver.

3. Transmission Lines as Circuit Elements

Lengths of transmission line are frequently used in microwave apparatus to perform the functions that ordinary circuit elements serve at lower frequencies. At very high frequencies the required lengths of line are small enough to be practical, and the efficiency of the lines employed as circuit elements is often very high.

Reactances.—As can be seen from Eqs. (3-9) and (3-11) and Figs. 3-1 and 3-2, lengths of low-loss transmission line that are terminated in an open or short circuit will serve as reactance elements. The input impedance of a shorted transmission line will be an inductive reactance if the line is shorter than a quarter wavelength. From a quarter to a half wavelength long, the input impedance will be capacitive, and the sign of the reactance will continue to reverse each time the length of the line is increased by a quarter wavelength.

A similar variation in reactance with changing length is found for the open-circuited line, but the reactance is capacitive rather than inductive for lengths less than a quarter wavelength.

Resistance.—The input impedance of a low-loss transmission line on which no standing waves exist is a pure resistance. The magnitude of the resistance is equal to the characteristic impedance of the line.

Resonant Circuits.—Low-loss transmission lines that are not terminated in their characteristic impedances will act much like resonant circuits over certain narrow bands of frequencies. This will be apparent by inspection of Fig. 3-3. The variation of impedance with frequency as the impedance passes through a maximum is similar to the behavior of a parallel resonant circuit. When the impedance goes through a minimum, its variation with changing frequency is similar to that occurring in a series resonant circuit.

If line losses are low, and the load at the far end does not absorb or radiate power, the Q of a resonant circuit made in this fashion may be quite high, of the order of several thousand. In spite of the low inductance, large shunt impedances (of the order of megohms) may be developed.

The effective L/C ratio of the equivalent resonant circuit will depend upon the length of line and its characteristic impedance. The parallel resonant circuit most commonly used in practice is the shorted line a quarter wave long. The equivalence is illustrated in Fig. 3-4.

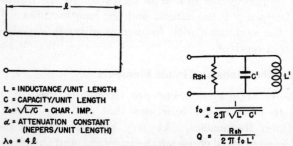

L = INDUCTANCE/UNIT LENGTH
C = CAPACITY/UNIT LENGTH
$Z_0 = \sqrt{L/C}$ = CHAR. IMP.
α = ATTENUATION CONSTANT
    (NEPERS/UNIT LENGTH)
$\lambda_0 = 4l$

$f_0 = \dfrac{1}{2\pi \sqrt{L' C'}}$

$Q = \dfrac{R_{sh}}{2\pi f_0 L'}$

Fig. 3-4.—A quarter-wave shorted transmission line, and the parallel resonant circuit to which it is equivalent.

For this special case, the constants of the equivalent resonant circuit may be found from the following equations (c = velocity of light = 3×10^{10} cm/sec.). With the length l specified in centimeters and the characteristic impedance Z_0 in ohms, the equivalent inductance is given by

$$L' = \frac{8lZ_0}{\pi^2 c} \qquad \text{henry} \qquad (3\text{-}13)$$

the equivalent capacitance by

$$C' = \frac{l}{2cZ_0} \qquad \text{farads} \qquad (3\text{-}14)$$

and the shunt impedance by

$$R_{SH} = \frac{Z_0}{\alpha l} \qquad \text{ohms} \qquad (3\text{-}15)$$

where α is the line attenuation in nepers per centimeter. The Q is given by

$$Q = \frac{\pi}{4\alpha l} \qquad (3\text{-}16)$$

An interesting relationship is

$$\sqrt{\frac{L'}{C'}} = \frac{4}{\pi}\sqrt{\frac{L}{C}} \qquad (3\text{-}17)$$

If the line were $3\lambda/4$ in length rather than $\lambda/4$, the Q and resonant frequency would be unchanged, but the shunt impedance and the equivalent inductance would be reduced by a factor of three.

4. Impedance Diagrams for Transmission Lines

Analytical solutions of low-loss transmission-line problems may be very time-consuming. A great deal of time may be saved by graphical analysis, and a number of charts have been developed to facilitate calculations. These are called "impedance" or "admittance" diagrams because they simplify impedance and admittance calculations. Sometimes they are referred to as "circle" diagrams, because the families of curves that give the desired information are usually circles. The charts are most suitable for calculations in which line loss may be neglected.

The normalized sending-end impedance of a lossless transmission line Z_s/Z_0 is given by

$$\frac{Z_s}{Z_0} = \frac{\frac{Z_r}{Z_0} + j \tan \beta l}{1 + j \frac{Z_r}{Z_0} \tan \beta l} \tag{3-18}$$

The normalized sending-end admittance Y_s/Y_0 is

$$\frac{Y_s}{Y_0} = \frac{\frac{Y_r}{Y_0} + j \tan \beta l}{1 + j \frac{Y_r}{Y_0} \tan \beta l} \tag{3-19}$$

In these equations $Z_r/Z_0 = 1/(Y_r/Y_0)$ is the normalized load impedance, l is the line length, and β is the phase constant of the line ($\beta = 2\pi/\lambda$). The similarity between these two equations is apparent. The same charts may be used for either impedance or admittance calculations, with only a corresponding change in the labeling of the various coordinate axes. Two types of charts have been found most generally useful, and the choice between these two depends upon the type of problem to be solved.

Rectangular Impedance Chart.—Examples of the rectangular impedance chart are given in Figs. 3-5 and 3-6. The chart is plotted on a base of a Cartesian coordinate system. The horizontal axis of these coordinates is labeled in values of normalized resistance R/Z_0, and the vertical axis in normalized reactance X/Z_0. Any value of normalized impedance may be plotted as a point on this impedance plane. The point $(1,0)$ represents the characteristic impedance of the line. In Fig. 3-7, the impedance $(Z_r/Z_0 = 1.3 + j0.75)$ is also plotted on the impedance plane.

It will be seen from Fig. 3-5 that a family of eccentric circles is grouped around the point (1,0) and that a circle of this family may be drawn passing through any point on the impedance plane. For

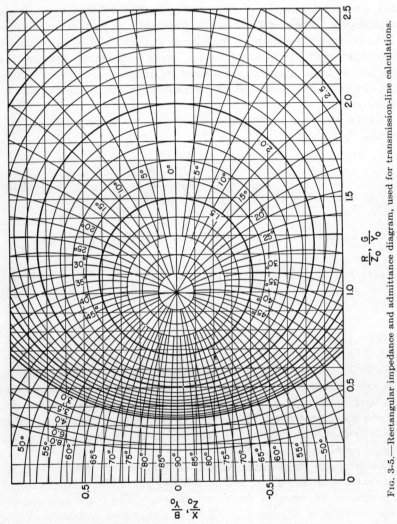

Fig. 3-5.—Rectangular impedance and admittance diagram, used for transmission-line calculations.

example, the particular circle that passes through the point

$$\left(\frac{Z_r}{Z_0} = 1.3 + j0.75\right)$$

is the one labeled 2.0, which passes through the point (2.0,0) on the real impedance axis. The input impedance to the transmission line at any arbitrary point on the line will fall somewhere on this circle (see Fig. 3-8). The exact point on the circle which determines the

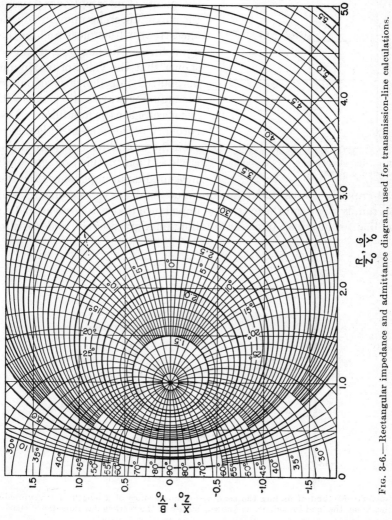

Fig. 3-6.—Rectangular impedance and admittance diagram, used for transmission-line calculations.

input impedance will depend upon the length of line between the load impedance and the point on the line at which the input impedance is measured.

Some properties of this family of circles are worth noting. For one thing, the center of all circles fall on the real axis of the impedance plane.   The circles intercept this real axis at two points, one at a value greater than unity, and one at a value less than unity.   These two intercepts are reciprocal values, and the points of interception represent the maximum and minimum impedances that will be measured on the input line.   Furthermore, it can be shown that the value of maximum normalized impedance is equal to the standing-wave ratio σ that will be measured on the input line.   The corollary of this statement is that if σ on the input line is measured the circle is then specified on which all measured input impedances and the load impedance must fall.   So the values that are labeled on circles of this family represent the maximum impedance that will be measured on the line for any load impedance falling on a given circle, and are also

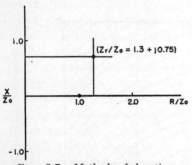

Fig. 3-7.—Method of locating a given impedance on a rectangular impedance plane.

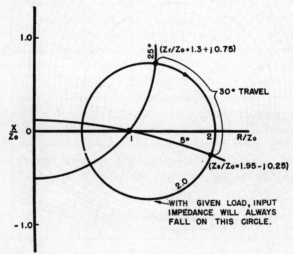

Fig. 3-8.—Method of finding the sending-end impedance of a length of transmission line, when the load impedance is known, by use of the rectangular impedance chart.

equal to the standing-wave ratio that will be measured on the input line. For the example that we have been following ($Z_r/Z_0 = 1.3 + j0.75$), the maximum normalized impedance that will be measured is $R/Z_0 = 2.0$, the minimum is $R/Z_0 = 1/2.0 = 0.5$, and $\sigma = 2$ on the input line.

It will be seen in Fig. 3-5 that there is a second family of circles superimposed upon the coordinate system which is orthogonal to the first family. All these circles pass through the point (1,0) on the impedance plane, and their centers are distributed along the reactive axis of that plane. These circles are labeled in electrical degrees of length and enable one to determine how far one must move around one of the first family of circles to account for a given length of transmission line between a known impedance and the impedance one wishes to know.

For example, assume that the load impedance of a transmission line is known to be $(Z_r/Z_0 = 1.3 + j0.75)$ and that one wishes to know the input impedance to a transmission line looking toward this load and a distance one-twelfth wavelength away. The load impedance has already been located as falling on the circle labeled 2.0, and the input impedance is also known to fall at some point on this circle; the problem is how far to proceed around this circle to account for the length of line in order to arrive at the precise point that represents the input impedance. It is this problem that the second family of circles enables one to answer.

First, in traveling along the transmission line from the load impedance *toward the generator*, one should proceed in a *clockwise direction* around the appropriate first circle that links the point (1,0). It is necessary to proceed in that direction a distance of one-twelfth wavelength or 30 deg as measured by the second family of circles. The required operation is illustrated in Fig. 3-8. The point representing the load impedance is intercepted by the circle of the second family labeled 25 deg. To account for the 30 deg of line, it is necessary to go beyond the real axis to the circle labeled 5 deg. This 5 deg of travel below the real axis added to the 25 deg of travel above the axis gives the full 30 deg of travel that is required by the given length of line. The required normalized sending-end impedance is given by the point of interception of the 2.0 circle and the 5-deg circle as

$$\left(\frac{Z_s}{Z_0} = 1.95 - j0.25 \right)$$

It will be seen from Fig. 3-5 that moving along the transmission line a distance of 180 deg or a half wavelength will bring one back to the original impedance. So if the load impedance and the sending end are separated by a considerable length of line, the sending-end impedance may be calculated by subtracting from that length of line as many half wavelengths as are required to bring the remaining length below a half wavelength. The calculation can then proceed as outlined above.

A type of problem more commonly encountered is the calculation of an unknown load impedance when the standing-wave ratio and position of the minimums are known on the input transmission line. For example, assume that the standing-wave ratio on the input line has been measured as $\sigma = 2.5$ and a voltage minimum is known to exist 210 deg away from the load. It is therefore known that the load impedance falls on the 2.5 circle and that, if there is a voltage

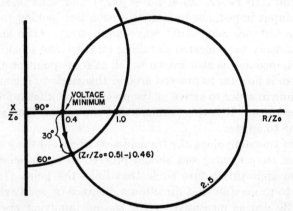

Fig. 3-9.—Method of determining the load impedance of a transmission line with the use of the rectangular impedance chart. The standing-wave ratio and position of the minimums on the line are known.

minimum 210 deg from the load, there must be another minimum a half wavelength closer, or 30 deg from the load. At the voltage minimum, the normalized input impedance is known to be a pure real quantity less than unity, which may be located on the impedance plane at the intercept of the 2.5 circle and the real axis at a real value less than unity, in this case 0.4. To proceed *toward the load impedance*, it is necessary to travel from this point in a *counterclockwise* direction around the 2.5 circle. This graphical solution is illustrated in Fig. 3-9. It is necessary to go 30 deg, which brings the impedance from the 90-deg circle to the 60-deg circle. The load impedance is then at the intercept of the 60-deg circle below the real axis and the 2.5 circle, and has a value $(Z_r/Z_0 = 0.51 - j0.46)$.

Figures 3-5 and 3-6 may be used with equal facility for impedance and admittance calculations, as is indicated by the labeling on the coordinate axes. When using the charts to calculate admittances, one should still proceed in a clockwise direction around the impedance circles when traveling toward the generator and in a counterclockwise direction when traveling toward the load. But it should be kept in mind that voltage minimums correspond to admittance maximums and that positive reactances are negative susceptances.

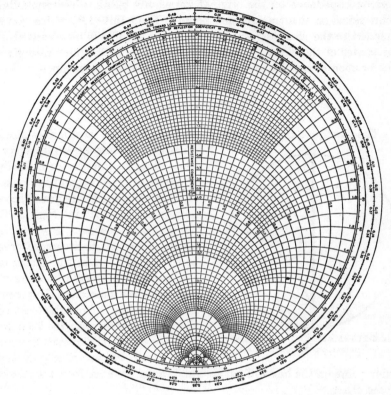

Fig. 3-10.—The Smith chart, an impedance chart used in transmission-line calculations.

Methods by which additional transmission-line problems may be solved with the use of this chart are indicated in Sec. 3-5, which deals with some simple impedance transformers.

Smith Chart.—A different version of this impedance diagram was developed by P. H. Smith.[2] The impedance plane has been transformed from a system of Cartesian coordinates to a system of two orthogonal families of circles. This chart is illustrated in Fig. 3-10. The family of straight lines that represent contours of constant react-

[2] SMITH, P. H., A Transmission Line Calculator, *Electronics*, **12** (No. 1), 29 (1939). Also Smith, P. H., An Improved Transmission Line Calculator, *Electronics*, **17** (No. 1), 130 (1944).

ance and that include the horizontal axis have been transformed to one family of circles, and the family of lines that represent contours of constant resistance and include the vertical axis have been transformed to the other family of circles. For any point that represented a given impedance on the original impedance plane, a corresponding point exists on this transformed plane. The point (1,0) which corresponded to the characteristic impedance of the line is now located at the center of the chart. This is shown in Fig. 3-11, which also gives the location of a point representing the normalized impedance

$$\left(\frac{Z_r}{Z_0} = 1.3 + j0.75 \right)$$

The family of circles that represent the locus of impedances along

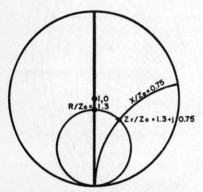

FIG. 3-11.—Method of locating a given impedance on the Smith chart.

mismatched transmission lines [corresponding to the eccentric family of circles grouped around the point (1,0) in the original diagram] have not been plotted in Fig. 3-10. They have become, however, a family of concentric circles centered at the point (1,0) in the center of the impedance chart which corresponds to the characteristic impedance of the line. Once the location of a point representing the load impedance on a transmission line has been found, the impedance at any other point on the line will fall an equal radial distance from the center of the chart.

The standing-wave ratio that a given load impedance will cause on the input line may be found by drawing one of these circles, which is centered at the point (1,0) and passes through the load impedance, and noting where this circle intercepts the real impedance axis at a value greater than unity. This value then represents the maximum impedance that will be measured on the input line and also gives the standing-wave ratio σ that will be set up on the transmission line by the known load impedance. This is illustrated in Fig. 3-12, where it is seen that a load impedance $(Z_r/Z_0 = 1.3 + j0.75)$ will give a standing-wave ratio $\sigma = 2.0$ on the input line, and the maximum normalized impedance value will be 2.0.

It is worth noting that, although the standing-wave ratio varies in a nonlinear way with changing radius from 1.0 at the center of the diagram to infinity at the edge, a radial scale that is drawn in terms of reflection coefficient is linear and varies from zero at the center of the chart to unity at the edge.

The second family of circles in the rectangular impedance diagram, which were labeled in electrical degrees and represented contours of constant position on the transmission line, are also not plotted on the

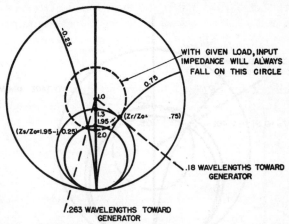

Fig. 3-12.—Method of finding the sending impedance of a length of transmission line, when the load impedance is known, by use of the Smith chart.

Smith chart. These have transformed, however, to a family of uniformly spaced straight lines radiating from the center of the chart. The azimuth reading that corresponds to a given position on the transmission line is given on the graduated scale that forms the border of the chart. There are two scales, one measuring from the real axis toward the load and one toward the generator. Both scales are graduated in fractions of a wavelength, rather than in electrical degrees of line length, which were used in the first chart. So to move along the transmission line a given distance, it is only necessary to move at a constant radial distance to a new azimuth position as indicated by the scale on the border. For example, suppose that it is desired to know the normalized input impedance at a distance of one-twelfth wavelength from a normalized load impedance $(Z_r/Z_0 = 1.3 + j0.75)$. The solution of this problem is indicated in Fig. 3-12. The load impedance is located on the concentric circle that passes through a maximum impedance of 2.0 and at an azimuth setting of 0.18 wavelength on the scale labeled "wavelengths toward generator." To find the input impedance one-twelfth (0.0833) wavelength away, it is necessary to travel around the circle to a new azimuth setting of $0.18 + 0.0833 = 0.2633$ wavelength. This new point falls on the impedance plane at a value $(Z_s/Z_0 = 1.95 - j0.25)$, which is the normalized input impedance.

The more common problem of an unknown load impedance at the end of a line on which the standing-wave ratio and position of a voltage minimum are known is as easily solved. For example, assume again

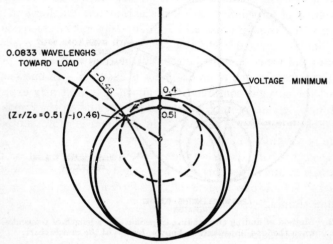

FIG. 3-13.—Method of determining the load impedance of a transmission line, with the use of the Smith chart. The standing-wave ratio and position of the minimums on the line are known.

that a standing-wave ratio $\sigma = 2.5$ has been measured on the input line, and a voltage minimum is known to exist 210 deg away from the load impedance (see Fig. 3-13). If there is a voltage minimum 210 deg from the load, there must be one a half wavelength closer, or 30 deg (0.0833 wavelength) from the load. At the voltage minimum, there is known to be an impedance minimum that has a value of

$$\frac{R}{Z_0} = \frac{1}{\sigma} = \frac{1}{2.5} = 0.4$$

and is located on the real axis. This sets the radius of the circle on which the load impedance falls.

The azimuth setting at the voltage minimum corresponds to a scale reading of zero on the "wavelengths toward load" scale. So it is necessary to move at the specified radial distance to a scale setting of 0.0833 wavelength toward the load. This will bring one to a point on the impedance plane that corresponds to the desired load impedance $(Z_s/Z_0 = 0.51 - j0.46)$.

The Smith chart has several advantages over the rectangular chart, including the following:

1. On the rectangular chart the impedance plane is semiinfinite, but on the Smith chart all impedances are confined within the limiting radius.

2. If a locus of points is plotted on the Smith chart to represent the variation of impedance with some parameter, this locus of points will maintain a constant size and configuration as the reference point on the line is changed. On the rectangular chart, the curve that represents the locus of impedances will be distorted as the position on the line chosen as the reference point is changed. In one section of the chart the curve is compressed; in another, it is greatly expanded.

3. Line attenuation may be taken into account in the Smith chart by a simple reduction in radius. The problem is more complicated with the rectangular chart.

On the other hand, certain types of problems, notably those involving changes in line impedance, are more easily solved on the rectangular chart. Which one is generally preferred is largely a matter of individual training.

5. Some Simple Impedance Transformers

Some of the reasons for matching the impedances of various microwave components to the impedance of the interconnecting lines have been outlined in Sec. 2-2. Some of the general principles and simpler techniques are outlined in this section, and additional information on specific devices that are applicable is contained in Chaps. 6 and 10, which deal with coaxial lines and wave guides, respectively.

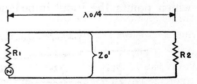

Fig. 3-14.—A quarter-wave transmission line used to match two unequal resistances.

Half-wave Lines.—Values of sending-end impedance repeat every half wavelength along a mismatched transmission line. A line that is a half wavelength or any integral multiple half wavelengths long will therefore match any two impedances that are equal.

Quarter-wave Lines.—A quarter wavelength of transmission line of characteristic impedance Z_0' will match any two resistive impedances of which Z_0' is the geometric mean. A generator of known resistive internal impedance R_1 may be matched to an unequal load resistance

R_2 (as illustrated in Fig. 3-14) by a quarter wavelength of interconnecting line whose characteristic impedance is given by

$$Z_0' = \sqrt{R_1 R_2} \tag{3-20}$$

At microwave frequencies, the generator impedance is frequently the characteristic impedance of a transmission line Z_0, and the quarter-

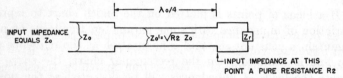

Fig. 3-15.—A quarter-wave transmission line used in conjunction with an additional length of line to match a complex load impedance to a transmission line.

wave section will match the resistive load R_2 to the line impedance Z_0.

If the load impedance Z_r of the transmission line is not a pure resistance, it may still be matched to Z_0 by a quarter-wave line, plus an additional length of line between Z_r and the quarter-wave matching section. This additional length of line should be of such length that the impedance looking into its input terminals is a pure resistance R_2. This means that the load end of the matching section should be placed at a voltage maximum or minimum in the input line, at which points the input impedance looking

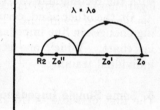

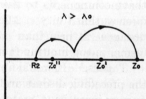

Fig. 3-16.—Multiple quarter-wave transmission lines used to provide a broad-band impedance match between a resistance and a transmission line.

Fig. 3-17.—Illustrating on a rectangular impedance chart the broad-band operation of multiple quarter-wave matching sections.

toward the load is real.   The various impedances must then satisfy the relation.

$$Z_0' = \sqrt{Z_0 R_2} \tag{3-21}$$

This is illustrated in Fig. 3-15.

Multiple Quarter-wave Lines.—A single quarter-wave line used as a transformer has the disadvantage that it is resonant; *i.e.*, it matches perfectly at only one frequency. The band width over which the match is good can be extended by using two or more quarter-wave matching sections, placed together and properly chosen in impedance. This is illustrated in Fig. 3-16. The design equation for such a transformer is

$$2(\log Z_0 - \log Z_0') = (\log Z_0' - \log Z_0'') = 2(\log Z_0'' - \log R_2)$$
$$(3\text{-}22)$$

where as before R_2 is the purely resistive impedance measured at a point of minimum voltage in the input line ($R_2 = Z_0/\sigma$ or $R_2 = Z_0\sigma$). The compensating action of a two-section matching transformer is illustrated in Fig. 3-17, where the variation of impedance with position along the line is shown on a rectangular impedance chart, not normalized.

Devices using multiple sections can be made less and less frequency sensitive by using more and more sections. The increment in the logarithm of the impedance between succeeding sections should follow the binomial coefficients:

$$
\begin{array}{ccccc}
1 & 2 & 1 & & \\
1 & 3 & 3 & 1 & \\
1 & 4 & 6 & 4 & 1
\end{array}
$$

The first of these is the double section illustrated in Fig. 3-16, the second is a three-section transformer, and so on. It should be observed that nothing is to be gained by the use of multiple sleeves if the frequency sensitivity of the load impedance rather than the transformer is the limiting factor.

Tapers.[3]—It would appear from the preceding discussion that a frequency-insensitive match between two impedances can be obtained

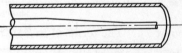

Fig. 3-18.—A tapered section connecting coaxial lines of different characteristic impedance.

by using a length of tapered transmission line whose impedance varies continuously but slowly throughout its length, and whose impedance at each end is equal to the impedance to be matched at that end. This is nearly true, provided that the change in line impedance per wavelength is sufficiently small. Such a tapered section in coaxial line is illustrated in Fig. 3-18.

[3] FRANK, N. H., Reflections from Sections of Tapered Transmission Line and Wave Guides, M.I.T. Radiation Laboratory Sec. 43, Rept. 17, Jan. 6, 1943. Also from some unpublished notes of W. W. Hansen.

An approximation to the reflection introduced by the tapered section is given by

$$\frac{V_2}{V_1} = \frac{1}{4\gamma_0}\left[\frac{d(\ln Z)}{dx}\right]_0 - \frac{1}{4\gamma_1}\left[\frac{d(\ln Z)}{dx}\right]_1 \exp\left(-2\int_0^d \gamma\,dx\right) \quad (3\text{-}23)$$

where V_1 is the incident wave of voltage and V_2 is the reflected wave. In this expression, the subscript 0 means the value for the taper at point x_0, while the subscript 1 means the value for the taper at the

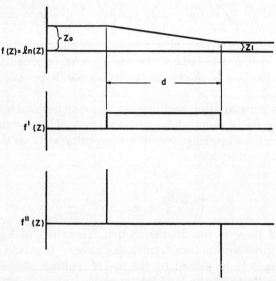

Fig. 3-19.—Impedance functions associated with a tapered transmission line of the type shown in Fig. 3-18.

point x_1. The terms $d(\ln Z)/dx$ are discontinuous at the points x_1 and x_0, so the values that are approached as a limit at the ends of the taper should be used. The term γ is the propagation constant of the line. To the extent for which the above expression is valid, i.e., for small reflections, the standing-wave ratio σ introduced by the taper is

$$\sigma = 1 + 2\left|\frac{V_2}{V_1}\right| \quad (3\text{-}24)$$

The optimum condition corresponding to minimum reflection occurs when no discontinuity exists in the function $f(Z) = \ln Z$ or any of its derivatives. This means that the impedance variation between Z_1 and Z_0 should be such that

$$\ln \frac{Z}{Z_0} = \frac{h}{\sqrt{\pi}} \ln \frac{Z_1}{Z_0} \int_{-\infty}^{x} e^{-h^2 x^2}\,dx \quad (3\text{-}25)$$

In this expression x is the distance as measured from the center of the taper, Z is the impedance at the point x, and h is an arbitrary constant.

Example: Consider the case where $f(Z) = \ln Z$ varies linearly with distance throughout the region x_0 to x_1. This is illustrated in Fig. 3-19. The reflection introduced by the taper is given by

$$\frac{V_2}{V_1} = \frac{\lambda}{8\pi jd} \ln \frac{Z_1}{Z_0} \left(1 - e^{-\frac{4\pi jd}{\lambda}}\right) \tag{3-26}$$

The variation of reflection with length of taper as calculated by this formula is illustrated in Fig. 3-20 for a taper from 46-ohm to 75-ohm

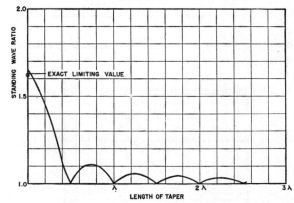

FIG. 3-20.—Standing-wave ratio introduced by a linear-tapered line, 75 to 46 ohms, theoretical calculation.

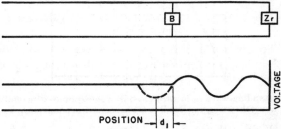

FIG. 3-21.—Use of a shunting susceptance to match a load impedance to a transmission line.

line, and it is seen that the standing-wave ratio will be less than 1.05 for any frequency at which the taper is more than two wavelengths long.

Shunt Susceptance.—A mismatched load on the end of a transmission line is frequently matched to the line by inserting a shunt susceptance at the proper point in the line (see Fig. 3-21). The required value of susceptance is determined by the standing-wave ratio which must be matched. This value of susceptance is the one that will set up the same standing-wave ratio on the input when shunted across a matched line. The required susceptance is related to the standing-wave ratio σ by

$$\frac{B}{Y_0} = \frac{\sigma - 1}{\sqrt{\sigma}} \tag{3-27}$$

which may also be written as

$$\sigma = \frac{\sqrt{4 + \left(\dfrac{B}{Y_0}\right)^2} + \left(\dfrac{B}{Y_0}\right)}{\sqrt{4 + \left(\dfrac{B}{Y_0}\right)^2} - \left(\dfrac{B}{Y_0}\right)} \tag{3-28}$$

This relationship between σ and B/Y_0 is shown graphically in Fig. 3-22.

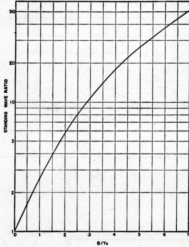

FIG. 3-22.—The standing-wave ratio introduced by a susceptance of magnitude B shunting a matched transmission line of characteristic admittance Y_o.

When B/Y_0 is of the proper magnitude, it sets up a reflected wave on the line which just cancels the one already present from the mismatched load. But the phase relationship must be right for complete cancellation, which means that the susceptance must be properly positioned along the line. This proper position is given by

$$d_1 = \frac{(\pi/2) - \tan^{-1}\left|\dfrac{B}{2Y_0}\right|}{4\pi} \lambda_g \tag{3-29}$$

where d_1 is the distance between the matching susceptance and a voltage minimum. If the susceptance is inductive (B/Y_0 is negative), it should be placed at a distance d_1 on the load side of a minimum;

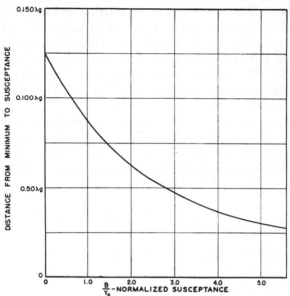

Fig. 3-23.—The distance between the voltage minimum of standing waves and a shunt susceptance positioned to eliminate the standing waves, plotted as a function of the required susceptance.

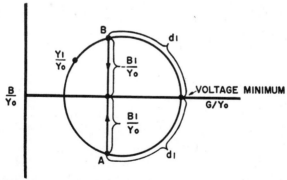

Fig. 3-24.—Illustrating on a rectangular admittance chart the operation of a shunt susceptance used for impedance matching.

if it is capacitive, it should be at a distance d_1 on the generator side of a minimum. The distance d_1 is plotted against B/Y_0 in Fig. 3-23.

The required susceptance and position may be determined by graphical calculation. The impedance chart in Figs. 3-5 and 3-6 is chosen for illustration, but as shunt elements are being dealt with, it is used as an admittance chart. An arbitrary load admittance Y_1/Y_0 will fall on some constant standing-wave ratio circle, as shown in Fig. 3-24. The two positions at which a shunt susceptance will match the line are the points A and B on this circle. At point A, a distance d_1 on the generator side of a voltage minimum, a capacitive susceptance $+B_1/Y_0$ added to the load admittance will match the line admittance. At point B, a distance d_1 on the load side of a voltage minimum, the inductive susceptance $-B_1/Y_0$ added to the load admittance will match the line.

The shunt susceptances used in actual practice take a variety of forms. Shorted stub lengths of line are frequently used, and in wave guides metallic diaphragms find wide application. Metallic posts may be used in either coaxial lines or wave guides. Particular structures that may be suitable are discussed in Chaps. 6 and 9.

CHAPTER 4

GENERAL FORMULAS FOR COAXIAL LINES

1. Introduction

Coaxial lines are transmission systems in which electromagnetic waves are transmitted through a dielectric medium bounded by two coaxial cylinders. The skin depth at microwave frequencies is small enough so that for most purposes of calculation the conducting boundaries may be considered to be of infinite thickness.

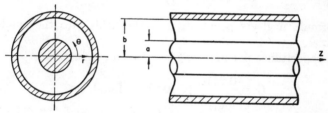

FIG. 4-1.—A section of coaxial transmission line, illustrating some of the notation used.

Having two separated conductors, coaxial lines are capable of carrying energy in the principal (TEM) mode of propagation and are generally used with this mode carrying energy. Operated in this fashion, they are used at low frequencies. At high radio frequencies the dimensions of the line are generally restricted to an extent that the line is unable to transmit energy in any of the modes other than the principal mode. The characteristics that follow should therefore be considered applicable only for the principal mode of transmission, except where otherwise noted.

The principal symbols used in this chapter are defined as follows, and some are illustrated in Fig. 4-1:

λ wavelength
f frequency
ω angular frequency $= 2\pi f$
v velocity of propagation
c velocity of light $= 3 \times 10^{10}$ cm/sec
a outer radius of inner conductor
b inner radius of outer conductor

ϵ dielectric constant = unity in free space
ϵ_1 dielectric constant of propagating medium
μ permeability = unity in free space
μ_1 permeability of medium separating the conductors
R resistance per unit length
L inductance per unit length
G conductance per unit length
C capacity per unit length
Z_0 characteristic impedance

2. Parameters of Coaxial Lines

The inductance per unit length of a coaxial line is

$$L = 0.4605 \, \mu_1 \left(\log_{10} \frac{b}{a} \right) \times 10^{-8} \quad \text{henry/cm} \quad (4\text{-}1)$$

This formula neglects penetration of the fields into the conducting boundaries.

The capacitance per unit length between conductors is

$$C = \frac{0.241 \epsilon_1}{\log_{10} \dfrac{b}{a}} \times 10^{-12} \quad \text{farad/cm} \quad (4\text{-}2)$$

The resistance per unit length is given by

$$R = \frac{\rho}{2\pi\delta} \left(\frac{1}{b} + \frac{1}{a} \right) = \sqrt{\frac{f\mu\rho}{10^9}} \left(\frac{1}{b} + \frac{1}{a} \right) \quad (4\text{-}3)$$

where δ is the skin depth in centimeters (see Chap. 2), f is the frequency in cycles per second, ρ is the resistivity in ohm-centimeters, μ is the permeability, and the radii of the line are in centimeters. It will be seen that the resistance of the line is proportional to the square root of the resistivity of the conductors; this is because of the skin effect. For copper conductors,

$$R = 4.14 \times 10^{-8} \sqrt{f \left(\frac{1}{b} + \frac{1}{a} \right)} \quad \text{ohms/cm} \quad (4\text{-}4)$$

If the inner and outer conductors are constructed of materials of different resistivity, the effective line resistance per unit length is

$$R = \sqrt{\frac{f}{10^9}} \left(\frac{\sqrt{\rho_a \mu_a}}{a} + \frac{\sqrt{\rho_b \nu_b}}{b} \right) \quad (4\text{-}5)$$

where ρ_a is the resistivity of the inner conductor, ρ_b is the resistivity of the outer conductor, and μ_a and μ_b are the respective permeabilities of the two conductors.

The appearance of μ in these equations is mostly of theoretical interest, as $\mu = 1$ for most practical conductors. When μ is greater

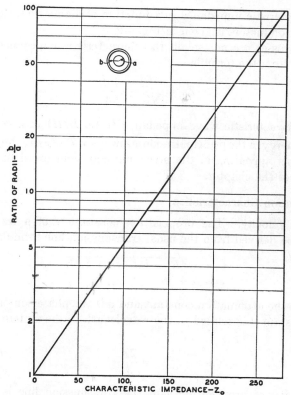

FIG. 4-2.—The characteristic impedance of an air-filled coaxial line as a function of the ratio of radii of outer and inner conductors.

than one, the above formulas give the loss resulting from finite conductivity, but do not include the hysteresis loss which may also be present.

The conductance per unit length of a coaxial line may usually be neglected if the line has an air or gaseous dielectric. But for a solid dielectric line, there is an effective conductance resulting from the energy loss in the dielectric. With a dielectric medium of loss tangent (tan δ), the effective conductance is

$$G = \omega C \tan \delta \qquad (4\text{-}6)$$

The characteristic impedance (surge impedance) of a low-loss coaxial line is

$$Z_0 = \sqrt{\frac{L}{C}} = 138 \sqrt{\frac{\mu_1}{\epsilon_1}} \log_{10} \frac{b}{a} = 60 \sqrt{\frac{\mu_1}{\epsilon_1}} \ln \frac{b}{a} \qquad (4\text{-}7)$$

The characteristic impedance as a function of diametric ratio of outer and inner conductors is given in Fig. 4-2.

Where losses are not small, the characteristic impedance may be calculated from the formula

$$Z_0 = \sqrt{\frac{R + j\omega L}{G + j\omega C}} \qquad (4\text{-}8)$$

The characteristic wave impedance (ratio E/H) in a coaxial line carrying energy in the principal mode is always $377 \sqrt{\mu_1/\epsilon_1}$ ohms. Various symbols appearing in the preceding equations are defined at the beginning of the chapter.

3. Propagation Characteristics

Phase Velocity.—The propagation constant γ of a transmission line may be derived from the usual transmission-line formulas

$$\gamma = \sqrt{(R + j\omega L)(G + j\omega C)}$$
$$= \alpha + j\beta \qquad (2\text{-}1)$$

where α is the attenuation constant and β is the phase constant. The phase constant β is related to the wavelength in the system λ_1 by the formula

$$\lambda_1 = \frac{2\pi}{\beta} \qquad (4\text{-}9)$$

The velocity of propagation v in the transmission line is given by

$$v = \frac{\omega}{\beta} \qquad (4\text{-}10)$$

Where losses are small, this velocity becomes

$$v = \frac{c}{\sqrt{\mu_1 \epsilon_1}} \qquad (4\text{-}11)$$

which is the same as the velocity of an unbounded plane wave in the dielectric medium characterized by μ_1, ϵ_1. In an air-filled line, the velocity of the wave is very nearly equal to the velocity of light in a vacuum.

The wavelength in the line λ_1 is related to the wavelength in free space λ by

$$\lambda_1 = \frac{\lambda}{\sqrt{\mu_1 \epsilon_1}} \qquad (4\text{-}12)$$

An air-filled coaxial line operating in the principal mode may therefore be used as a Lecher-wire system on which wavelength measurements are made directly.

Attenuation.—For nearly all coaxial lines used at microwave frequencies, the attenuation per wavelength is small enough so that the following approximate formula may be used

$$\alpha = \frac{R}{2Z_0} + \frac{G}{2Y_0} \qquad \text{nepers/unit length} \qquad (4\text{-}13)$$

It is usually simpler, however, to divide the sources of attenuation into conductor losses and dielectric losses.

Attenuation Resulting from Conductor Losses.—The attenuation resulting from conductor losses in a coaxial line is given by

$$\alpha_c = \frac{\pi}{2} \frac{\delta\mu}{\lambda} \frac{1}{b} \left(1 + \frac{b}{a}\right) \frac{\sqrt{\epsilon_1}}{\ln\dfrac{b}{a}} \qquad \text{nepers/unit length}$$

$$= 13.6 \frac{\delta\mu}{\lambda} \frac{1}{b} \left(1 + \frac{b}{a}\right) \frac{\sqrt{\epsilon_1}}{\ln\dfrac{b}{a}} \qquad \text{db/unit length} \qquad (4\text{-}14)$$

where δ is the skin depth, λ is the wavelength, b and a are the outer and inner radii of the line, all in similar units. Also, μ is the permeability of the conductors, and ϵ_1 is the dielectric constant of the medium separating the conductors. For a copper line, this formula reduces to

$$\alpha_c = 2.98 \times 10^{-9} \sqrt{f} \frac{1}{b} \left(1 + \frac{b}{a}\right) \frac{\sqrt{\epsilon_1}}{\ln\dfrac{b}{a}} \qquad \text{db/cm} \qquad (4\text{-}15)$$

with the dimensions b and a in centimeters and the frequency f in cycles per second. If the inner and outer conductors are of different material, the attenuation formula may be written

$$\alpha_c = \frac{13.6}{\lambda} \left(\frac{\delta_a\mu_a}{a} + \frac{\delta_b\mu_b}{b}\right) \frac{\sqrt{\epsilon_1}}{\ln\dfrac{b}{a}} \qquad \text{db/unit length} \qquad (4\text{-}16)$$

where the subscripts a and b refer to the inner and outer conductors, respectively.

The attenuation increases as the square root of frequency, assuming that ϵ_1 is independent of frequency, and also varies as the square root of the resistivity of the conductors. Table 2-1 gives the resistivity of a number of conducting materials and also the attenuation as compared with the attenuation of copper.

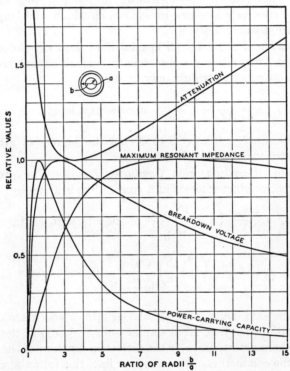

Fig. 4-3.—Various characteristics of a coaxial transmission line plotted as functions of the ratio of radii of outer and inner conductors.

An optimum ratio $b/a = 3.6$ exists for a fixed dimension of the outer radius b, and minimum attenuation occurs at this value. This corresponds to a characteristic impedance of 77 ohms for a line with air dielectric. The minimum is rather broad, and impedance values can vary considerably about this value without a marked change in the attenuation. The variation of attenuation with diametric ratio, assuming a fixed diameter outer conductor, is shown in Fig. 4-3.

Attenuation Resulting from Dielectric Losses.—Solid dielectric coaxial lines are not widely used at microwave frequencies when low attenuation is important because even a very good dielectric has losses that are very appreciable at these frequencies. To express these losses mathematically, it is convenient to consider the dielectric constant ϵ as complex and of the form

$$\epsilon = \epsilon' - j\epsilon'' \tag{4-17}$$

The loss tangent of the dielectric is defined as

$$\tan \delta = \frac{\epsilon''}{\epsilon'} \tag{4-18}$$

Usually the angle δ (not to be confused with skin depth) is small, and it can be said that the loss tangent is very nearly equal to the power factor of a condenser using the dielectric. The true power factor is defined as

$$\text{Power factor} = \cos \theta \tag{2-10}$$

with

$$\theta = 90° - \delta$$

The attenuation in a coaxial line α_D resulting from dielectric losses is given by

$$\alpha_D = \pi \frac{\sqrt{\epsilon_1'}}{\lambda} \tan \delta \qquad \text{nepers/unit length}$$

$$= 27.3 \frac{\sqrt{\epsilon_1'}}{\lambda} \tan \delta \qquad \text{db/unit length} \tag{4-19}$$

Attenuation in a Coaxial Line with Both Conductor and Dielectric Losses.—The total attenuation in a coaxial line is the sum of the attenuation resulting from the conductor losses and the dielectric losses, *i.e.*,

$$\alpha_T = \alpha_C + \alpha_D \tag{4-20}$$

where α_T is the total attenuation, α_C is the attenuation resulting from conductor losses, and α_D is the attenuation resulting from dielectric losses.

It will be seen from an inspection of the attenuation formulas that, if the dielectric constant and power factor are independent of frequency, the following is true:

1. The conductor losses are proportional to the square root of frequency.

2. The dielectric losses are linearly proportional to frequency.

Hence at higher frequencies the dielectric losses become increasingly important.

4. Field Configuration

The field configuration of the principal mode of transmission is illustrated in Fig. 4-4. Solid lines are used to indicate the electric field and broken lines the magnetic field. Where I_0 is the conduction current amplitude along the inner conductor associated with the incident wave, the field is specified by the following equations, which

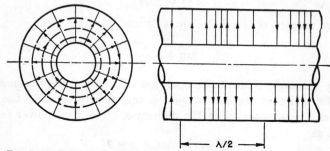

Fig. 4-4.—Field distribution for the principal mode in a coaxial line.

apply throughout the dielectric medium separating the conductors:

$$H_r = 0$$

$$H_\theta = \frac{I_0}{2\pi r} \left(e^{j\omega t - \gamma z} - \rho e^{j\omega t + \gamma z} \right)$$

$$H_z = 0$$

$$E_r = 377 \sqrt{\frac{\mu_1}{\epsilon_1}} \frac{I_0}{2\pi r} \left(e^{j\omega t - \gamma z} + \rho e^{j\omega t + \gamma z} \right) \qquad (4\text{-}21)$$

$$E_\theta = 0$$

$$E_z = 0$$

With I_0 in amperes, the magnetic field H is in ampere turns per meter, the electric field E is in volts per meter, and the radius r is in meters. The term ρ indicates the reflection coefficient, γ the propagation constant, μ and ϵ the permeability and dielectric constant of the dielectric medium (both unity in free space). The coordinates are indicated in Fig. 4-1. It will be seen that the electric and magnetic field intensities decrease inversely with radial distance from the axis of the line.

The field patterns for other higher modes of transmission are illustrated in Sec. 4-8.

5. Breakdown in a Coaxial Line

Breakdown will occur in a coaxial line when the maximum voltage gradient exceeds a limiting value. This limiting gradient is approximately 30,000 volts/cm for an air-filled line under ordinary atmospheric conditions.

The electric field intensity E at any point in the region between the inner and outer conductors of a coaxial pair is given by

$$E = \frac{V}{r \ln \dfrac{b}{a}} \quad \text{volts/cm} \tag{4-22}$$

when the voltage between conductors is V. The gradient is a maximum when the radius r is equal to the radius of the inner conductor a. For a specified outer radius b and maximum field strength E_m, the allowed potential difference between conductors is

$$V = E_m b \frac{\ln \dfrac{b}{a}}{\dfrac{b}{a}} \quad \text{volts} \tag{4-23}$$

For maximum voltage between conductors, the optimum ratio b/a is 2.718. This corresponds to a characteristic impedance of 60 ohms. The variation in breakdown voltage as a function of the ratio of radii with a constant-radius outer conductor is shown in Fig. 4-3.

6. Maximum Power That Can Be Carried by a Coaxial Line

The power that can be transferred by a matched line will depend upon the ratio V^2/Z_0. Hence the maximum power P that can be carried in a coaxial line is

$$P = \frac{E_m{}^2 b^2}{60} \frac{\ln \dfrac{b}{a}}{\left(\dfrac{b}{a}\right)^2} \quad \text{watts} \tag{4-24}$$

where E_m is the maximum allowable voltage gradient. For a specified outer radius b, the maximum power can be carried by a line when the ratio $b/a = 1.65$. This gives a characteristic impedance of 30 ohms.

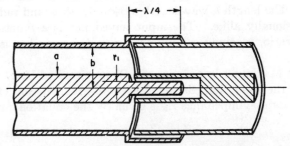

Fig. 4-5.—Choke connection for a coaxial line.

This is the theoretical maximum power-carrying capacity, but in actual practice it is necessary to limit maximum powers to values considerably less than the theoretical limit. The maximum voltage that will exist on the line for a given net power flow will increase if the load is mismatched (see Sec. 2-3). Also, gradients may be higher at line supports, and there is more likelihood of breakdown in a rotating joint, or choke connection. The breakdown in a choke connector is most likely to occur at the center conductor. As Fig. 4-5 shows, the maximum gradient in the line will be increased as the ratio a/r_1, and the power-carrying capacity is therefore reduced by a factor $(a/r_1)^2$.

Information on the variation of power-carrying capacity with altitude for an air-filled unpressurized line is given in Sec. 2-3.

7. Impedance of Resonant Lines

At microwave frequencies, it is often desirable to use concentric lines as circuit elements, particularly as resonant circuits in which the line presents a minimum or maximum resonant impedance.

Case 1: Minimum Impedance of an Open-circuited Line.— Neglecting losses, the input impedance Z of an open-circuited transmission line of length l and characteristic impedance Z_0 is given by

$$Z = -jZ_0 \cot \beta l \qquad (4\text{-}25)$$

This would indicate that the input impedance passes through zero at the odd quarter-wave points. Actually, because of the presence of conductor losses, the input impedance does not reach zero at these points but is given by the expression

$$Z = 60\pi \frac{\delta}{\lambda} \frac{l}{b} \left(1 + \frac{b}{a}\right) \qquad (4\text{-}26)$$

as the reactive component approaches zero. In this expression, Z is in ohms. The length l, wavelength λ, skin depth δ, and radii b and a are dimensionally alike. The input impedance is a function of the diametric ratio, reaching a minimum when the ratio b/a is equal to unity.

Case 2: Maximum Impedance of a Short-circuited Line.—Neglecting losses, the input impedance of a short-circuited line of length l and characteristic impedance Z_0 is given by the equation

$$Z = jZ_0 \tan \beta l \qquad (4\text{-}27)$$

indicating that the input impedance passes through infinity at odd quarter wavelengths. Because of the presence of conductor losses, the impedance, although high, is not infinite and is given by the equation

$$Z = \frac{120}{\pi} \frac{\lambda}{\delta} \frac{b}{l} \frac{\ln^2\left(\dfrac{b}{a}\right)}{1 + \dfrac{b}{a}} \qquad \text{ohms} \qquad (4\text{-}28)$$

where the terms are defined as in Eq. (4-26). This neglects losses in the shorting plug or plate. The optimum ratio of b/a for high resonant impedance occurs when $b/a = 9.2$, corresponding to a line whose characteristic impedance is $Z_0 = 133$ ohms, but the maximum is quite broad. The variation in resonant impedance with changing diametric ratio for a constant-radius outer conductor is plotted in Fig. 4-3.

8. Higher Modes in Coaxial Lines

Coaxial lines are usually operated with energy transmitted in the principal (TEM) mode and will transmit a wave of any frequency in this mode. But higher order (wave guide) modes can also exist. For these higher modes, the coaxial line acts like a high-pass filter, and a given line will carry energy in one of the higher modes only if excited at a frequency above the critical or cutoff frequency for the given mode. This cutoff frequency depends upon the mode in question. At frequencies below cutoff, the higher modes may be excited at a source of energy or at a discontinuity in the line, but will attenuate rapidly with distance and draw no real power.

Lines that are designed to operate at a given frequency are usually restricted in size so that none of these higher modes can carry energy down the line. An approximate formula that specifies this critical wavelength within 8 per cent is

$$\lambda = \pi(b + a) \qquad (4\text{-}29)$$

i.e., the limiting wavelength is approximately equal to the circumference at the arithmetic mean diameter.

The configuration of all these higher modes will approach the configuration of modes that exist in round wave guide as the diameter of the center conductor approaches zero. In Fig. 4-6, the electric fields of a number of these higher modes are shown, and their notation is that of the corresponding limiting modes in round wave guide. The cutoff wavelength λ_c of some of these modes is given in Fig. 4-7 as a function of the diametric ratio of the coaxial line.

The field components for all higher modes may be expressed in

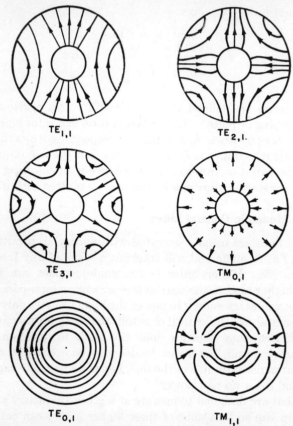

FIG. 4-6.—The electric field of some of the higher modes in a coaxial line.

terms of the cylindrical coordinates r, θ, z as follows:[1]
For TE waves:

$$H_z = \frac{k^2}{j\omega\mu} e^{j\omega t - \gamma z} [AJ_n(kr) + BN_n(kr)] \cos n\theta$$

$$H_\theta = -\frac{\gamma}{rk^2} \frac{\partial H_z}{\partial \theta}$$

$$H_r = -\frac{\gamma}{k^2} \frac{\partial H_z}{\partial r} \tag{4-30}$$

$$Z_w = \frac{j\omega\mu}{\gamma} = \text{wave impedance}$$

[1] In Eqs. (4-30) and (4-31) rationalized mks units are used. In this system the fundamental units are the meter, kilogram, second, and coulomb. The dielectric constant ϵ is in farads per meter, equal to 8.85×10^{-12} in empty space. The permeability μ is in henrys per meter, equal to 1.26×10^{-6} in empty space.

For *TM* waves:

$$E_z = \frac{k^2}{j\omega\epsilon} e^{j\omega t - \gamma z} [AJ_n(kr) + BN_n(kr)] \cos n\theta$$

$$E_\theta = -\frac{\gamma}{rk^2} \frac{\partial E_z}{\partial \theta}$$

(4-31)

$$E_r = -\frac{\gamma}{k^2} \frac{\partial E_z}{\partial r}$$

$$Z_w = \frac{\gamma}{j\omega\epsilon}$$

For all waves:

$$E_r = Z_w H_\theta \qquad k^2 = k_0{}^2 + \gamma^2$$

$$E_\theta = -Z_w H_r \qquad k_0 = \frac{2\pi}{\lambda}$$

In these equations, λ_1 is the wavelength in the line and λ is the wavelength of a plane wave in the material forming the line dielectric

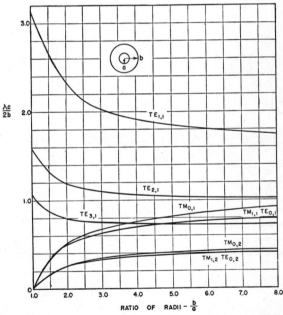

FIG. 4-7.—Cutoff wavelengths of higher modes in a coaxial line.

(assumed lossless). The values of k for the various modes are the roots of the following transcendental equations in the unknown k, which ensure that the proper boundary conditions are met.

For *TE* waves:

$$-\frac{B}{A} = \frac{J_n{}'(ka)}{N_n{}'(ka)} = \frac{J_n{}'(kb)}{N_n{}'(kb)}$$

(4-32)

For *TM* waves:

$$-\frac{B}{A} = \frac{J_n(ka)}{N_n(ka)} = \frac{J_n(kb)}{N_n(kb)} \tag{4-33}$$

where J_n and N_n are Bessel functions of the first and second kind, respectively. The prime denotes differentiation. The modes are identified by the subscripts n, m where n is the order of the Bessel functions involved and the value of k used is the mth root of Eq. (4-32) or (4-33). The cutoff wavelength λ_c is

$$\lambda_c = \frac{2\pi}{k} \tag{4-34}$$

for any mode. The attenuation of any mode in the cutoff region is

$$\alpha = \frac{54.6}{\lambda_c} \sqrt{1 - \left(\frac{\lambda_c}{\lambda}\right)^2} \quad \text{db/unit length} \tag{4-35}$$

CHAPTER 5

FLEXIBLE CABLES

1. General Information[1]

A large number of designs of flexible coaxial cable were developed during the war years for higher frequency use. The development and production were the work of a number of cable manufacturers and were

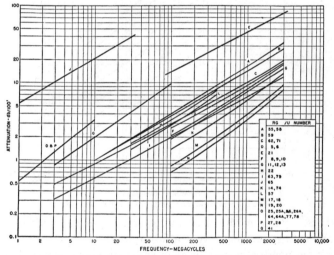

Fig. 5-1.—Attenuation of standard R.F. Cables.

coordinated by an Army-Navy R.F. Cable Coordinating Committee. As a result of this work, there are a number of types of high-frequency cable, all of which are produced by several manufacturers, and all of which have been assigned Army-Navy type numbers of the form RG-n/U, with the n identifying the particular type of cable. A number of these have been adopted as standard cables. A list of these cables and their characteristics as of Oct. 15, 1944, is given in Table 5-1. The expected attenuation of these cables is given as a function of

[1] The tabulated information and charts in this chapter are taken from the Index of Army-Navy R.F. Transmission Lines and Fittings (Army No. 71-4925 Navships 900102), issued by the Army-Navy R.F. Cable Coordinating Committee.

frequency in Fig. 5-1.   A list of nonstandard cables still in use is given
in Table 5-2.   In Table 5-3 is a list of standard radio-frequency cables
in order of diameter over dielectric, and in Table 5-4 is a list of manufacturers of radio-frequency cables.   Figure 5-2 gives the power-
handling capacity of various cables as a function of frequency.

The high-frequency cables all have the common feature of a solid
dielectric of stabilized polyethylene separating the inner and outer

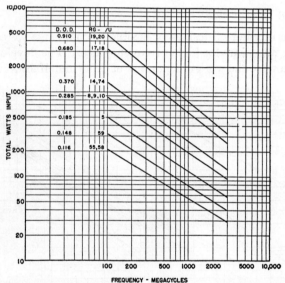

Fig. 5-2.—Power-carrying capacity of cables.

conductors.   Pulse cables used at lower frequencies and lossy high-
frequency cables may have synthetic-rubber dielectric.

The inner conductor may be solid or stranded and is usually copper,
although Nichrome is used in some lossy cables.   The outer conductors
are single or double layers of braid, usually copper, which may or may
not be tinned.   The outer protective cover is usually vinyl, and some
of the cables are armored for additional protection.

Most of the cables are still in a state of development, and changes
are being made in their design and construction.   It is to be expected
therefore that not all the characteristics outlined in the various tables
will still apply at some future date.   These changes have been and
are being dictated by troubles that are encountered in the use of these
cables.   Their performance is not yet completely satisfactory, and
some care must be taken when they are used.

2. High-frequency Phenomena

Attenuation.—At lower frequencies, the attenuation in a cable is primarily the result of conductor losses and, therefore, increases as the square root of frequency. But the dielectric losses increase linearly with frequency and become increasingly important at high frequencies. When they are appreciable, they increase the frequency sensitivity of the cable attenuation.

The conductor losses are somewhat higher than predicted by simple theory because of the "braid factor," the ratio of resistivity of the outer braid to the resistivity of a solid outer conductor. There is some experimental evidence to indicate that the braid factor may increase with increasing frequency. In particular, the frequency sensitivity at the highest frequencies is somewhat greater than expected.

The attenuation in the cable is also likely to vary with time for a variety of reasons. For one thing, it was found for an early design of cable that, with prolonged temperature cycling, the polyethylene dielectric was sufficiently contaminated by the outer cover material to raise the attenuation at high frequencies (9,500 mc) by as much as 300 per cent. This situation has been greatly improved by addition of a stabilizer to the dielectric and by use of a noncontaminating vinyl jacket.

Chemicals in the outer jacket are also likely to increase attenuation by corroding the outer braid. Bare copper is most susceptible; silver braid or tinned copper have shown more resistance to corrosion. When the braid has corroded, it is sometimes found that repeated flexing of the cable will reduce attenuation by polishing the braid contacts. But if the braid is not corroded, the attenuation may be increased by flexing, which tends to loosen the braid. When this has happened, the former characteristics may be regained by leaving the cable motionless for a period of a day or so.

Some experiments show that repeated flexing or temperature cycling may cause the center conductor to drift or wander through the dielectric. With severe temperature cycling, the differential expansion of the metal and polyethylene may cause the center conductor to short against the outside braid.

Another effect that has been observed with temperature cycling is that the plasticizer from the outer covering may diffuse through the polyethylene and form a waxy deposit around the center conductor.

Temperature cycling and flexing will cause increasingly erratic

TABLE 5-1

ARMY-NAVY STANDARD LIST OF R.F. CABLES

October 15, 1944

Class of cables		Army-Navy type number	Inner conductor	Dielec. material*	Nominal diameter of dielectric(in.)	Shielding braid	Protective covering	Nominal over-all diam. (in.)	Weight (lb/ft)	Nominal impedance (ohms)	Nominal capacitance ($\mu\mu$f/ft)	Max. operating voltage (rms)	Remarks
50-55 ohms	Single braid	RG-58/U	No. 20 AWG copper	A	0.116	Tinned copper	Vinyl	0.195	0.025	53.5	28.5	1,900	General-purpose small-size flexible cable
		RG-8/U	7/21 AWG copper	A	0.285	Copper	Vinyl	0.405	0.106	52.0	29.5	4,000	General-purpose medium-size flexible cable
		RG-10/U	7/21 AWG copper	A	0.285	Copper	Vinyl (noncontaminating) and armor	0.475 (max)	0.146	52.0	29.5	4,000	Same as RG-8/U armor for naval equipment
		RG-17/U	0.188 copper	A	0.680	Copper	Vinyl (noncontaminating)	0.870	0.460	52.0	27.5	11,000	Large high-power low-attenuation transmission cable
		RG-18/U	0.188 copper	A	0.680	Copper	Vinyl (noncontaminating) and armor	0.945 (max)	0.585	52.0	29.5	11,000	Same as RG-17/U armor for naval equipment
		RG-19/U	0.250 copper	A	0.910	Copper	Vinyl (noncontaminating)	1.120	0.740	52.0	29.5	14,000	Very large high-power low-attenuation transmission cable
		RG-20/U	0.250 copper	A	0.910	Copper	Vinyl (noncontaminating) and armor	1.195 (max)	0.925	52.0	29.5	14,000	Same as RG-19/U armor for naval equipment
	Double braid	RG-55/U	No. 20 AWG copper	A	0.116	Tinned copper	Polyethylene	0.206 (max)	0.034	53.5	28.5	1,900	Small-size flexible cable
		RG-5/U	No. 16 AWG copper	A	0.185	Copper	Vinyl	0.332	0.087	53.5	28.5	2,000	Small microwave cable
		RG-9/U	7/21 AWG silvered copper	A	0.280	Inner—silver-coated copper, outer—copper	Vinyl (noncontaminating)	0.420	0.150	51.0	30.0	4,000	Medium-size low-level circuit cable
		RG-14/U	No. 10 AWG copper	A	0.370	Copper	Vinyl (noncontaminating)	0.545	0.216	52.0	29.5	5,500	General-purpose semiflexible power transmission cable

		RG No.	Inner conductor			Shield	Dielectric/Jacket						Application
70–80 ohms	Single braid	RG-74/U	No. 10 AWG copper	A	0.370	Copper	Vinyl (noncontaminating) and armor	0.615	0.310	52.0	29.5	5,500	Same as RG-14/U armor for naval equipment
		RG-59/U	No. 22 AWG copperweld	A	0.146	Copper	Vinyl	0.242	0.032	73.0	21.0	2,300	General-purpose small-size video cable
		RG-11/U	7/26 AWG tinned copper	A	0.285	Copper	Vinyl	0.405	0.096	75.0	20.5	4,000	Medium-size flexible video and communication cable
		RG-12/U	7/26 AWG tinned copper	A	0.285	Copper	Vinyl (noncontaminating) and armor	0.475	0.141	75.0	20.5	4,000	Same as RG-11/U armor for naval equipment
	Double braid	RG-6/U	No. 21 AWG copperweld	A	0.185	Inner—silver-coated copper, outer—copper	Vinyl (noncontaminating)	0.332	0.082	76.0	20.0	2,700	Small-size video and i-f cable
		RG-13/U	7/26 AWG tinned copper	A	0.280	Copper	Vinyl	0.420	0.126	74.0	20.5	4,000	I-f cable
Cables of special characteristics	Twin conductor	RG-22/U	2 Cond. 7, No. 18 AWG copper	A	0.285	Single—tinned copper	Vinyl	0.405	0.107	95.0	16.0	1,000	Small-size twin conductor cable
		RG-57/U	2 Cond. 7/21 AWG copper	A	0.472	Single—tinned copper	Vinyl	0.625	0.225	95.0	16.0	3,000	Large-size twin conductor cable
	High attenuation	RG-21/U	No. 16 AWG resistance wire	A	0.185	Inner—silver-coated copper, outer—copper	Vinyl (noncontaminating)	0.332	0.087	53.0	29.0	2,700	Special attenuating cable with small temperature coefficient of attenuation
	High impedance	RG-65/U	No. 32 Formex F Helix diam. 0.128 in.	A	0.285	Single copper	Vinyl	0.405	0.096	950	44.0	1,000	High-impedance video cable. High delay
Low capacitance	Single braid	RG-62/U	AWG copperweld	A	0.146	Copper	Vinyl	0.242	0.0382	93.0	13.5 (max 14.5)	750	Small-size low-capacitance air-spaced cable
		RG-63/U	No. 22 AWG copperweld	A	0.285	Copper	Vinyl	0.405	0.0832	125	10.0 (max 11.0)	1,000	Medium-size low-capacitance air-spaced cable
	Double braid	RG-71/U	No. 22 AWG copperweld	A	0.146	Inner—plain copper, outer—tinned copper	Polyethylene	0.250 (max)	0.0457	93.0	13.5 (max 14.5)	750	Small-size low-capacitance spaced cable for i-f purposes

TABLE 5-1.—(Continued)

Class of cables		Army-Navy type number	Inner conductor	Dielec. material*	Nominal diameter of dielectric (in.)	Shielding braid	Protective covering	Nominal over-all diam. (in.)	Weight (lb/ft)	Nominal impedance (ohms)	Nominal capacitance (μμf/ft)	Max. operating voltage (rms)	Remarks
Pulse applications	Single braid	RG-26/U	19/0.0117 tinned copper	D	0.308†	Tinned copper	Synthetic rubber and armor	0.525 (max)	0.189	48.0	50.0	8,000 (peak)	Medium-size pulse cable armored for naval equipment
		RG-27/U	19/0.0185 tinned copper	D	0.455†	Single—tinned copper	Vinyl and armor	0.675 (max)	0.304	48.0	50.0	15,000 (peak)	Large-size pulse cable armored for naval equipment
	Double braid	RG-64/U	19/0.0117 tinned copper	D	0.308†	Tinned copper	Neoprene	0.495	0.205	48.0	50.0	8,000 (peak)	Medium-size pulse cable
		RG-25/U	19/0.0117 tinned copper	D	0.308†	Tinned copper	Neoprene	0.565	0.205	48.0	50.0	8,000 (peak)	Special twisting pulse cable for naval equipment
		RG-28/U	19/0.0185 tinned copper	D	0.455†	Inner—tinned copper, outer galvanized steel	Synthetic rubber	0.805	0.370	48.0	50.0	15,000 (peak)	Large-size pulse cable
Twisting application	Single braid	RG-41/U	16/30 AWG tinned copper	C	0.250	Tinned copper	Neoprene	0.425	0.150	67.5	27.0	3,000 (peak)	Special twist cable

* Dielectric materials: A—Stabilized polyethylene. C—Synthetic rubber compound. D—Layer of synthetic rubber dielectric between thin layers of conducting rubber.
† This value is the diameter over the outer layer of conducting rubber.

TABLE 5-2

NONSTANDARD CABLES STILL IN USE

(1) Army-Navy type No.	(2) Inner conductor	(3) Dielectric material*	(4) Nominal diam. of dielectric (in.)	(5) No. of shielding braids	(6) Protective covering	(7) Nominal over-all diam. (in.)	(8) Weight (lb/ft)	(9) Nominal impedance (ohms)	(10) Nominal capacitance ($\mu\mu f/ft$)	(11) Max. operating volts (rms)	(12) Replaced by standard
RG-4/U	No. 20 AWG copper	A	0.116	2	Vinyl	0.226	0.025	51	30	1,900	RG-58/U
RG-7/U	No. 19 AWG copper	A	0.250	1	Vinyl	0.370	0.080	95	14		RG-62/U
RG-15/U	No. 15 AWG copperweld	A	0.370	2	Vinyl	0.545	0.197	75	20	5,500	RG-11/U
RG-16/U	0.125 in. copper tube	A	0.460	1	Vinyl	0.630 ×	0.254	52	30	7,500	RG-12/U
RG-23/U	2 Con. 7/26 copper	A	0.400	2	Vinyl	0.650 × 0.945	0.490	125	13	3,000	Not used
RG-24/U	2 Con. 7/26 copper	A	0.400	2	Vinyl and armor	0.735 × 1.034 (max)	0.670	125	13	3,000	Used for DF only
RG-29/U	No. 20 AWG copper	A	0.116	1	Polyethylene	0.184	0.021	53	29	1,900	Used for DF only
RG-31/U	7/21 AWG copper	B	0.285	1	Vinyl	0.405	0.106	51	30	2,000	RG-58/U
RG-33/U	No. 10 AWG copper	A	0.370	None	Lead sheath	0.470	0.390	51	30	6,000	RG-8/U
RG-34/U	7/21 AWG copper	A	0.460	1	Vinyl	0.625	0.224	72	21	5,200	None
RG-35/U	No. 9 AWG copper	A	0.680	1	Vinyl and armor	0.945 (max)	0.525	72	21	10,000	None
RG-36/U	0.162 copper	A	0.910	1	Vinyl and armor	1.160	0.805	72	21	10,000	None
RG-37/U	No. 20 AWG tinned copper	C	0.140	1	Polyethylene	0.210 (max)	0.040	53	29	750	RG-58/U
RG-38/U	No. 17 AWG tinned copper	C	0.196	2	Polyethylene	0.312 (max)	0.110	53	29	1,000	RG-21/U
RG-39/U	No. 22 AWG copperweld	C	0.196	2	Polyethylene	0.312 (max)	0.100	73	28	1,000	RG-6/U
RG-40/U	No. 22 AWG copperweld	C	0.196	2	Synthetic rubber	0.420 (max)	0.150	73	28	1,000	RG-59/U
RG-42/U	No. 21 AWG resistance wire	A	0.196	2	Vinyl	0.342	0.050	76	20	2,700	RG-6/U
RG-54A/U	7/0.0152 copper	A	0.178	1	Noncontaminating polyethylene	0.250 (max)	0.041	58	27	3,000	None

* Dielectric materials. A—Stabilized polyethylene. B—Polyisobutylene mixtures. C—Synthetic rubber compounds.

TABLE 5-3
STANDARD R.F. CABLES IN ORDER OF DIAMETER OVER DIELECTRIC

D.O.D.	RG-/U type	No. of braids	Nominal impedance, (ohms)	Jacket type	Armored	Remarks
0.116	55	2	53.5	III	..	Small-size i-f cable
0.116	58	1	53.5	I	..	General-purpose small-size flexible cable
0.146	59	1	73.0	I	..	General-purpose small-size video cable
0.146	62	1	93.0	I	..	Low-capacitance cable
0.146	71	2	93.0	III	..	Low-capacitance cable
0.185	5	2	53.5	I	..	Small microwave cable
0.185	6	2	76.0	II	..	Small microwave i-f cable, double shielded
0.185	21	2	53.0	II	..	Special attenuating cable
0.250	41	1	67.5	IV	..	Cable designed for twisting
0.280	9	2	51.0	II	..	Medium-size low-level circuit cable
0.280	13	2	74.0	I	..	Double-shielded i-f cable
0.285	8	1	52.0	I	..	General-purpose medium-size flexible cable
0.285	10	1	52.0	II	x	Armored RG-8/U
0.285	11	1	75.0	I	..	Medium-flexible video and communication cable
0.285	12	1	75.0	II	x	Armored RG-11/U
0.285	22	1	95.0	I	..	Small-size twin conductor cable
0.285	65	1	950.0	I	..	High impedance-delay line video cable
0.285	63A	1	125.0	I	..	Low-capacity cable
0.285	79A	1	125.0	I	x	Armored RG-63A/U. 0.475 in. max. diam. over armor
0.288	25A	2	48.0	V	..	Replaces RG-25/U. Uses field-assembly connectors

behavior at the higher frequencies, because of the greater importance of the braid contacts.

Periodicity.—Periodicity is the name applied to the anomalous behavior of different cables at different specific frequencies or frequency bands and their harmonics. Periodicity shows as a high standing-wave ratio and increased attenuation. No cable checked has been found completely free of this effect.

The sources of this effect are periodic variations in the physical construction of the cable that result from the process of manufacture. When the spacing of the variations is some multiple of a half wavelength, the effects add in such a fashion as to affect seriously the overall behavior of a length of cable.

TABLE 5-4
R. F. CABLE MANUFACTURERS

Manufacturer	Cable type			Mfgs. index no.
	Polyethylene	Pulse	Rubber	
American Phenolic Corp.................	x	..	..	3
American Steel & Wire Co...............	..	x	..	6
Anaconda Wire & Cable Co..............	x	..	..	7
Federal Telephone & Radio Corp..........	x	..	..	31
General Cable Corp......................	x	..	..	32
General Electric Co.....................	x	..	x	33A
Okonite Company.......................	x	x	x	56
Phelps Dodge Copper Prod. Co............	x	..	..	59
Philadelphia Insulated Wire Co...........	..	..	x	60
Simplex Wire & Cable Co................	x	x	x	69
Western Electric Co.....................	..	x	x	77
Whitney Blake Wire & Cable Co..........	x	x	x	79

The most serious cause of periodicity is variation in the outer diameter of the dielectric. The wavelengths corresponding to the frequencies of measured disturbances have been checked experimentally with mechanically measured variations in the core diameter, and variations of 1 or 2 mils are sufficient to cause pronounced resonances in the region of 3,000 mc. Other sources are variations in braid uniformity, pitch of braid, jacket uniformity, and armor.

In general, the smaller diameter cables are likely to show periodicity effects in the region of 1,000 to 10,000 mc, while larger diameter cables have shown effects at frequencies as low as 175 mc.

Heating cables to 85°C for several hours and subsequent cooling increases the number and severity of the periodicity effects. This indicates that the polyethylene is not stress-free when extruded.

In general, periodicity effects are serious enough to warrant careful consideration when it is planned to use the cable in a critical application.

Power-handling Capacity.—The power-handling capacity of a high-frequency cable is usually limited by the heating of the cable, and the maximum voltage is limited by the dielectric strength of the polyethylene and fittings. The two ratings do not necessarily agree, and if a cable is run at its maximum voltage rating, the service must usually be interrupted if the power rating is not to be exceeded.

CHAPTER 6

COAXIAL LINE STRUCTURES AND TRANSFORMERS

1. Miscellaneous Structures

Sleeves.—A quarter-wave line is frequently used as an impedance-matching device at high frequencies (Sec. 3-5). In coaxial lines this matching section frequently takes the form of a metal sleeve placed over the inner conductor or inside the outer conductor, as in Fig. 6-1. The impedance of the transformer section is then less than the line

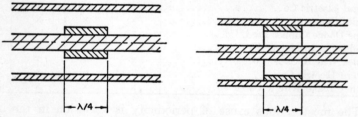

FIG. 6-1.—Quarter-wave sleeves used for impedance matching in a coaxial line.

impedance, and the resistance that is matched to the line must be less than Z_0. This means that the end of the sleeve facing the load must be placed at a voltage minimum in the line.

The dimensions of sleeve necessary for matching are determined by the standing-wave ratio σ to be eliminated. If the sleeve is on the inner conductor, its outer diameter d_1 should be

$$d_1 = \frac{2b}{\left(\dfrac{b}{a}\right)^{\sigma - \frac{1}{2}}} \tag{6-1}$$

where b and a are the outer and inner radii of the line, respectively. If the sleeve is inside the outer conductor, its inner diameter should be

$$d_2 = 2a \left(\frac{b}{a}\right)^{\sigma - \frac{1}{2}} \tag{6-2}$$

The ratios $d_1/2a$ and $d_2/2b$ are plotted as functions of the standing-wave ratio they will match in 46-ohm line in Fig. 6-2. For minimum

82

frequency sensitivity, the sleeve should be placed as close to the load as possible.

This simple theory neglects the discontinuity capacities set up by the fringing fields at the ends of the transformer. This is usually justified because, even if the capacities are appreciable, their spacing is such that the effects tend to cancel.

Multiple quarter-wave sleeves may be used to increase the band width of the matching transformer. Tapers may be even more satisfactory if their length is not too short. The general principles that should be followed in their use are outlined in Sec. 3-5.

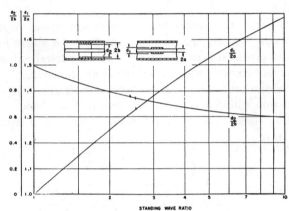

FIG. 6-2.—The dimensions of quarter-wave sleeves used for impedance matching in a 46-ohm coaxial line.

Sometimes the quarter-wave transformer is constructed by using a slug of dielectric material that reduces the line impedance. If the dielectric completely fills the line, the characteristic impedance of the line is reduced by a factor $\sqrt{\epsilon}$. The phase velocity and wavelength are also reduced by the same factor, and the length of the dielectric slug must be $\lambda/4 \sqrt{\epsilon}$ if it is to be electrically a quarter-wave long. If the dielectric only partially fills the line, the characteristic impedance and phase velocity are reduced by a lesser amount. The reduction in characteristic impedance and phase velocity will be proportional to the square root of the increase in capacity per unit length between conductors.

A combination metal and dielectric sleeve may be used; this is advantageous when the matching transformer is required to serve the additional function of supporting the center conductor or sealing or pressurizing the line. It also enables higher standing-wave ratios to be matched than the dielectric transformer alone is capable of matching.

Beads in Coaxial Lines.—The center conductor of a coaxial line must be supported clear of the outside conductor. This is often done in cables by using a continuous solid dielectric material between the conductors. But at microwave frequencies, even the best solid dielectrics introduce such a high amount of attenuation that solid dielectric cables cannot be used for transmitting power over any very large distances. A gaseous dielectric is required when low attenuation is desired, and the center conductor is supported only at discrete intervals. These supports must be used with care, because they represent discontinuities that are likely to cause reflections at microwave frequencies.

Single Beads.—The center conductor is sometimes supported by dielectric beads that are spaced along the line. A single bead introduced into an air-filled coaxial line will cause a partial reflection of an incident electromagnetic wave, resulting from the changed impedance of the line in the presence of the dielectric material. The magnitude of this reflection will depend upon the length of the bead.

Neglecting losses, the exact reflection coefficient ρ from a single bead is given by

$$\rho = \frac{-j\left(\sqrt{\epsilon} - \frac{1}{\sqrt{\epsilon}}\right)\tan\frac{2\pi\sqrt{\epsilon}\,l}{\lambda}}{2 + j\left(\sqrt{\epsilon} + \frac{1}{\sqrt{\epsilon}}\right)\tan\frac{2\pi\sqrt{\epsilon}\,l}{\lambda}} \tag{6-3}$$

where l is the length of the bead and ϵ is its dielectric constant. If the value of $\tan\frac{2\pi\sqrt{\epsilon}\,l}{\lambda}$ is small, this reduces to

$$\rho = -\frac{j}{2}(\epsilon - 1)\frac{2\pi l}{\lambda} \tag{6-4}$$

The absolute value of this expression is

$$|\rho| = \frac{\pi l}{\lambda}(\epsilon - 1) \tag{6-5}$$

The magnitude of the standing-wave ratio introduced by a bead is given graphically in Fig. 6-3. In this figure the standing-wave ratio is plotted against l/λ. Curves are given for several values of dielectric constant. These curves assume no loss in the dielectric. A bead that is electrically a half wavelength long introduces no net reflection. The advantages of a low dielectric-constant bead are apparent. The effective dielectric constant may be reduced at the cost of mechanical strength by cutting away part of the dielectric material of the bead.

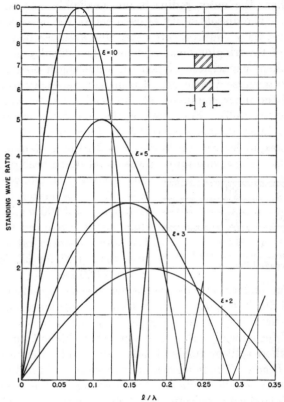

Fig. 6-3.—Standing-wave ratio introduced by a single dielectric bead in a coaxial line.

Undercut Beads.—The reflection from a dielectric bead may be minimized by adjusting the diametric ratio at the bead so as to hold constant the characteristic impedance. This is illustrated in Fig. 6-4. To maintain the characteristic impedance constant, the radius a' of the inner conductor at the bead should be

$$a' = \frac{b}{\left(\frac{b}{a}\right)^{\sqrt{\epsilon}}} \qquad (6\text{-}6)$$

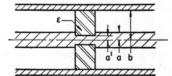

Fig. 6-4.—Undercut dielectric bead used to support the center conductor of a coaxial line.

where ϵ is the dielectric constant of the bead and b and a are the outer and inner radii of the air-filled line. This formula is derived from simple theory and neglects fringing effects. These effects are great enough to affect appreciably the performance of these beads at frequencies where the outer radius is not negligible compared with a wavelength. The discontinuity at each end of the bead is equivalent to a small capacity shunted across the line at those points, but the interaction of the fringing fields increases the difficulty of calculating these equivalent capacities. When the wavelength does not greatly exceed the transverse dimensions, it is usually necessary to reduce the diameter of the inner conductor at the bead a greater amount than predicted by Eq. (3-6). For example, the preceding formula predicts an optimum inner diameter of 0.265 in. for a bead $\frac{1}{4}$ in. long, of material whose dielectric constant is $\epsilon = 2.10$ in a 46-ohm line with $2a = 0.375$ in. Experimentally[1] it was found that a bead of this diameter

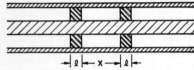

FIG. 6-5.—Paired dielectric beads in a coaxial line.

eter set up a standing-wave ratio $\sigma = 1.10$ in a matched line at a frequency of 3,000 mc, while if the diameter was reduced to 0.245 in., the standing-wave ratio remained less than 1.02 for all frequencies below 4,000 mc.

In general, undercut beads are not very frequency selective, and it is not too difficult to pick a design that will introduce only a small reflection over a very broad band of frequencies in the microwave spectrum Mechanically, they are somewhat difficult to handle in long lines, where split or molded beads seem to offer the best solution.

Pairs of Beads.—The reflection introduced by a single bead may be eliminated at a single frequency by inserting another similar bead which will introduce a reflection of such magnitude and phase as to cancel the reflection of the single bead. For the two reflections to cancel, the effective distance between the bead centers should be approximately a quarter wavelength. Referring to Fig. 6-5 the exact formula for proper spacing X between beads to cancel reflections is

$$X = \frac{\lambda}{2\pi} \tan^{-1}\left[\frac{2\sqrt{\epsilon}}{1+\epsilon}\cot\left(\frac{2\pi\sqrt{\epsilon}\,l}{\lambda}\right)\right] \tag{6-7}$$

where ϵ is the dielectric constant of the bead material. A disadvantage of pairing beads to cancel reflections is that the device is resonant and will introduce a reflection at frequencies differing from the designed frequency. For example, consider a concentric line in which the inner conductor is supported by two $\frac{1}{4}$-in. beads of dielectric constant

[1] Experiments performed in laboratories of Sperry Gyroscope Company, Inc.

$\epsilon = 2.6$. If the beads are properly spaced for no reflection at $\lambda = 10$ cm ($X = 0.548$ in.), the standing-wave ratio introduced into the line as a function of wavelength is given in Fig. 6-6.

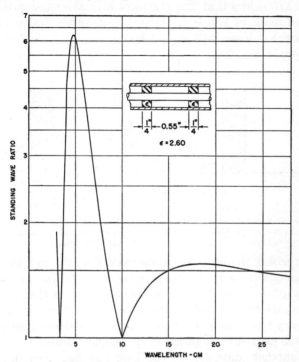

Fig. 6-6.—Standing-wave ratio introduced into a matched line by two dielectric beads properly spaced for a wavelength of 10 cm.

Multiple Beads.—If it is desired to use a long coaxial line for transmission of microwave signals, and the center conductor is supported by multiple beads of dielectric, some care must be taken in choosing the spacing between the beads.

Consider a large number of thin beads, of thickness d and uniformly spaced a distance l apart. This is illustrated in Fig. 6-7. It is readily apparent that, if the distance l were approximately a half wave, the reflections introduced by each bead would add in phase and the line would have very high attenuation, even if the dielectric were perfect and absorbed no power. The presence of this reflected wave makes

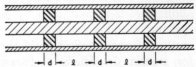

Fig. 6-7.—Multiple dielectric beads equally spaced in a coaxial line.

the input impedance highly reactive and prevents power from entering the line.

An approximate calculation based on filter theory and assuming that $d \ll \lambda/2$ shows that this region of high attenuation is found for values of l between $\lambda/2 - d\epsilon$ and $\lambda/2 - d$, as illustrated in Fig. 6-8. The presence of losses will modify this curve and leads to the general form shown in Fig. 6-9.

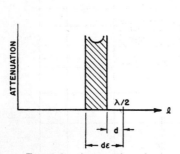

FIG. 6-8.—Attenuation characteristics of multiple dielectric beads in a coaxial line.

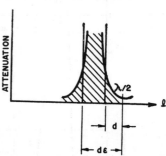

FIG. 6-9.—Attenuation characteristics of multiple dielectric beads as modified by losses.

A surprising distance exists between $l = \lambda/2$ and the region of high attenuation, and with losses present, a spacing of $\lambda/2$ actually gives less attenuation than a spacing of $\lambda/4$. But the $\lambda/2$ spacing is critical enough to frequency that it is very seldom used, a slight change in frequency resulting in a marked increase in attenuation. The $\lambda/4$ spacing has proved most satisfactory for general use.

Still another approach to the long line has been developed by Lawson. This starts with two beads, properly spaced so as to minimize reflections. Then two of these units are placed with their centers an odd number of quarter wavelengths apart. This means that in the neighborhood of the correct frequency the reflection will be a quadratic instead of a linear function of frequency. If the process of adding beads is continued by doubling sections and keeping section centers an odd number of quarter wavelengths apart, the reflections in the immediate vicinity of the correct frequency become less, but for greater deviations of frequency they become greater. As the number of sections increases, the pass band becomes narrower, until for an infinitely large number of sections, there is an infinitely narrow pass band.

Stub Supports for Coaxial Lines. *Straight-through Stubs.*—A lossless shorted transmission line that is electrically a quarter wavelength long has an infinite input impedance, and a stub line of this length may be used to support the center conductor of a coaxial line. It is a resonant device, however, that will introduce no reflection at only the designed frequency. The band width over which the reflection will be below a specified limit depends upon the ratio of the characteristic impedance of the stub line to the characteristic impedance of the main line and will increase as this ratio increases. But a higher impedance stub means reducing the diameter of its center conductor, which weakens the mechanical support that is provided. So a compromise must be made between mechanical strength and electrical band width.

At microwave frequencies where line diameters are usually an appreciable fraction of a wavelength, the behavior of the stub is con-

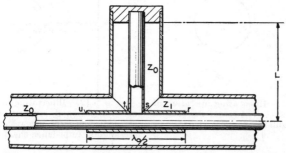

Fig. 6-10.—Broad-band tee stub support for a coaxial line.

siderably affected by the higher order modes or fringing fields that are set up at the junction. For instance, there is no one answer to the problem of whether the quarter wavelength should be measured from the inner or outer conductor, or somewhere in between. This must be determined experimentally for each size of line and frequency.

The band width over which a stub support introduces a small reflection may be increased by the addition of compensating devices. A good example is the half-wave transformer on the center conductor centered at the stub, developed by Pound.[2] This support is illustrated in Fig. 6-10. The transformer on the center conductor is made half a wavelength long at a wavelength λ_0 in the center of the band over which the line is to be used and provides a section of line of different impedance Z_1, but introduces no reflection at this center wavelength. Neither will the stub support, which is adjusted in length until it is electrically $\lambda_0/4$ long. The behavior of this support at resonance is illustrated on an admittance diagram in Fig. 6-11. If the load impedance is matched to the line, the admittance at point r in

[2] Pound, R. V., Stub Supports in $\frac{7}{8}$″ Coaxial Line, M.I.T. Radiation Laboratory, Sec. 53, Rept. 2, May 19, 1942.

Fig. 6-10 will be Y_0. From r to s is a quarter wavelength, bringing the admittance at point s back to the G-axis. The stub is exactly a quarter wavelength long, so the admittance at point t will be the same as at point s. From t to u is another quarter wavelength, and the admittance at u is again Y_0.

There are two other wavelengths, λ_1 and λ_2, one less and one greater than λ_0, at which no reflections occur. At $\lambda_1 < \lambda_0$, illustrated in

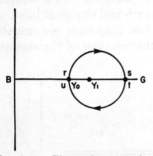

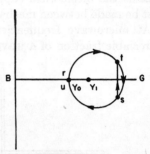

FIG. 6-11.—Illustrating operation of a broad-band stub at center wavelength on a rectangular impedance chart.

FIG. 6-12.—Illustrating the operation of a broad-band stub at wavelength shorter than center wavelength on a rectangular impedance chart.

Fig. 6-12, from r to s is greater than $\lambda_1/4$, and the admittance at s will therefore fall below the G-axis. But the stub is now longer than $\lambda_1/4$ and introduces a capacitive or positive susceptance that brings the admittance at t above the G-axis. From t to u is greater than $\lambda_1/4$, bringing the admittance at u around to Y_0.

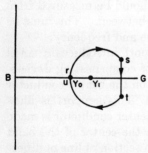

At $\lambda_2 > \lambda_0$, illustrated in Fig. 6-13, the section from r to s is less than $\lambda_2/4$, and the admittance at s therefore falls above the G-axis. The stub is now inductive and adds a negative susceptance that brings the admittance at t below the G-axis. The section from t to u is less than $\lambda_2/4$, but brings the admittance at u back again to Y_0.

FIG. 6-13.—Illustrating the operation of a broad-band stub at wavelength greater than center wavelength on a rectangular impedance chart.

The relation between the characteristic impedance of the line, Z_0, and the impedance of the $\lambda_0/2$ transformer, Z_1, obtained from transmission-line theory is as follows

$$\left(\frac{Z_1}{Z_0}\right)^3 + 2\left(\frac{Z_1}{Z_0}\right)^2 + \frac{1}{p^2}\frac{Z_1}{Z_0} - 2 = 0 \qquad (6\text{-}8)$$

where p is a compromise value taken from the two results given by the equations

$$p = \tan \frac{\pi\lambda_0}{2\lambda_1} \quad \text{and} \quad p = \tan \frac{\pi\lambda_0}{2\lambda_2} \qquad (6\text{-}9)$$

As an example, consider a coaxial line in which $\lambda_1 = 9.1$ cm, $\lambda_0 = 9.9$ cm, and $\lambda_2 = 10.7$ cm. The two equations for p yield values of $p = +8.15$ and $p = -7$. As a compromise, let $p^2 = 50$, which gives $Z_1/Z_0 = 0.835$.

With proper adjustment of the stub length, this type of support centered about $\lambda_0 = 10.0$ cm will exhibit the standing-wave ratio–

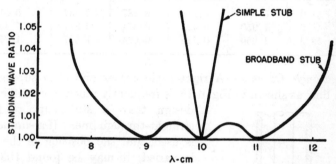

Fig. 6-14.—Standing-wave ratio introduced by a typical broad-band stub.

wavelength relation shown in Fig. 6-14. As indicated, the stub will introduce standing-wave ratios no greater than 1.02 for any wavelength between 8 and 12 cm.

The design procedure that has been found satisfactory is to calculate the dimensions of the half-wave transformer and then to fix the stub length by adjusting it experimentally until there are no reflections introduced at λ_0. The discontinuity effects at the ends of the half-wave transformer are compensated for by proper adjustment of the stub length.

There is phase distortion in one of these broad-band stub supports which makes the electrical and mechanical lengths unequal.[3] This is usually not important, but should be considered when measurements are made of impedances on the far side of a stub support. The dimensions of some typical broad-band stub supports are given in Table 6-1. In referring to the size of coaxial lines, the dimension given is the outer diameter of the outer conductor.

Stub supports are best applied where a very low standing-wave

[3] POUND, R. V., Phase Distortion in Broad Band Stub Supports, M.I.T. Radiation Laboratory, Sec. 53, Rept. 6, Aug. 17, 1942.

ratio is desired over a moderate band of frequencies. For narrow band work, a simple stub is satisfactory. For very wide bands, the broad-band stub is not adequate, and undercut beads are preferred.

TABLE 6-1
TEE STUB SUPPORTS
(All dimensions in inches)

Line size	Z_0	$\lambda_0/2$ transformer		Conductor		Length of stub short to center line
		Length	Diameter	O.D. inner	I.D. outer	
$\frac{1}{2}$	51.0	0.630	0.218	0.187	0.437	0.516
$\frac{7}{8}$	46.0	1.950	0.425	0.374	0.811	1.450
$1\frac{5}{8}$	53.3	1.950	0.725	0.624	1.527	1.750

Right-angle Corners.—A right-angle corner and stub support for coaxial line, as shown in Fig. 6-15, is frequently much more difficult to

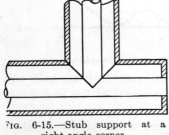

FIG. 6-15.—Stub support at a right-angle corner.

design than a stub support for a straight-through line. If a simple stub is used, and the position of the short is varied, it may be found that the minimum reflection from the stub and corner is not zero, but finite. For example, with 1-in. 75-ohm coaxial line, it is found that at a wavelength of 20 cm a stub can be designed with very little reflection. But at 11 cm the minimum standing-wave ratio is about 1.2, and at 7.75 cm the minimum is greater than 1.5. A completely reflectionless stub and corner must have some sort of transformer designed into it in larger diameter lines or at higher frequencies.

An adaptation of the broad-band stub is the universal stub shown in Fig. 6-16, which permits transmission around a right-angle corner without appreciable reflection over a fairly broad band of frequencies. If a short is properly located on the stub section (dotted lines), a straight-through tee support results which functions like the one described above. By placing a short slightly beyond one end of the $\lambda_0/2$ transformer and leaving the stub open, a signal may be fed around the corner without reflection. The transformer on the stub line cancels reflections at wavelengths λ_1 and λ_2 as in the straight-through stub. The diameter of the transformers may be obtained by Eq.

(6-8), but L_1, L_2, and d must be determined experimentally for each size line and frequency. A typical design is given in Fig. 6-16.

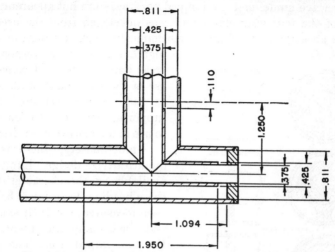

Fig. 6-16.—Broad-band stub support for a right-angle corner.

Resonant Beads for Coaxial Lines.[4]—The quarter-wave stub line often is a satisfactory support for the center conductor of a coaxial line because it is equivalent to a parallel resonant circuit shunting the transmission line. It is possible to build other structures that are parallel resonant and that are capable of supporting the center conductor. These may be built entirely of metal, or part metal and part dielectric, and at high frequencies they may be enclosed completely within the outer conductor of the line, in which event they are called "resonant beads." Band widths may be obtained that are comparable or superior to ordinary stub supports, and broad-banding devices such as the half-wave sleeve mentioned in the previous section are equally applicable. Because of the smaller size of the circuit, losses are generally greater than for conventional stubs, but are not great enough to be of serious consequence for most purposes.

Four typical structures are shown in Fig. 6-17. All these structures when built approximately to the scale shown will be parallel resonant in the neighborhood of 3,000 mc in ⅞-in. 50-ohm coaxial line. The resonant beads have both lumped and distributed constant circuits. In some, such as No. 3, the inductance and capacitance forming the resonant circuit are fairly well separated from each other. But in

---

[4] These resonant beads were first investigated by E. T. Jaynes, Sperry Gyroscope Company, Inc.

others, such as No. 1, the resonant wavelength will be found when the slot is approximately a half wave long, as in the well-known resonant slot in wave guide, and the lumped constants are not apparent. Yet each of the four examples shown was developed from the preceding one in an attempt to obtain a mechanically rugged structure with a high L/C ratio and correspondingly great band width. Of course, the use of these resonant beads as well as stubs is not restricted to line supports; they are often convenient to use in microwave filter designs.

Unfortunately, there is little quantitative design information available on the characteristics of these beads. Their losses have not been measured, but their shunt impedance is many times greater than the line impedance. The power-handling capacity of the line is obviously reduced, and the performance of the beads, such as Nos. 1 and 2, can be seriously affected by particles of dirt catching in the gap. In a 50-ohm line, the band width of beads Nos. 1 and 2 (which depends upon their characteristic impedance $Z_0 = \sqrt{L/C}$) is somewhat less than a simple stub support; the band width of Nos. 3 and 4, somewhat greater. It is possible to measure the resonant frequency of a bead

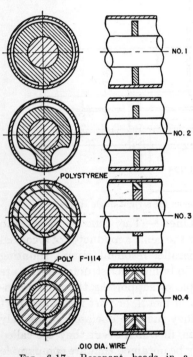

Fig. 6-17.—Resonant beads in a coaxial line, electrically equivalent to parallel resonant circuits shunting the transmission line.

by determining the wavelength at which the bead introduces minimum reflection into a matched line. The characteristic impedance may be measured by determining the slope of the susceptance-frequency characteristic at resonance and applying the equation

$$\frac{dB}{df} = \frac{2}{f_0} \frac{1}{\sqrt{\dfrac{L}{C}}} \tag{6-10}$$

Coaxial-line Junctions.—When three coaxial lines meet at a common junction, as illustrated in Fig. 6-18, the behavior at low frequencies is what would be expected, and any one of the lines may be considered as feeding the other two in parallel. If, as illustrated, the three lines are of equal impedance, the calculation of junction effects is further simplified. But there are higher order modes excited at the junction and at microwave frequencies these modes, though still

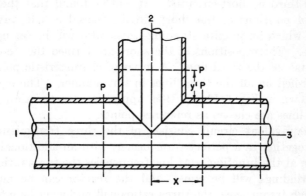

CHARACTERISTIC POINTS AT P

FIG. 6-18.—Illustrating the notation used with an equivalent circuit of a coaxial junction.

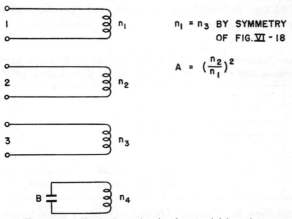

$n_1 = n_3$ BY SYMMETRY OF FIG. VI - 18

$$A = \left(\frac{n_2}{n_1}\right)^2$$

FIG. 6-19.—Equivalent circuit of a coaxial junction.

below cutoff, may appreciably change the behavior of the junction. For any given size line operating at a given frequency, it is possible to describe the behavior of the junction in terms of an equivalent circuit, but the parameters of this circuit will be functions of frequency. The nature of the equivalent circuit will depend upon what cross sections of the three lines are chosen as reference planes. One of the simplest equivalent circuits results when the reference planes or points are chosen by the following procedure.[5]

It is first necessary to introduce the concept of "characteristic points" on the three lines. These characteristic points are located as follows. Energy is fed in one line and extracted from a second, while the third is short-circuited. It will be found that there are a number of positions of the short circuit, spaced a half wavelength apart, at which an infinite standing-wave ratio will be set up in the input line. These positions of the short are termed the "characteristic points" of the third line. A series of characteristic points may be established on all the three lines in this manner. The equivalent circuit shown in Fig. 6-19 will then apply if characteristic points on the three lines are chosen as reference points.

This equivalent circuit consists of the three transmission lines coupled together in a perfect transformer, with an additional reactor coupled in at the junction. At low frequencies the turns ratios of the various windings will be equal, and the reactor can be neglected. But at high frequencies, the turns ratios will no longer be equal, and the susceptance of the reactor may be appreciable.

The results shown in Table 6-2 are illustrative. Measurements[5] were taken at two different wavelengths, and the effect of the fringing fields is seen to be greater at the shorter wavelength.

TABLE 6-2

MEASURED CONSTANTS OF EQUIVALENT CIRCUIT OF COAXIAL LINE STUB
$2b = 2.54$ cm.　　$2a = 0.715$ cm.　　$Z_0 = 75.9$ ohms

λ	Mean circumference in wavelengths	$A = \left(\dfrac{n_2}{n_1}\right)^2$	$\dfrac{B}{Y_0}$ $(n_4 = n_1)$	y'	x
10.88 cm	2.13	0.81	0.28	0.422λ	0.475λ
7.74	1.52	0.64	0.35	0.380λ	0.477λ

Discontinuities in Coaxial Lines.[6]—General considerations that apply to abrupt changes in the cross section of a coaxial line were

[5] LAMB, J., The Experimental Behavior of the Coaxial Line Stub, *J. Inst. Elec. Engrs.* (*London*), May, 1946, p. 188–190.

[6] The material in this section is largely from the following two papers: WHINNERY, J. R., and H. W. JAMIESON, Equivalent Circuits for Discontinuities in Transmission Lines, *Proc. Inst. Radio Engrs.*, **32**, 98–114 (1944); and WHINNERY, J. R., H. W. JAMIESON, and T. E. ROBBINS, Coaxial Line Discontinuities, *Proc. Inst. Radio Engrs.*, **32**, 695–709 (1944).

discussed in Sec. 1-5. It is assumed here that the coaxial line is restricted in diameter so that higher modes cannot carry energy at the operating frequency. To summarize, higher modes that are below cutoff (local waves) are excited at discontinuities and account for fringing fields that are present at abrupt changes in cross section. If the discontinuity has longitudinal dimensions that are small compared with a wavelength, the effect of these fringing fields is equivalent to a

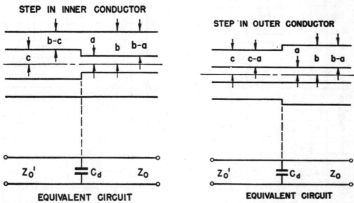

FIG. 6-20.—Step discontinuities in coaxial lines, and their equivalent circuits.

lumped susceptance shunted across the line at the point of discontinuity. This equivalent shunt susceptance must be considered in addition to any change in impedance at the discontinuity, but if both the impedance change and the shunt susceptance are considered, the behavior of the discontinuity is completely predictable. It is the purpose of this section to discuss the equivalent susceptance that results from the higher order modes.

Simple Discontinuities.—For a step in the inner conductor, shown in Fig. 6-20, the discontinuity capacitance divided by the outer circumference is plotted in Fig. 6-21 as a function of $\alpha = (b - c)/(b - a)$. There are several curves, each corresponding to different values of the parameter $(\tau = b/a)$, and intermediate values may be obtained by interpolation. It is assumed here that the line diameter is small compared with a wavelength.

For a step in the outer conductor, shown in Fig. 6-20, the discontinuity capacitance divided by the outer circumference is plotted in Fig. 6-22 as a function of $\alpha = (c - a)/(b - a)$. Again several curves are required for different values of the parameter $(\tau = b/a)$.

Complex Discontinuities.—The equivalent capacitance associated with more complex discontinuities can often be determined by considering the structure as composed of two or more simple discontinuities. This is permissible if the fringing fields of the simple discontinuities do not occupy the same region and hence do not couple together and affect each other. For example, the discontinuity capacitance associated with an infinitely thin disk on the center conductor of a coaxial line is twice the capacitance associated with a step

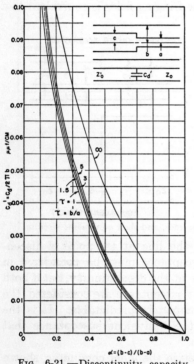

Fig. 6-21.—Discontinuity capacity of a step on inner conductor of a coaxial line.

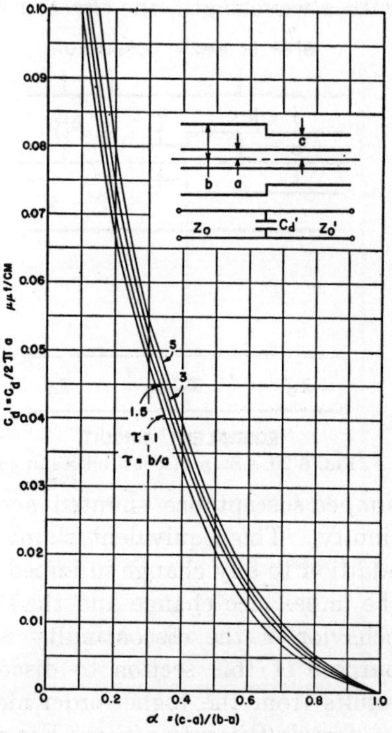

Fig. 6-22.—Discontinuity capacity of a step on outer conductor of coaxial line.

up to the disk diameter. There are fringing fields on both sides of the disk, and the over-all effect may be considered as the sum of two steps, one up to disk diameter, and one back down.

A number of these more complex discontinuities are shown in Fig. 6-23, along the with formulas by which their equivalent circuits may be calculated when the diameter is small compared with a wavelength.

The Effect of Dielectric Materials.—If the fringing fields of a step discontinuity occupy a region filled with dielectric material, the equivalent capacitance of the discontinuity as obtained from Figs. 6-21 and 6-22 must be multiplied by the dielectric constant of the material.

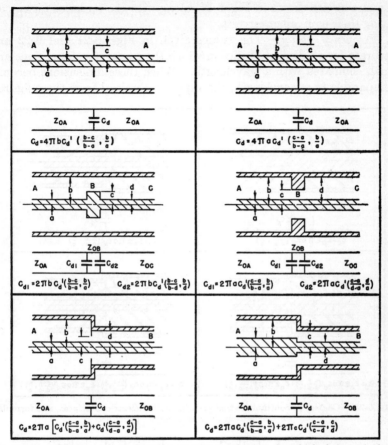

Fig. 6-23.—Miscellaneous coaxial discontinuities and means by which their equivalent circuits may be calculated from the data of Figs. 6-21 and 6-22.

Two steps are shown in Fig. 6-24. For the left-hand step the fringing fields are in the dielectric-filled region, and the equivalent capacity must be multiplied by ϵ. The fringing fields of the right-hand step are not in the dielectric-filled region, and the dielectric therefore does not affect the equivalent capacitance of this step.

A number of examples in which a dielectric discontinuity coincides with a step discontinuity of the

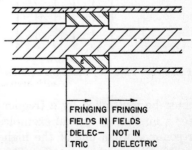

Fig. 6-24.—Coaxial discontinuities that coincide with dielectric interfaces.

conductors are shown in Fig. 6-25, along with the formulas for calculating their equivalent circuits.

Frequency Factor.—The values given in Figs. 6-21 and 6-22 are accurate for all discontinuities in which the transverse dimensions are small compared with a wavelength. When these dimensions become comparable to a wavelength, the capacity obtained from these figures

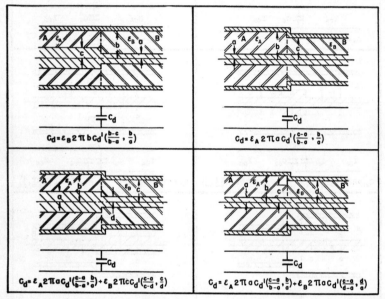

Fig. 6-25.—Coaxial discontinuities that coincide with dielectric interfaces, and formulas for calculating their equivalent capacities.

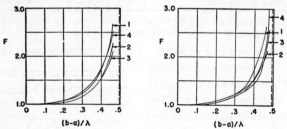

Fig. 6-26.—Factor by which the equivalent capacity of discontinuities must be modified with decreasing wavelength.

must be multiplied by a frequency factor F. This factor F is given for a number of typical examples in Fig. 6-26. There is an effective resonance when one of the higher modes that is excited by the discontinuity reaches cutoff. This is not, however, the lowest mode other than the principal mode that the coaxial line can carry (see Sec. 4-8). The discontinuities shown do not couple between this lowest mode and the principal mode except when the inner conductor is off center.

Proximity Factor.—If the fringing fields of a discontinuity interact with those of another discontinuity or with a short circuit, the equivalent circuit of the discontinuity will be modified. This may be taken

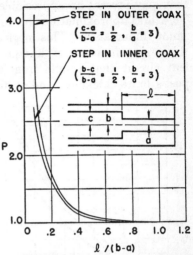

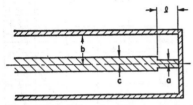

Fig. 6-27.—Discontinuity near a short in a coaxial line.

Fig. 6-28.—Factor by which the equivalent capacity of a discontinuity must be modified when the discontinuity is near a short circuit.

into account by multiplying the values of Figs. 6-21 and 6-22 by a proximity factor P. For a discontinuity near a short circuit in which the short circuit interferes with the fringing fields (see Fig. 6-27), this proximity factor is plotted in Fig. 6-28 for two typical examples.

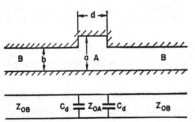

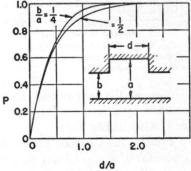

Fig. 6-29.—Two discontinuities close together in a plane transmission line.

Fig. 6-30.—Factor by which the equivalent capacities of discontinuities must be modified when the discontinuities are close together.

When two discontinuities are close together and interact (Fig. 6-29), typical proximity factors are as given in Fig. 6-30. This was calculated for parallel plate lines, but the results are similar for coaxial lines.

Posts in Coaxial Line.—A round post or wire that connects the inner and outer conductors of a coaxial line has a finite inductance that may present an appreciable reactance at microwave frequencies. To a first approximation the equivalent circuit of the post will be a shunt inductance. This neglects the series component of the equivalent circuit that results from the post's finite thickness, and at high

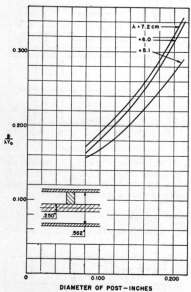

FIG. 6-31.—The measured shunt susceptance of some round posts short-circuiting a coaxial line.

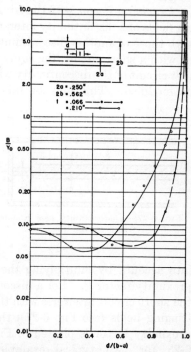

FIG. 6-32.—The measured shunt susceptance of some round metal probes extending into a coaxial line. $\lambda = 6.0$ cm.

frequencies the magnitude of the equivalent inductance will also be modified by a frequency factor. The results of some measurements[7] are plotted in Fig. 6-31.

Probes in Coaxial Line.—A probe extending from the outer conductor of a coaxial line part way toward the center conductor will cause reflections. To a first approximation, its equivalent circuit is a shunt susceptance, whose magnitude varies with the probe length. For short lengths the probe is equivalent to a shunt capacity. As the end of the probe nears the center conductor, the probe impedance

[7] Measurements performed in laboratories of the Sperry Gyroscope Company, Inc.

passes through a series resonance, becoming inductive when very close to the center conductor. It should be noted that the probe must be very close to the center conductor before introducing a large reflection.

No theoretical solution has been attempted. The susceptance as a function of probe depth is plotted in Fig. 6-32 for two experimental measurements.[7] The residual susceptance at zero probe length results from imperfections in the trap through which the probe was fed.

2. Impedance Transformers in Coaxial Line

Single-stub Transformer.—The input admittance Y of a shorted length l of lossless transmission line is a pure susceptance given by

$$Y = -jY_0 \cot \beta l$$

where Y_0 is the characteristic admittance of the line and β is its phase constant. A shorted stub line is often placed in shunt with a trans-

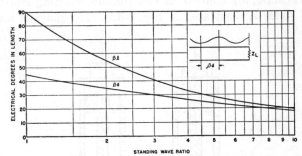

FIG. 6-33.—The length and location of a shorted stub line used for impedance matching, plotted as a function of the standing-wave ratio to be canceled.

mission line for the purpose of matching the load impedance of the line to the line impedance. The general principles that apply to its use were given in Sec. 3-5. The required length of a stub line and its position on the line are plotted as functions of the standing-wave ratio in Figs. 6-33 and 6-34 for two possible solutions, in one of which the stub is inductive and in the other capacitive. In both of these figures the length is given in electrical degrees, as is also the distance between the voltage minimum and the required stub position. As shown, the distance between the voltage minimum and stub should be measured from the minimum toward the load.

A shorted stub line whose length and position may be continuously and separately varied is an impedance transformer capable of matching any generator impedance to any load impedance within limits set by losses in the system, provided that neither impedance is a pure reactance.

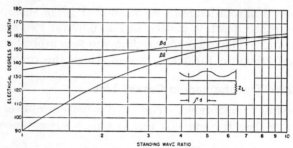

FIG. 6-34.—An alternative length and position of a shorted stub line used for impedance matching, plotted as a function of the standing-wave ratio to be canceled.

Double-stub Transformer.—Another type of transformer used for impedance matching consists of two tunable shorting stubs, fixed in position. This is illustrated in Fig. 6-35. The range of impedances

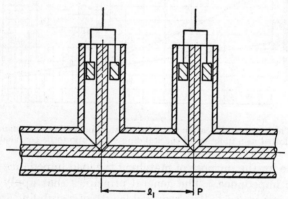

FIG. 6-35.—A tunable double-stub transformer, used for impedance matching in a coaxial line.

seen by the transformer at the point P which can be matched to the impedance of the line Z_0 depends upon the length of line between the two shorting stubs. Specifically, a transformer with two shorting stubs spaced βl_1 electrical degrees apart will match to the line admittance Y_0 any load whose conductance component G_1 at the point P is less than $Y_0(1 + \cot^2 \beta l_1)$. This is illustrated in Fig. 6-36, where the maximum allowable conductance component $G_{1(\text{max})}$ of the admittance at point P is plotted as a function of the distance between stubs. It would appear from Fig. 6-36 that the double-stub transformer could match the greatest range of impedances if the spacing between the stubs were very nearly some multiple of a half wavelength. But such

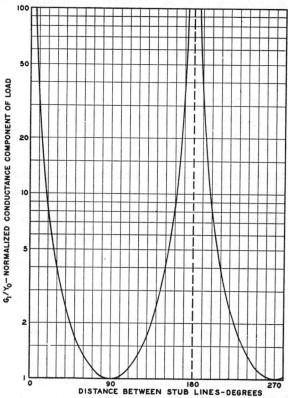

FIG. 6-36.—The maximum conductance component of a load admittance that can be matched to a transmission line by the double-stub transformer of Fig. 6-35, plotted as a function of the spacing between the two stubs.

a transformer would require that the stubs present a very low admittance across the line, which may not be obtainable in practice because of losses in the stub. Also, the tuning will be very critical and the match very sensitive to slight changes in frequency.

In actual practice, a compromise must be made between the range of impedances which the transformer is capable of matching and the ease of obtaining a match. An odd multiple eighth wave spacing is frequently used; this will match to Y_0 any admittance whose conductance component is less than $2Y_0$ at the point P.

An identical analysis holds when the stubs are in series rather than in shunt except that, in the above expressions, impedance should be substituted for admittance, reactance for susceptance, etc.

A double-stub transformer will match any impedance to the line impedance if provision is made for inserting an additional quarter wavelength of line between the transformer and the load when required.

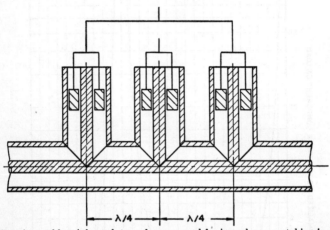

Fig. 6-37.—A tunable triple-stub transformer, used for impedance matching in a coaxial line.

Triple-stub Transformer.—A transformer suitable for matching any impedance to any other impedance can be constructed by placing three adjustable shorting stubs in shunt with line, spaced a quarter wave apart. If the first and third are ganged together, this transformer (see Fig. 6-37) has only two adjustments and has an advantage over the single movable stub in that there is no joint in the main line requiring sliding contacts.

Eccentric Line Transformer.—To construct an adjustable quarter-wave transformer, it is necessary to have the characteristic impedance of the quarter-wave section continuously variable. One way to do this is to leave the diametric ratio fixed in the quarter-wave section, but to have the eccentricity between inner and outer conductors variable. Making the conductors eccentric increases their capacity and so reduces the characteristic impedance of the line. For the transformer to cover the entire range of impedances, the eccentricity should be continuously adjustable from a point where the two conductors are coaxial to where they are just grazing. The grazing limit cannot be approached too closely if the transformer is to carry any considerable amount of power because of the increased possibility of voltage breakdown with closer spacing.

If the position as well as the eccentricity of the quarter-wave section is made variable, this type of transformer will match any impedance to the characteristic impedance of the line.

The characteristic impedance of an eccentric line is given by

$$Z_0 = 60 \cosh^{-1}\left[\frac{b}{2a}(1 - \epsilon^2) + \frac{a}{2b}\right] \tag{6-11}$$

where the displacement of the axis of the inner conductor from the axis of the outer conductor is ϵb. Curves that give the variation in char-

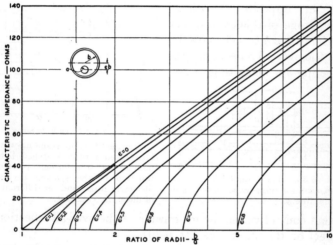

Fig. 6-38.—The characteristic impedance of an eccentric coaxial transmission line.

acteristic impedance as a function of the displacement of the center conductor are given in Fig. 6-38.[8] The curves are self-explanatory.

Line-stretcher Transformer.—The power delivery from a generator to a load, neither of which is matched to the line impedance, can be varied by varying the length of line between them. This is frequently done with a "line stretcher." Although line stretchers in general will not produce a perfect match, they are widely used because of their simplicity and because they usually increase the power transfer over what would otherwise be obtained with an arbitrary length of line.

[8] BROWN, G. H., Impedance Calculations for Eccentric Lines, *Electronics,* **15,** 49 (1942); and BARCLAY, W., and K. SPANGENBERG, Characteristic Impedance of Eccentric Lines, *Electronics,* **15,** 50 (1942).

Double-slug Transformer.—A convenient impedance transformer with no sliding contacts may be made using two reflecting elements, usually slugs of metal or dielectric. The reflection introduced by these slugs is used to cancel any reflected wave already existing on the line. Two controls are provided for these slugs: (1) With the spacing between held constant, the slugs are moved along the line. (2) The spacing between the slugs is varied by moving each slug an equal amount in opposite directions. The advantage of this transformer is that the first control changes the phase of the over-all reflection without affecting its magnitude, while

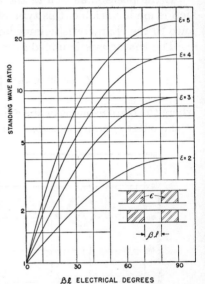

Fig. 6-40.—The standing-wave ratio introduced into a matched line by a double-slug transformer, plotted as a function of the spacing between the dielectric slugs, and for different values of dielectric constant.

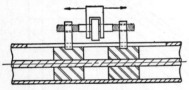

Fig. 6-39.—The double-slug transformer, used for impedance matching in a coaxial line.

the second control varies the magnitude of the over-all reflection with little effect on the phase (see Fig. 6-39).

It is customary but not necessary to make the two reflecting slugs electrically a quarter wave long. If this is true, there will be no net reflection when the two slugs are brought together, and the reflection will be maximized when the spacing between them is a quarter wavelength. If the electrical length of the slugs somewhat exceeds a quarter wavelength, zero reflection will not be found until the spacing between the slugs approaches a half wavelength. But if the slug length is less than a quarter wave, a point of zero reflection will be reached as the slug spacing approaches zero. If a double-slug transformer is to cover a band of wavelengths, it is advisable to make the slug length not greater than a quarter wave for the shortest operating wavelength, as this will minimize the required size of the transformer.

The following analysis assumes that the slugs are electrically a quarter wave long, fill the line, and are made of dielectric material whose constant is ϵ. The results are equally applicable, however, for any sort of slug that reduces the characteristic impedance of the line by a factor $\sqrt{\epsilon}$.

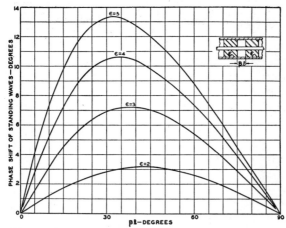

FIG. 6-41.—The shift in phase of the standing waves introduced into a matched transmission line by the double-slug transformer, plotted as a function of the spacing between the dielectric slugs.

The magnitude of reflection introduced into a matched line by the transformer is given by

$$\left|\frac{V_2}{V_1}\right| = \left|\frac{j\left(\dfrac{1}{\epsilon} - \epsilon\right)\tan \beta l}{2 + j\left(\dfrac{1}{\epsilon} + \epsilon\right)\tan \beta l}\right| \tag{6-12}$$

where βl is the electrical distance between the two quarter-wave slugs. The standing-wave ratio as a function of βl is plotted in Fig. 6-40 for various values of ϵ. The maximum standing-wave ratio that can be reached or matched is ϵ^2.

The shift in phase $\Delta\phi$ of the standing waves with increasing βl is given by

$$\Delta\phi = \frac{1}{2}\beta l - \frac{1}{2}\tan^{-1}\left[\frac{\left(\dfrac{1}{\epsilon} + \epsilon\right)}{2}\tan \beta l\right] \tag{6-13}$$

This shift in phase is a measure of the extent to which the phase of the standing-wave ratio is dependent upon the second control, which primarily controls amplitude. The shift is arbitrarily chosen as zero when βl is zero.   Curves are given in Fig. 6-41 of this shift as a function of βl for various values of ϵ.   Maximum shift in phase is given by

$$(\Delta\phi)_{max} = \frac{1}{2}\tan^{-1}\sqrt{\frac{2}{\frac{1}{\epsilon}+\epsilon}} - \frac{1}{2}\tan^{-1}\sqrt{\frac{\frac{1}{\epsilon}+\epsilon}{2}} \qquad (6\text{-}14)$$

CHAPTER 7

GENERAL FORMULAS FOR WAVE GUIDES

1. General Discussion of Wave Guides[1]

Definition.—Any transmission line is a wave guide in the sense that it guides electromagnetic waves. The general properties of transmission lines have been discussed in Chaps. 1 to 3. An arbitrary transmission line has an infinite number of possible modes of transmission, which may be divided into three classes. The first class includes transverse electromagnetic (*TEM*) waves. These are limited in number. When there are only two conductors, only a single *TEM* wave, usually known as the "principal" wave, can exist. With more than two conductors, there are more than two principal waves (*e.g.*, balanced and unbalanced currents with two wires over ground). The other two classes (higher modes), transverse electric (*TE*) and transverse magnetic (*TM*), are both infinite in number. For the principal mode to exist, the transmission line must have two separated conductors, and this mode may be carried at any frequency. But any line will support higher modes if the frequency is sufficiently

[1] Some of the references in which modern wave-guide theory has been developed are as follows:

BARROW, W. L., Transmission of Electromagnetic Waves in Hollow Tubes of Metal, *Proc. Inst. Radio Engrs.*, **24**, 1298–1328 (1936).

SOUTHWORTH, G. C., Hyper Frequency Wave Guides—General Considerations and Experimental Results, *Bell System Tech. J.*, **15**, 284–309 (1936).

CARSON, J. R., S. P. MEAD, and S. A. SCHELKUNOFF, *Bell System Tech. J.*, **15**, 310–333 (1936).

CHU, L. J., and W. L. BARROW, Electromagnetic Waves in Hollow Metal Tubes of Rectangular Cross Section, *Proc. Inst. Radio Engrs.*, **26**, 1520–1555 (1938).

Since that time detailed discussions have been included in a number of books, including the following:

BRAINARD, *et al.*, "Ultra High Frequency Techniques," pp. 455–494, D. Van Nostrand Company, Inc., New York, 1942.

SARBACHER, R. I., and W. A. EDSON, "Hyper and Ultra High Frequency Engineering," John Wiley & Sons, Inc., New York, 1943, Chaps. 6-8.

RAMO, S., and J. R. WHINNERY, "Fields and Waves in Modern Radio," John Wiley & Sons, Inc., New York, 1944.

SCHELKUNOFF, S. A., "Electromagnetic Waves," D. Van Nostrand Company, Inc., New York, 1943.

high.   Two separated conductors are not required for lines carrying energy in the higher modes, and these modes may exist on a line that is incapable of supporting a principal mode.   However, any transmission line of finite cross-sectional dimensions will carry energy in one or more of these higher modes only if the frequency is above a critical or cutoff frequency, which is in general different for each mode.

A wave guide is a transmission line in which the wave propagation is not in the form of a *TEM* mode.   In this section, consideration will be limited to transmission lines incapable of supporting *TEM* waves. This implies that the transmission lines must not have two separated conductors.   Usually a wave guide consists of a dielectric cylinder (usually air) of arbitrary cross section, with a closed conducting boundary within which the electromagnetic fields are contained.   The conducting boundary may be omitted, however, and the dielectric cylinder immersed in a medium of lower dielectric constant; these wave guides are sometimes called "dielectric wave guides," or "wave guide without metal walls."   The latter notation will be adhered to.

Modes of Transmission.—There are a doubly infinite number of possible modes by which energy may be carried in a wave guide.   Each of these modes is characterized by a distinctive field configuration, and each represents a solution of Maxwell's equations that will fit the boundary conditions imposed by the particular wave guide.

In any wave guide, the possible modes of transmission may be divided into two classes, both infinite in number.   In one class, the magnetic field has a component parallel to the guide axis, but the electric field is everywhere transverse to the axis.   For this reason, waves of this class are referred to as transverse electric, or *TE* waves. Waves of this type are also called *H* waves, as it is only the magnetic field that has an axial component.

Waves of the second class are characterized by having components of electric field parallel to the guide axis, but a magnetic field that is everywhere transverse to the axis.   These waves are therefore known as transverse magnetic, or *TM*, waves.   They are also called *E* waves.

It is customary to identify individual modes by an additional subscript notation, the rules of which depend upon the guide configuration.   These are discussed in Sec. 7-2 for rectangular, circular, and elliptical guides.

For any wave guide, the mode of transmission that has the lowest cutoff frequency is called the *dominant* mode.

In this chapter it is assumed that the wave guides are lossless dielectric cylinders bounded by walls of infinite conductivity. The effects of imperfections in the dielectric and conducting boundary are discussed in Chap. 8.

Some definitions introduced and used in this chapter are as follows:

f frequency

f_c frequency at cutoff $\lambda = c/f$

λ wavelength in free space

λ_g wavelength in the wave guide

λ_c wavelength at cutoff

v_p phase velocity

v_g group velocity

2. Field Distribution in Wave Guides

Rectangular Wave Guides.—The notation applied to rectangular wave guides is that illustrated in Fig. 7-1.

Individual modes in rectangular wave guide are identified by giving the class of the transmission mode, followed by two numerical subscripts. These two subscripts are integers that indicate the number of half-period variations in transverse field intensity along the x and y dimensions of the guide, respectively. For example, the dominant mode in rectangular wave guide is the $TE_{1,0}$ mode, indicating that the wave is of the transverse electric type, that there is a single half-wave variation of transverse field along the x-axis, and that there is no variation of transverse field along the y-axis.

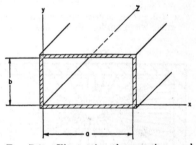

Fig. 7-1.—Illustrating the notation used with rectangular wave guides.

The field distribution of the dominant, or $TE_{1,0}$, mode is shown in Fig. 7-2. The field equations of this mode are as follows (mks units, see footnote on page 70):

$$E_z = E_x = H_y = 0 \tag{7-1}$$

$$E_y = B \frac{\mu\omega\pi}{k^2 a} \sin \frac{\pi x}{a} \sin (\omega t - \beta z) \tag{7-2}$$

$$H_z = -B \cos \frac{\pi x}{a} \cos (\omega t - \beta z) \tag{7-3}$$

$$H_x = B \frac{\beta\pi}{k^2 a} \sin \frac{\pi x}{a} \sin (\omega t - \beta z) \tag{7-4}$$

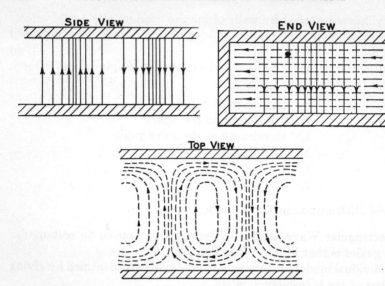

FIG. 7-2.—The electric and magnetic field of the dominant $TE_{1,0}$ mode in a rectangular wave guide. Solid lines indicate electric field, broken lines magnetic field.

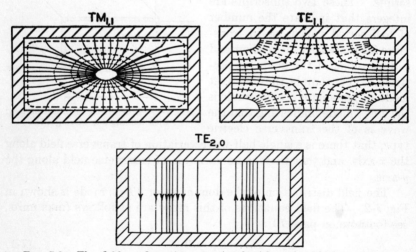

FIG. 7-3.—The field configurations associated with various higher modes in a rectangular wave guide. Solid lines indicate electric field, broken lines magnetic field.

where B is an arbitrary constant of amplitude. The phase constant β is given by

$$\beta^2 = \frac{\omega^2}{c^2} - \frac{\pi^2}{a^2} \tag{7-5}$$

the quantity k is defined by the equation

$$k^2 = \frac{\pi^2}{a^2} \qquad (7\text{-}6)$$

Field configurations for a few of the higher modes of transmission are given in Fig. 7-3, and the corresponding field equations are as follows (mks units, see footnote on page 70):

$TM_{m,n}$ waves:

$$E_z = A \sin \frac{n\pi y}{b} \sin \frac{m\pi x}{a} \cos (\omega t - \beta z) \qquad (7\text{-}7)$$

$$E_y = A \frac{\beta}{k^2} \frac{n\pi}{b} \cos \frac{n\pi y}{b} \sin \frac{m\pi x}{a} \sin (\omega t - \beta z) \qquad (7\text{-}8)$$

$$E_x = A \frac{\beta}{k^2} \frac{m\pi}{a} \sin \frac{n\pi y}{b} \cos \frac{m\pi x}{a} \sin (\omega t - \beta z) \qquad (7\text{-}9)$$

$$H_z = 0 \qquad (7\text{-}10)$$

$$H_y = -A \frac{\epsilon\omega}{k^2} \frac{m\pi}{a} \sin \frac{n\pi y}{b} \cos \frac{m\pi x}{a} \sin (\omega t - \beta z) \qquad (7\text{-}11)$$

$$H_x = A \frac{\epsilon\omega}{k^2} \frac{n\pi}{b} \cos \frac{n\pi y}{b} \sin \frac{m\pi x}{a} \sin (\omega t - \beta z) \qquad (7\text{-}12)$$

$TE_{m,n}$ waves:

$$E_z = 0 \qquad (7\text{-}13)$$

$$E_y = -B \frac{\omega\mu}{k^2} \frac{m\pi}{a} \cos \frac{n\pi y}{b} \sin \frac{m\pi x}{a} \sin (\omega t - \beta z) \qquad (7\text{-}14)$$

$$E_x = B \frac{\omega\mu}{k^2} \frac{n\pi}{b} \sin \frac{n\pi y}{b} \cos \frac{m\pi x}{a} \sin (\omega t - \beta z) \qquad (7\text{-}15)$$

$$H_z = -B \cos \frac{n\pi y}{b} \cos \frac{m\pi x}{a} \cos (\omega t - \beta z) \qquad (7\text{-}16)$$

$$H_y = B \frac{\beta}{k^2} \frac{n\pi}{b} \sin \frac{n\pi y}{b} \cos \frac{m\pi x}{a} \sin (\omega t - \beta z) \qquad (7\text{-}17)$$

$$H_x = B \frac{\beta}{k^2} \frac{m\pi}{a} \cos \frac{n\pi y}{b} \sin \frac{m\pi x}{a} \sin (\omega t - \beta z) \qquad (7\text{-}18)$$

In these equations, A and B are arbitrary constants of amplitude. The quantity β is given by

$$\beta_{m,n}{}^2 = \frac{\omega^2}{c^2} - \pi^2 \left(\frac{m^2}{a^2} + \frac{n^2}{b^2} \right) \qquad (7\text{-}19)$$

and the quantity k by

$$k^2 = \pi^2 \left(\frac{m^2}{a^2} + \frac{n^2}{b^2} \right) = \frac{\omega^2}{c^2} - \beta^2 \qquad (7\text{-}20)$$

The conduction current in a wave guide is confined to the inner surface of the guide, the depth of penetration being determined by skin-depth considerations, as outlined in Sec. 2-1. The direction of current flow is orthogonal to the direction of magnetic field at the inner surface of the guide. The lines of current flow for the dominant mode are shown in Fig. 7-4.

Circular Wave Guides.—The notation applied to circular wave guides is that shown in Fig. 7-5.

For any mode of transmission in a circular wave guide, the transverse field may be resolved into two components, tangential and radial. Both of these components vary periodically along a circular path concentric with the wall and vary in a manner related to a Bessel function of order m along a radius. Any particular mode is identified

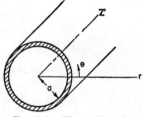

FIG. 7-4.—Current flow in the walls of a rectangular wave guide propagating the $TE_{1,0}$ mode.

FIG. 7-5.—Illustrating the notation used with circular wave guides.

by the notation $TE_{m,n}$ or $TM_{m,n}$, where m is the total number of full period variations of either component of field along a circular path concentric with the wall and n is one more than the total number of reversals of sign of either component of field along a radial path.

Alternatively, the modes have been identified by the notation $TE_{n,m}$ and $TM_{n,m}$, where the variation of transverse field with radial distance is related to a Bessel function of order n. Either definition identifies a given mode with the same numerical subscripts.

The dominant mode in circular wave guides, that with the longest cutoff wavelength, is the $TE_{1,1}$ mode, which corresponds to the $TE_{1,0}$ mode in rectangular guide. This mode is shown in Fig. 7-6, along with a number of other possible modes of transmission. The field equations of some of these possible modes are as follows (mks units, see footnote on page 70):

$TE_{1,1}$ wave (dominant mode):

$$H_z = BJ_1\left(u'\frac{r}{a}\right)\cos\theta\cos(\omega t - \beta z) \tag{7-21}$$

$$H_r = B\frac{\beta a}{u'}J_1'\left(u'\frac{r}{a}\right)\cos\theta\sin(\omega t - \beta z) \tag{7-22}$$

$$H_\theta = -B \frac{\beta a^2}{u_1 r} J_1\left(u' \frac{r}{a}\right) \sin\theta \sin(\omega t - \beta z) \tag{7-23}$$

$$E_z = 0 \tag{7-24}$$

$$E_r = -\mu \frac{\omega}{\beta} H_\theta \tag{7-25}$$

$$E_\theta = \mu \frac{\omega}{\beta} H_r \tag{7-26}$$

$$u' = 1.841 \qquad u_1 = 3.39 \qquad \beta^2 = \left(\frac{\omega}{c}\right)^2 - \left(\frac{u'}{a}\right)^2 \tag{7-27}$$

TE$_{1,1}$

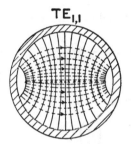

TE$_{2,1}$

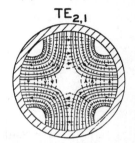

TM$_{0,1}$

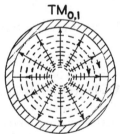

TE$_{0,1}$

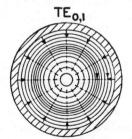

TM$_{1,1}$

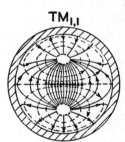

FIG. 7-6.—The field configurations of various modes in a circular wave guide. Solid lines indicate electric field, broken lines magnetic field.

$TE_{0,1}$ mode (circular electric mode):

$$H_z = -B J_0\left(u' \frac{r}{a}\right) \cos(\omega t - \beta z) \tag{7-28}$$

$$H_r = B \frac{\beta a}{u'} J_1 \left(u' \frac{r}{a} \right) \sin (\omega t - \beta z) \qquad (7\text{-}29)$$

$$H_\theta = E_z = E_r = 0 \qquad (7\text{-}30)$$

$$E_\theta = \mu \frac{\omega}{\beta} H_r \qquad (7\text{-}31)$$

$$u' = 3.832 \qquad \beta^2 = \left(\frac{\omega}{a} \right)^2 - \left(\frac{u'}{a} \right)^2 \qquad (7\text{-}32)$$

$TM_{0,1}$ mode (circular magnetic mode):

$$E_z = A J_0 \left(u \frac{r}{a} \right) \cos (\omega t - \beta z) \qquad (7\text{-}33)$$

$$E_r = -A \frac{\beta a}{u} J_1 \left(u \frac{r}{a} \right) \sin (\omega t - \beta z) \qquad (7\text{-}34)$$

$$E_\theta = H_z = H_r = 0 \qquad (7\text{-}35)$$

$$H_\theta = -A \frac{\omega a}{u} J_1 \left(u \frac{r}{a} \right) \sin (\omega t - \beta z) \qquad (7\text{-}36)$$

$$u = 2.405 \qquad \beta^2 = \left(\frac{\omega}{c} \right)^2 - \left(\frac{u}{a} \right)^2 \qquad (7\text{-}37)$$

In these equations, A and B are arbitrary constants determining amplitude.

Elliptical Wave Guide.[2]—A knowledge of the behavior of elliptical wave guides is of some importance because the inevitable deformations encountered in a round guide will result in an equivalent ellipticity. A few of the possible modes in an elliptical wave guide are shown in Fig. 7-7, along with the corresponding mode in round pipe.   In general, if a round wave guide is deformed, the wave being transmitted will split into two components that proceed down the pipe with different phase velocities and different attenuation.   This instability will be found in all cases except the following:

1. When deformation is along an axis of symmetry of the wave.

2. When the wave has circular symmetry (*e.g.*, $TE_{0,1}$ or $TM_{0,1}$ wave).

The notation for elliptical wave guides is similar to that for circular guides except that there is an additional preceding subscript, indicating whether the wave is classed as even or odd.   The field in an elliptical wave guide is specified in terms of Mathieu functions, which are of two kinds, even and odd.   Those waves which are specified by the

[2] CHU, L. J., Electromagnetic Waves in Hollow Pipes of Metal, *J. Appl. Phys.* **9**, 483–591 (1938).

even functions are termed "even" waves, and those specified by the odd functions are termed "odd" waves.

3. Cutoff in Wave Guides

All modes of transmission in wave guides, and all modes except the principal mode in any transmission line, will carry energy down the

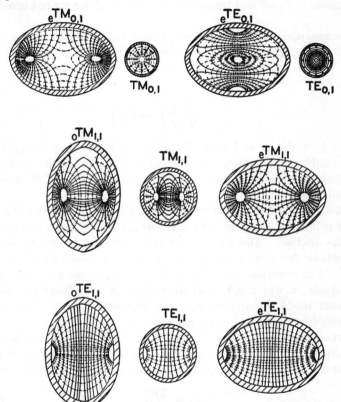

Fig. 7-7.—Various modes of transmission in an elliptical wave guide and the corresponding transmission modes in a circular wave guide. Solid lines indicate electric field, broken lines magnetic field.

line only if the frequency is over a certain limiting or cutoff value. This value depends upon the size and configuration of the line as well as upon the particular mode of transmission. If these modes are excited on a line at frequencies below their cutoff frequencies, they will carry no real energy down the line, and the electric and magnetic fields associated with any given mode will diminish exponentially with distance from the point of excitation. (The rate of attenuation in the cutoff region is covered in Sec. 8-4.)   In other words, the action of a wave guide for any given mode of transmission is similar to a high-pass filter, with reactive attenuation at frequencies below cutoff. When the conducting walls are assumed to have infinite conductivity, the cutoff wavelength and frequency for any given mode have unique values.   But finite losses in the walls will blend together slightly the regions of cutoff and transmission.   Finite losses are not considered here.

Rectangular Wave Guide.—For any mode of transmission, the cutoff wavelength λ_c is given in terms of the guide dimensions a and b by

$$\lambda_c = \frac{2}{\sqrt{\left(\frac{m}{a}\right)^2 + \left(\frac{n}{b}\right)^2}} \tag{7-38}$$

In this formula, m and n are the subscripts denoting the particular mode under consideration (*e.g.*, $TE_{m,n}$) and λ_c is the limiting or cutoff wavelength.   The equation holds for either *TE* or *TM* modes of transmission.

The size of guide necessary for transmission of some of the lower modes is illustrated in Fig. 7-8.   In this figure, b/λ is the ordinate and a/λ the abcissa.   The various curves mark the boundary between sizes where the modes will carry energy and where they are below cutoff.   For example, the $TE_{2,0}$ mode will carry energy in all sizes of wave guide in which a/λ is greater than unity.   To allow only the dominant mode to carry energy, one dimension of the guide should not exceed λ and the other should not exceed $\lambda/2$.

Circular Wave Guide.—The cutoff wavelength in a circular wave guide for all modes depends upon the ratio of diameter to wavelength.

For the $TE_{m,n}$ wave, the cutoff wavelength is given by the formula

$$\lambda_c = \frac{2\pi a}{u'_{m,n}} \tag{7-39}$$

where a is the radius of the guide.   The constant $u'_{m,n}$ is the nth root of the equation $J_m'(u) = 0$.   Some of the lower values of $u'_{m,n}$ are

$$u'_{0,1} = 3.832 \qquad u'_{0,2} = 7.016$$
$$u'_{1,1} = 1.841 \qquad u'_{1,2} = 5.332$$
$$u'_{2,1} = 3.054 \qquad u'_{2,2} = 6.706$$
$$u'_{3,1} = 4.201 \qquad u'_{3,2} = 8.016$$

A more extensive listing of these roots is given in Table 13-1.

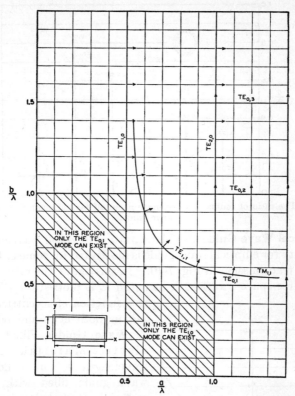

FIG. 7-8.—The size of pipe necessary for propagation of some of the lower modes in a rectangular wave guide. The solid lines indicate the boundaries between above cutoff and below cutoff.

For the $TM_{m,n}$ wave, the cutoff wavelength is given by

$$\lambda_c = \frac{2\pi a}{u_{m,n}} \qquad (7\text{-}40)$$

where a is the guide radius and $u_{m,n}$ is the nth root of the equation $J_m(u) = 0$. Some of the lower values of $u_{m,n}$ are

$$u_{0,1} = 2.405 \qquad u_{0,2} = 5.520 \qquad u_{0,3} = 8.654$$
$$u_{1,1} = 3.832 \qquad u_{1,2} = 7.016$$
$$u_{2,1} = 5.136$$

A more extensive listing is given in Table 13-1.

In Fig. 7-9 is shown the relation between the ratio a/λ and the cutoff wavelength for several of the lowest modes in circular wave guide.

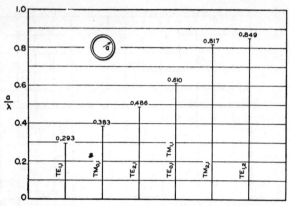

Fig. 7-9.—The ratio of radius to wavelength at cutoff for various modes in a circular wave guide.

Elliptical Wave Guides.[3]—The variation in cutoff wavelength with eccentricity for elliptical wave guide is illustrated for some of the lowest modes of transmission in Fig. 7-10. In this figure, the ratio of periphery s to free-space wavelength at cutoff λ_c is plotted for some modes as a function of eccentricity resulting in both even and odd waves.

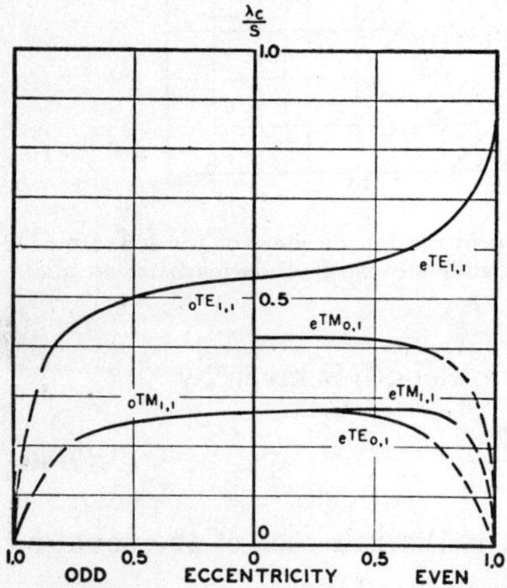

Wave Guides Filled with Dielectric Material.—The cutoff wavelength λ_c' in a hollow-pipe wave guide filled with dielectric material of constant ϵ is related to the cutoff wavelength λ_c of the same pipe when air filled by the formula

$$\lambda_c' = \sqrt{\epsilon}\,\lambda_c \qquad (7\text{-}41)$$

Fig. 7-10.—Variation of cutoff wavelength with eccentricity for elliptical wave guides of periphery s.

4. Wavelength in Wave Guides

In uniform coaxial lines filled with air dielectric, the wavelength in the line is approximately equal to the free-space wavelength, provided that the attenuation is small.

In uniform hollow-pipe wave guides, filled with air dielectric and neglecting attenuation, the wavelength in the guide always exceeds the free-space wavelength. As the frequency is unchanged, this would appear to indicate that the velocity

[3] CHU, L. J., *Loc. cit.*

of propagation of waves in a wave guide exceeds the velocity of light. Actually, the phase velocity v_p in an air-filled wave guide given by the formula

$$v_p = f\lambda_g \tag{7-42}$$

is greater than the velocity of light by the factor λ_g/λ. But the actual rate of transmission of energy down the guide is the group velocity v_g; this is related to the phase velocity by the equation

$$v_g = \frac{c^2}{v_p} \tag{7-43}$$

where c is the velocity of propagation in free space, *i.e.*, the velocity of light.

The wavelength in an air-filled hollow-pipe wave guide λ_g is related to the cutoff wavelength in the guide λ_c and the free-space wavelength of the transmitted radiation λ by the formula

$$\lambda_g = \frac{\lambda}{\sqrt{1 - \left(\dfrac{\lambda}{\lambda_c}\right)^2}} \tag{7-44}$$

The wavelength in the guide is always greater than the wavelength in free space, but only very slightly greater if the guide is operated at a frequency far above cutoff. As the frequency is decreased, the free-space wavelength approaches the cutoff wavelength of the guide; with increasing frequency the guide wavelength becomes increasingly greater and reaches infinity at cutoff. The relationships given in Eq. (7-44) are plotted graphically in Fig. 7-11. In this figure the ratio λ/λ_g is plotted against the ratio λ/λ_c, and the relationship between the two quantities is seen to be a quarter circle of unity radius.

If the wave guide is filled with a perfect dielectric of constant ϵ_1, the wavelength in the guide is given by the equation

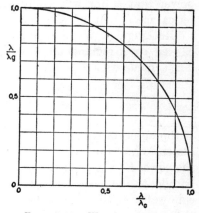

Fig. 7-11.—Wavelength relationships for any mode of propagation in any air-filled wave guide.

$$\lambda_g = \frac{\lambda}{\sqrt{\epsilon_1 - \left(\dfrac{\lambda}{\lambda_c}\right)^2}} \tag{7-45}$$

where λ is still the free-space wave-length in air and λ_c the cutoff wave-length of the guide when air filled.

5. Power-carrying Capacity of Wave Guides.

The maximum power that can be transmitted through a wave guide will depend upon the maximum electric field strength that can exist without breakdown. If this maximum allowable field strength is specified, the maximum power-carrying capacity of the wave guide can be calculated when the wavelength and the size of the guide are known. The following theoretical formulas give the maximum power in terms of the maximum allowable field strength. Experimental data on allowable field strengths at ultrahigh frequencies indicate that the value of 30,000 volts/cm is applicable for air-filled guides under standard sea-level conditions of temperature, pressure, and humidity.

The values given by the equations below are theoretical maximum powers. Voltage gradients are likely to be higher if there are discontinuities in the line, or particles of dirt and dust. Also, voltage gradients will be higher if the line is not terminated in its characteristic impedance, and for a given net power flow down the line, the maximum voltage gradient will be increased by the square root of the voltage standing-wave ratio on the line. For these reasons the maximum power that a line will safely carry is usually a fraction of the theoretical maximum unless extraordinary precautions are taken.

Rectangular Wave Guide.—The maximum power that can be carried by a rectangular wave guide operating in the dominant, or $TE_{1,0}$, mode with $a > b$ is

$$\frac{P}{E_{\max}{}^2} = 6.63 \times 10^{-4}ab\left(\frac{\lambda}{\lambda_g}\right) \tag{7-46}$$

If the potential gradient $E_{\max}$ is expressed in volts per centimeter, the dimensions of the guide a and b should be expressed in centimeters for the power P to be given in watts. The maximum field intensity occurs parallel to the narrower dimension of the guide, midway between the side walls, and is independent of the distance from the wide faces of the guide.

Circular Wave Guide.—For the dominant, or $TE_{1,1}$, mode in circular wave guide, the relation between maximum power and maximum allowable field strength is

$$\frac{P}{E_{\max}{}^2} = 1.99 \times 10^{-3}a^2\left(\frac{\lambda}{\lambda_g}\right) \tag{7-47}$$

where a is the radius of the guide, λ is the free-space wavelength, and λ_g is the guide wavelength. Maximum field strength is at the center of the guide.

For the circular magnetic, or $TM_{0,1}$, mode, there are two separate cases:

CASE 1: $a/\lambda < 0.761$

$$\frac{P}{E_{max}^2} = 7.69 \times 10^{-3} \frac{a^4}{\lambda^2}\left(\frac{\lambda}{\lambda_g}\right) \tag{7-48}$$

In this case the maximum field intensity is at the center of the guide.

CASE 2: $a/\lambda > 0.761$

$$\frac{P}{E_{max}^2} = 3.33 \times 10^{-3} a^2 \left(\frac{\lambda_g}{\lambda}\right) \tag{7-49}$$

In this case the maximum field intensity is at $r = 0.765a$ and is independent of angle.

Variation of Power-carrying Capacity with Altitude.—The variation of power-carrying capacity with altitude is discussed in Sec. 2-3.

6. Wave Guides without Metal Walls

It is possible for a dielectric cylinder immersed in a medium of lower dielectric constant to act as a wave guide and transmit energy in any of a doubly infinite number of higher modes, if the frequency is above cutoff for these modes. But there are a number of difficulties that arise in the practical application of these guides.

The fields are not confined within the boundaries of the dielectric cylinder but extend off toward infinity in the external dielectric medium. Even when the modes of transmission are a long way from cutoff, a very considerable fraction of the energy will be carried through the external dielectric.

Any higher or below-cutoff modes that are excited at a discontinuity will radiate power transversely, and a power loss is associated with any such discontinuity. In other words, the equivalent circuit of a discontinuity will contain resistive as well as reactive components. Any bend or change of direction will excite higher modes and a resulting energy loss by radiation.

Because the fields extend outside the dielectric cylinder, any mechanical support for the guide will represent a discontinuity, with a corresponding loss of power; this is generally true of any mechanical structure brought in proximity with the guide.

7. Commercially Available Wave Guides and Their Selection

For most practical applications, a wave guide is a rather narrow band transmission system. If a rectangular wave guide is used in the customary manner to carry only the dominant mode of transmission, the free-space wavelength must not exceed twice the width of the guide, or the guide will be below cutoff for the dominant mode. On the other end, if the free-space wavelength is equal to or less than the guide width, the guide will be above cutoff for the $TE_{2,0}$ mode of transmission. So a 2:1 frequency range is the theoretical maximum if higher modes are to be avoided.

For most applications, it is desirable that the frequency range be still further restricted. The attenuation rises very sharply as cutoff is approached, and for this reason it is usually desirable to restrict the maximum operating wavelength to 1.60 or 1.65 times the inside width of the wave guide. At the short-wavelength end, one should not approach too near cutoff for the $TE_{2,0}$ mode, as it will then attenuate very slowly when excited by a discontinuity. The minimum operating wavelength that is recommended is about 1.05 times the inside width of the guide. If these limits are adhered to, the wave guide may be used over a frequency range only slightly greater than 1.5:1.

To avoid the $TE_{0,1}$ mode of transmission, the inside height of the guide should be less than a half wavelength at the shortest operating wavelength and should, therefore, not exceed half the inside width of the guide. But decreasing the height still further below this value will increase the attenuation in the guide, which in this region will be approximately inversely proportional to the height of the guide. So for minimum attenuation, the inside height of the guide should be nearly half the width.

The practical band width of a circular wave guide is even less than a rectangular wave guide. The cutoff wavelength of the dominant, or $TE_{1,1}$, mode is given by $\lambda_c = 2\pi a/1.841$, and for the next mode, which is the $TM_{0,1}$ mode, $\lambda_c = 2\pi a/2.405$. So if the dominant mode is to be transmitted, and the next mode kept below cutoff, the guide may be used over a maximum theoretical frequency range of only 1.31:1. The practical necessity of avoiding the very high attenuation close to cutoff reduces the working range to about 1.15:1.

The $TM_{0,1}$ mode in circular guide is sometimes used because of its circular symmetry. The next mode that is likely to be transmitted is the $TE_{2,1}$ mode, whose cutoff wavelength is given by $\lambda_c = 2\pi a/3.05$. The maximum theoretical frequency range of a circular guide operating in the $TM_{0,1}$ mode is therefore 1.27:1 and the practical operating range correspondingly less. The $TE_{1,1}$ mode can also be carried in the guide and must be avoided by using the proper means of excitation, or by the use of mode filters.

The working range of the circular guides can in theory be considerably extended by the use of mode filters, which will permit one mode

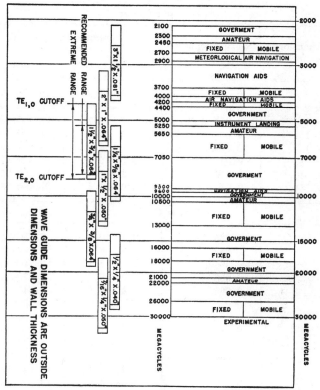

Fig. 7-12.—FCC allocations of Nov. 19, 1945, compared with the range for single-mode propagation of various rectangular wave guides.

to operate but suppress others. Many designs have been proposed, but there is little information available on their experimental use.

The wall thickness and material of a wave guide should be chosen primarily on a basis of desired strength and weight, although attenuation and methods of fabrication must also be considered. Brass is the most widely used material because of its low cost, availability, and ease of fabrication. Furthermore, the attenuation is not too high and may be improved by plating. Silver offers lower attenuation, but the cost is much greater, and it merits practical consideration only at frequencies above 10,000 mc. Copper is sometimes used. Aluminum offers advantages in light weight, but fabrication is more difficult. Iron or stainless steel tubing is occasionally used, but must be

TABLE 7-1
RECOMMENDED SIZES OF WAVE GUIDES
Rectangular Guides

Outer dimensions (in.)	Wall thickness (in.)	Recommended for range	
		Wavelength (cm)	Frequency (mc)
1½ × 3	0.081	7.6 –11.8	2,540– 3,950
1 × 2	0.064, 0.081	5 – 7.6	3,950– 6,000
¾ × 1½	0.064, 0.081	3.7 – 5.7	5,250– 8,150
⅝ × 1¼	0.064	3.0 – 4.7	6,400–10,000
½ × 1	0.050, 0.064	2.4 – 3.7	8,100–12,500
⅜ × ¾	0.064	1.7 – 2.6	11,500–17,700
¼ × ½	0.040	1.2 – 1.8	16,600–25,000
¼ × ⁷⁄₁₆	0.050	0.9 – 1.4	21,400–33,300

Circular Guides

3	0.065	9.6 –10.9	2,750– 3,130
2⅝	0.062	8.3 – 9.6	3,130– 3,610
2¼	0.065	7.1 – 8.1	3,710– 4,230
2	0.065	6.2 – 7.2	4,170– 4,840
1¾	0.065	5.4 – 6.2	4,840– 5,500
1½	0.042	4.7 – 5.4	5,550– 6,380
1⅜	0.065	4.15– 4.8	6,250– 7,230
1⅛	0.032	3.6 – 4.15	7,230– 8,330
1	0.032	3.1 – 3.6	8,330– 9,680
⅞	0.035	2.7 – 3.1	9,680–11,100
¾	0.032	2.3 – 2.7	11,100–13,050
⅝	0.020	1.95– 2.3	13,050–15,400
⁹⁄₁₆	0.028	1.7 – 2.0	15,000–17,650
½	0.032	1.45– 1.7	17,650–20,700
⁷⁄₁₆	0.042	1.2 – 1.45	20,700–25,000
⅜	0.042	1.0 – 1.2	25,000–30,000

carefully plated to avoid high attenuation. Plated plastic tubing has also been proposed.

Various standard sizes of round and rectangular pipe that are suitable for wave guides have been recommended by the Subcommittee on Wave Guide Connectors of the RMA Committee on H.F. Line

Connectors. These are listed in Table 7-1, along with the range of wavelengths for which each is suitable.

Unfortunately, the ranges over which the recommended wave guides may be used do not in all cases agree with the later frequency allocations of the Federal Communications Commission, and there are certain assigned bands that are narrow enough to be covered by a single wave guide, but which are not covered by any of the recommended list of guide sizes. These allocations in the microwave region

TABLE 7-2

ARMY-NAVY STANDARD LIST OF RIGID WAVE GUIDES

AN Type No.	Dimensions (in.)		Material
	Outside	Wall thickness	
RG 69/U	6.66 × 3.41	0.065	Brass
RG 48/U	3 × 1½	0.080	Brass
RG 75/U	3 × 1½	0.080	Aluminum
RG 49/U	2 × 1	0.064	Brass
RG 50/U	1½ × ¾	0.064	Brass
RG 51/U	1¼ × ⅝	0.064	Brass
RG 68/U	1¼ × ⅝	0.064	Aluminum
RG 52/U	1 × ½	0.050	Brass
RG 67/U	1 × ½	0.050	Aluminum
RG 53/U	½ × ¼	0.040	Brass
RG 66/U	½ × ¼	0.040	Silver

are given in Fig. 7-12, along with the frequency ranges for which each of the recommended guides is suitable.

A further difficulty that arises in the use of standard brass tubing for wave guides is the lack of close manufacturing tolerances. This is particularly true of rectangular tubing, which was manufactured primarily for decorative purposes before being used as wave guides and is, therefore, held to no manufacturing tolerances. This difficulty has been corrected in part by Army-Navy standardization of certain of the recommended guide sizes; these sizes may readily be obtained held to sufficiently close manufacturing tolerances. These standard guides are listed in Table 7-2, along with the Army-Navy designation.

CHAPTER 8

ATTENUATION IN WAVE GUIDES

In the previous chapter, it was assumed that the wave-guide walls were of infinite conductivity and that the wave guides were filled with lossless dielectric. If these assumptions were completely justified, power would be carried down the inside of the wave guide with no attenuation, provided that the wave guide was not below cutoff dimensions for the wave being transmitted. In physically realizable wave guides, the conductivity of the walls is finite, and as a result the wave is attenuated because of losses in the metal. In addition, if some dielectric other than air is used inside the guide, the losses in the dielectric may result in a very rapid attenuation of the transmitted waves.

1. Conductor Losses

The conductor losses in a wave guide are dependent upon the skin-depth considerations outlined in Chap. 2. For a given size of wave guide operating at a given frequency, the attenuation will increase as the square root of the resistivity of the conducting boundary. This is the same variation with resistivity that is encountered with coaxial lines. The variation of attenuation with frequency is a more complex function. Equations for attenuation that apply when the wave guide is above cutoff are given below. Without exception, these equations indicate that the attenuation approaches infinity as the frequency decreases toward cutoff, but the approximations under which these equations were developed are not valid in the region immediately adjacent to the cutoff wavelength. More accurate formulas applied to this region indicate that there is a smooth transition between the more approximate results that are given below for the above-cutoff and the below-cutoff regions.

Rectangular Wave Guides.—For a rectangular copper air-filled wave guide operating in the dominant, or $TE_{1,0}$, mode, the attenuation is given by

$$\alpha_c = \frac{0.01107}{a^{3/2}} \left[\frac{\frac{1}{2}\frac{a}{b}\left(\frac{f}{f_c}\right)^{3/2} + \left(\frac{f}{f_c}\right)^{-1/2}}{\sqrt{\left(\frac{f}{f_c}\right)^2 - 1}} \right] \quad \text{db/ft} \quad (8\text{-}1)$$

where f is operating frequency and f_c is the cutoff frequency. The inner dimensions of the guide, a and b, are in inches. The larger dimension is a. If some metal other than copper is used as a conductor, the attenuation given by this formula should be multiplied by the square root of the ratio of the resistivities. This relative loss factor is given for a number of metals in Table 2-1.

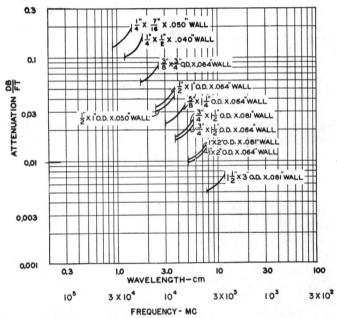

Fig. 8-1.—Attenuation as a function of wavelength and frequency in recommended sizes of a rectangular copper wave guide. Recommended limits of operating frequency are indicated by the vertical bars.

The variation of attenuation with frequency for the various recommended wave guides of Sec. 7-7 is given in Fig. 8-1 over the frequency range for which each size of guide is recommended. It is assumed that the guides are copper, and the results are derived from theory. Experimental values are likely to be slightly higher, depending upon the surface finish.

Formulas giving attenuation as a function of frequency and guide dimensions for some other modes of propagation in a rectangular copper wave guide are

$TE_{2,0}$ mode:

$$\alpha_c = \frac{0.01565}{a^{3/2}} \left[\frac{\frac{a}{2b}\left(\frac{f}{f_c}\right)^{3/2} + \left(\frac{f}{f_c}\right)^{-1/2}}{\sqrt{\left(\frac{f}{f_c}\right)^2 - 1}} \right] \qquad \text{db/ft} \qquad (8\text{-}2)$$

$TE_{1,1}$ mode:

$$\alpha_c = \frac{0.01107}{a^{3/2}} \left\{ \frac{\frac{a}{b}\left(1 + \frac{a}{b}\right)\left(\frac{f}{f_c}\right)^{3/2} + \left[1 + \left(\frac{a}{b}\right)^3\right]\left(\frac{f}{f_c}\right)^{-1/2}}{\left[1 + \left(\frac{a}{b}\right)^2\right]^{3/4} \sqrt{\left(\frac{f}{f_c}\right)^2 - 1}} \right\}$$

$$\text{db/ft} \qquad (8\text{-}3)$$

$TM_{1,1}$ mode:

$$\alpha_c = \frac{0.01107}{a^{3/2}} \left\{ \frac{\left[1 + \left(\frac{b}{a}\right)^3\right]\left(\frac{f}{f_c}\right)^{3/2}}{\left[1 + \left(\frac{b}{a}\right)^2\right]^{3/4} \sqrt{\left(\frac{f}{f_c}\right)^2 - 1}} \right\} \qquad \text{db/ft} \qquad (8\text{-}4)$$

As before, the guide dimensions a and b are in inches, f is frequency and f_c is the cutoff frequency.

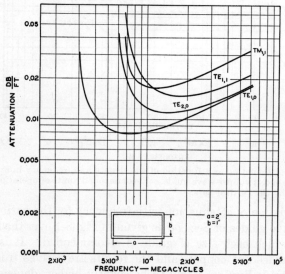

Fig. 8-2.—Attenuation as a function of frequency for various modes in a typical copper rectangular wave guide.

The variation with frequency of the attenuation in a typical rectangular wave guide ($a = 2$ in., $b = 1$ in.) is plotted in Fig. 8-2 for some of the lower modes of propagation. The variation with frequency is seen to be similar for all the modes, although the magnitude of attenuation differs with the mode of propagation.

A term L may be defined as the loss length, or length per unit attenuation. In Fig. 8-3, the dominant, or $TE_{1,0}$, mode of transmission

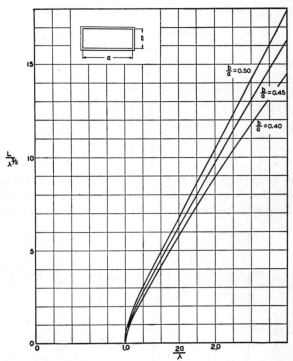

FIG. 8-3.—The loss length, or length per unit attenuation, for a rectangular copper wave guide, as related to the operating wavelength and the guide dimensions.

is assumed and $L/\lambda^{3/2}$ is plotted against $2a/\lambda$ for values of the ratio b/a that cover the range most commonly used. In this figure the loss length is in feet per decibel and the factor $\lambda^{3/2}$ is in centimeters$^{3/2}$. The free-space wavelength is λ. The conducting material is assumed to be copper. These curves permit rapid calculation of attenuation for any signal of arbitrary wavelength in a wave guide chosen within the range commonly used.

Circular Wave Guides.—The attenuation formulas for conductor losses in circular wave guides are as follows:

For $TE_{1,1}$ mode (dominant mode):

$$\alpha_c = \frac{0.00423}{a^{3/2}} \frac{\left(\dfrac{f}{f_c}\right)^{-1/2} + \dfrac{1}{2.38}\left(\dfrac{f}{f_c}\right)^{3/2}}{\sqrt{\left(\dfrac{f}{f_c}\right)^2 - 1}} \quad \text{db/ft} \quad (8\text{-}5)$$

For $TM_{0,1}$ mode (circular magnetic mode):

$$\alpha_c = \frac{0.00485}{a^{3/2}} \frac{\left(\dfrac{f}{f_c}\right)^{3/2}}{\sqrt{\left(\dfrac{f}{f_c}\right)^2 - 1}} \quad \text{db/ft} \quad (8\text{-}6)$$

For $TE_{0,1}$ mode (circular electric mode):

$$\alpha_c = \frac{0.00611}{a^{3/2}} \frac{\left(\dfrac{f}{f_c}\right)^{-1/2}}{\sqrt{\left(\dfrac{f}{f_c}\right)^2 - 1}} \quad \text{db/ft} \quad (8\text{-}7)$$

where f is frequency and f_c the cutoff frequency. These formulas assume air-filled copper guides with the radius a in inches. For different conductor materials, the attenuation given by these formulas

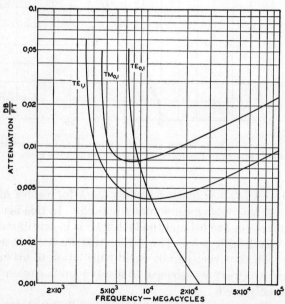

Fig. 8-4.—Attenuation as a function of frequency for some of the lower transmission modes in a circular copper wave guide, 2 in. in diameter.

should be multiplied by the square root of the ratio of the resistivities of the different conductors. This factor is given for a number of different materials in Table 2-1.

The variation of attenuation with frequency for a round copper wave guide 2 in. in diameter for each of the foregoing modes is given

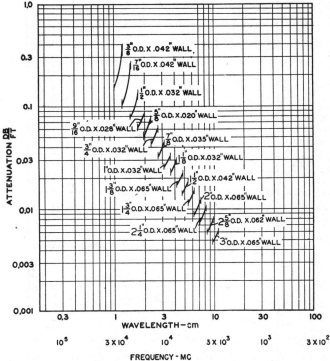

FIG. 8-5.—Attenuation as a function of wavelength and frequency for recommended sizes of circular copper wave guides. The vertical bars indicate the limits of the recommended operating range.

in Fig. 8-4. It is interesting to note that, for a given size guide, the attenuation of the $TE_{0,1}$ mode decreases without limit with increasing frequency. Experimental verification of this is lacking, and the anomalous attenuation characteristic is lost if the guide is elliptical. Additional effects of ellipticity are given in the following section of this chapter.

The variation of attenuation with wavelength for the various recommended circular wave guides of (Sec. 7-7) is plotted in Fig. 8-5. This is for the $TE_{1,1}$ mode of transmission in airfilled copper wave guide. For different conductor materials the value of attenuation given by this figure should be multiplied by the appropriate loss factor given in Table 2-1.

The loss length L is defined as the length of line per unit attenuation. In Fig. 8-6 the term $L/\lambda^{3/2}$ is plotted against $2a/\lambda$ for the fore-

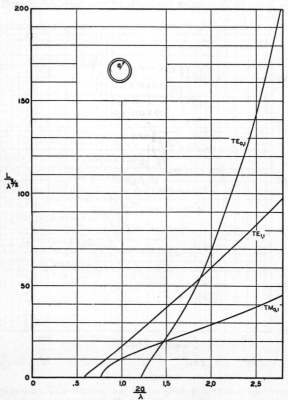

FIG. 8-6.—Loss length, or length per unit attenuation, for three transmission modes in circular copper wave guides.

going three modes of transmission. In this figure, L is in feet per decibel, the radius a is in centimeters, and the factor $\lambda^{3/2}$ is in centimeters$^{3/2}$. The free-space wavelength is λ. The wave guide is assumed to be copper, air filled.

Effect of Ellipticity on Attenuation in Circular Wave Guides.[1]—If a circular wave guide is deformed or made elliptical, the transmission through the guide will be affected, as outlined in Sec. 7-2, page 118. The attenuation of the guide will also be affected. The notation

[1] CHU, L. J., Electromagnetic Waves in Hollow Pipes of Metal, *J. Appl. Phys.*, **9**, 483–591 (1938).

applied here to modes of transmission in elliptical guide shall be the same as used in Chap. 7. The following conclusions may be drawn regarding the effect of ellipticity upon attenuation, with the perimeter of the pipe held constant.

1. The attenuation of the $_eTE_{0,1}$ and $_eTM_{0,1}$ waves will always increase as the ellipticity increases. In addition, the $_eTE_{0,1}$ wave will not have an attenuation that decreases indefinitely with increasing frequency unless the ellipticity is zero.

2. The attenuation of the $_0TE_{1,1}$ and $_eTE_{1,1}$ waves will not be appreciably affected by the ellipticity.

3. The attenuation of the $_eTE_{1,1}$ and the $_0TM_{1,1}$ waves will increase with increasing ellipticity except in the case of the $_eTE_{1,1}$ wave very near cutoff.

The minimum attenuation that can be obtained as a function of frequency is plotted in Fig. 8-7 as a function of the ellipticity of the guide for the preceding modes of propagation. The periphery is assumed to be held constant at 40 cm, and the minimum attenuation is given in decibels per mile for copper air-filled guide. In general, the variations in attenuation are not important except for large deformations.

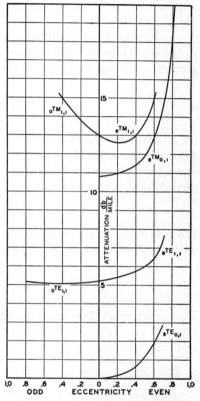

Fig. 8-7.—The minimum attenuation that can be attained by varying the frequency in an elliptical copper wave guide, with the periphery held constant at 40 cm.

Comparison of Theoretical and Measured Attenuation in Wave Guides.—The preceding sections of this chapter have given values of attenuation that are derived from theoretical considerations. These values represent minimum limits of attenuation that are approached more or less closely by the actual guides. General considerations that apply to the problem of losses in a practical guide are discussed in Sec. 2-1.

The losses in a drawn-brass rectangular wave guide usually approach closely the minimum values predicted by theory.

Conductor Losses in Dielectric-filled Wave Guides.—If a wave guide is filled with a dielectric, there will be losses introduced by the dielectric, and in addition, the copper losses will be affected by the presence of the dielectric material. The equations given in this section for losses in an air-filled guide may be applied to wave guides filled with a dielectric whose constant is ϵ_1 if some slight corrections are made, as follows:

1. Wherever the cutoff frequency f_c in the air-filled guides appears in the equations, substitute the cutoff frequency in the dielectric-filled guide f_c'. These terms are related by the equation

$$f_c' = \frac{f_c}{\sqrt{\epsilon_1}} \tag{8-8}$$

2. Multiply the modified expression by the factor $\epsilon_1^{1/4}$. In other words, if the original expression for attenuation in an air-filled guide was a known function of the frequency f, cutoff frequency f_c, and wave-guide dimensions a and b,

$$\alpha = F(f, a, b, f_c)$$

the modified expression for attenuation in the same wave guide filled with a dielectric whose constant is ϵ_1 will be

$$\alpha = \epsilon_1^{1/4} F(f, a, b, f_c') = \epsilon_1^{1/4} F\left(f, a, b, \frac{f_c}{\sqrt{\epsilon_1}}\right) \tag{8-9}$$

This expression takes into consideration only the effect upon conductor losses of having a dielectric inside the guide and does not include losses resulting from the finite power factor of the dielectric.

2. Dielectric Losses

In a wave guide filled with dielectric material, there will be losses resulting from the imperfections of the dielectric as well as from the finite conductivity of the conducting walls. These dielectric losses may be calculated by assuming the dielectric constant to be complex for actual dielectrics although real for perfect dielectrics. The dielectric constant may therefore be written

$$\epsilon_1 = \epsilon_1' - j\epsilon_1'' \tag{8-10}$$

and the loss tangent of the dielectric is defined as

$$\tan \delta = \frac{\epsilon_1''}{\epsilon_1'} \tag{8-11}$$

The loss tangent of the dielectric is equal to the power factor, defined by

$$\text{Power factor} = \cos(90° - \delta) \tag{8-12}$$

for all but very lossy dielectrics.

If an ideal dielectric whose constant is ϵ_1 is assumed, the cutoff wavelength λ_c' in the dielectric-filled guide will be

$$\lambda_c' = \sqrt{\epsilon_1}\,\lambda_c \tag{8-13}$$

where λ_c is the cutoff wavelength in the same guide when filled with air. Inserting a dielectric with a constant greater than unity will increase the cutoff wavelength of the guide and permit it to transmit power at lower frequencies than would otherwise be possible. But, in general, losses in the dielectric are so high that the saving in space is more than compensated for by the increased attenuation. On the other hand, it is quite feasible to construct satisfactory fixed attenuators by using a wave guide filled with a lossy dielectric.

The wavelength in a guide filled with an ideal dielectric whose constant is ϵ_1 has been given in Sec. 7-4, page 123,

$$\lambda_g = \frac{\lambda}{\sqrt{\epsilon_1 - \left(\dfrac{\lambda}{\lambda_c}\right)^2}} \tag{8-14}$$

where λ is the free-space wavelength and λ_c is the cutoff wavelength of the empty guide. If the dielectric is not perfect, the exact wavelength in the guide is

$$\lambda_g = \frac{\lambda}{\sqrt{\epsilon_1' - \left(\dfrac{\lambda}{\lambda_c}\right)^2}} \times \frac{1}{\sqrt{\dfrac{1}{2} + \dfrac{1}{2}\left\{\dfrac{\epsilon_1''^2}{[\epsilon_1' - (\lambda/\lambda_c)^2]^2} + 1\right\}^{\frac{1}{2}}}} \tag{8-15}$$

which reduces to the approximate formula

$$\lambda_g = \frac{\lambda}{\sqrt{\epsilon_1' - \left(\dfrac{\lambda}{\lambda_c}\right)^2}} \tag{8-16}$$

for all except the most lossy dielectrics.

The exact formula for attenuation in a wave guide resulting from an imperfect dielectric is

$$\alpha_D = 830 \frac{\epsilon_1''}{\lambda}\left(\frac{\lambda_g}{\lambda}\right) \quad \text{db/ft} \tag{8-17}$$

where λ_g, the guide wavelength given above, and the free-space wavelength λ are in centimeters. In all cases where the approximate calculation for wavelength is justified, the attenuation may be expressed as

$$\alpha_D = 830 \frac{\epsilon_1''}{\lambda} \frac{1}{\sqrt{\epsilon_1' - \left(\dfrac{\lambda}{\lambda_c}\right)^2}} \quad \text{db/ft} \tag{8-18}$$

3. Attenuation Resulting from Both Conductor and Dielectric Losses

The total attenuation in a wave guide resulting from both conductor and dielectric losses may be obtained from the equation

$$\alpha_T = \alpha_c + \alpha_D \tag{8-19}$$

in which α_T is the total attenuation, α_c is the attenuation resulting from conductor losses, and α_D is the attenuation resulting from dielectric losses. When conductor losses are calculated, care should be taken to use the modified equations that take into account the effect of the dielectric upon conductor losses. In the practical problems usually encountered, however, the dielectric losses are considerably greater than the conductor losses.

4. Attenuation in a Wave Guide below Cutoff

If, in a wave guide with perfectly conducting walls, a possible mode of transmission is excited at a frequency that is below cutoff for that particular mode, no energy will be transmitted through the guide from the point of excitation. The input impedance of the guide will be a pure reactance for the mode below cutoff, and the field intensity associated with the cutoff mode will diminish exponentially from the point of excitation.

The field strength in the guide, as a function of distance from the point of excitation, will vary as

$$E = E_0 e^{-\alpha z} \tag{8-20}$$

where E_0 is the initial amplitude at the point of excitation. The attenuation is given by

$$\alpha = 8.69 \sqrt{\left(\frac{2\pi}{\lambda_c}\right)^2 - \epsilon \left(\frac{2\pi}{\lambda}\right)^2} \quad \text{db/unit length} \tag{8-21}$$

where λ_c is the cutoff wavelength of the air-filled guide, λ is the wavelength in free space at the frequency of excitation, and ϵ is the dielectric constant of the dielectric medium inside the conducting boundary.

The attenuation in a guide below cutoff is plotted as a function of the ratio λ_c/λ in Fig. 8-8. When the free-space wavelength is much greater than the cutoff wavelength, *i.e.*, when the frequency of excitation is much less than the cutoff frequency, the attenuation in the

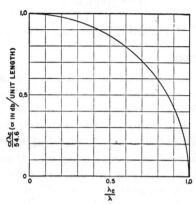

FIG. 8-8.—The attenuation in below-cutoff wave guides.

guide becomes very nearly independent of frequency and approaches a limiting value of

$$\alpha = \frac{54.6}{\lambda_c} \quad \text{db/unit length} \tag{8-22}$$

as the wavelength becomes very large and the frequency correspondingly low. As before, the term λ_c is the cutoff wavelength of the guide when air-filled, but in both Eqs. (8-21) and (8-22) the answer will be correct whether the guide is air-filled or filled with a dielectric with a constant of ϵ.

Wave guides below cutoff frequency are frequently used as variable attenuators, because for any single mode of excitation, the attenuation measured in decibels is a linear function of the length of the wave guide. The two modes most commonly used in circular guide and their respective attenuations are

$TE_{1,1}$ mode:

$$\alpha = 8.69 \sqrt{\left(\frac{1.841}{a}\right)^2 - \left(\frac{2\pi}{\lambda}\right)^2} \quad \text{db/unit length} \tag{8-23}$$

$TM_{0,1}$ mode:

$$\alpha = 8.69 \sqrt{\left(\frac{2.405}{a}\right)^2 - \left(\frac{2\pi}{\lambda}\right)^2} \quad \text{db/unit length} \tag{8-24}$$

where a is the guide radius and λ is the free-space wavelength.

CHAPTER 9

OBSTACLES, DISCONTINUITIES, AND JUNCTIONS

1. General Discussion

Coupling between Modes at an Obstacle.—In general, a metallic obstacle placed in a wave guide will affect the transmission of an electromagnetic wave through the guide. The guide may be restricted in size so that only the dominant mode is above cutoff. The obstacle will then cause a partial reflection of a traveling wave in the dominant mode and is equivalent to a discontinuity on a transmission line (see Sec. 1-5). In addition, higher modes that are below cutoff will usually be excited at the discontinuity. These will diminish rapidly with distance from the point of excitation and are usually of no consequence at a distance from the discontinuity equal to or greater than the transverse dimensions of the guide.

If there is more than one mode above cutoff, but only one mode is being used for energy transmission, a metallic obstacle may excite other modes above cutoff, and in general an obstacle will couple energy between the different modes of transmission unless reasons of polarization or symmetry prevent interaction.

Equivalent Circuit Representation of Wave-Guide Structures.—The effect of an obstacle in a wave guide may be accounted for by setting up an equivalent circuit in terms of lumped constants. This may be done at any single frequency, but in general the parameters of the equivalent circuit will vary with frequency, and the sign of a circuit parameter does not necessarily imply anything as to its frequency dependence. The choice of an equivalent circuit will depend upon what planes in the wave guide are chosen for reference.

Furthermore, if two obstacles are placed sufficiently close together to permit interaction of the below-cutoff modes excited at the obstacles, the equivalent circuit of the obstacles will be modified by this coupling between them.

If the obstacle has longitudinal dimensions that are very small, an equivalent circuit may be used which consists of a single shunting reactance located precisely at the point of discontinuity. If the obstacle has finite thickness, and a single reference plane is chosen at the center of the obstacle, the equivalent circuit is usually a more complex tee or pi network, which approaches a simple shunting reactance as the thickness approaches zero.

For more complex structures, such as tee junctions, a variety of equivalent circuits may be determined with different planes chosen for reference, and the ones that are shown in this chapter have no special virtues other than possible simplicity and ease of application.

Applicability of Equivalent Circuits.—In general, the results given in this chapter should be applied only when the wave guide is restricted in size so as to be above cutoff for only the dominant mode. Some of the results, in theory at least, may be extended outside this range when the discontinuities do not excite other modes that are above cutoff, but machining inaccuracies in a practical structure will often make it impossible to meet the theoretical requirements.

The accuracy of the theoretical curves given in this section varies, but most of the theoretical values are good within ±5 per cent or less.

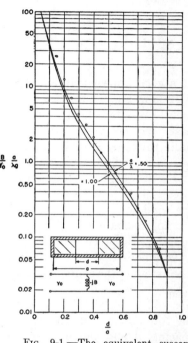

Fig. 9-1.—The equivalent susceptance of a thin, symmetrical inductive window in a rectangular wave guide. The curves are theoretical, and experimental points are given for $a/\lambda = 0.80$, $\lambda = 6.0$ cm, and thickness of $\frac{1}{32}$ in.

Greater discrepancies with experimental results are usually attributable to experimental error.

2. Metallic Windows

A thin plate of metal that partially blocks the guide and is placed perpendicular to the axis of a wave guide has an equivalent circuit consisting of a susceptance shunted across the guide, at the location of the plate. The magnitude of the susceptance, its frequency dependence, and its sign depend upon the size and location of the opening in the plate.

Rectangular Wave Guides. *Symmetrical Inductive Windows.*—When the window opening in a thin diaphragm extends completely across the guide and is symmetrically located with the sides parallel to the electric field (Fig. 9-1), the equivalent circuit is an inductive reactance shunted across the guide. The theoretical reactance is given by

$$\frac{X}{Z_0} = \frac{Y_0}{B} = \frac{a}{\lambda_g} \tan^2 \frac{\pi d}{2a} \left[1 + \frac{3}{4} \sin^2 \frac{\pi d}{a} \left(\frac{1}{\sqrt{1 - \left(\frac{2a}{3\lambda}\right)^2}} - 1 \right) \right] \quad (9\text{-}1)$$

to a good approximation. Results that are predicted by theory are plotted in Fig. 9-1 for two values of the parameter a/λ. Some experimental results, which were measured with windows of $\frac{1}{32}$-in. thickness, are compared with this theory.[1] The quantitative effect of finite thickness is difficult to calculate theoretically, but finite thickness will tend to increase the equivalent susceptance of the windows, and series-resistance terms will also be introduced into the equivalent circuit of the structure if the reference plane is chosen at the center of the window.

Approximate calculations have been made which estimate the coupling (between symmetrical inductive windows in rectangular wave guide) that results from interaction of the higher order fields. The extent of the coupling will increase with window susceptance. For a half wave-guide wavelength spacing between windows, the interaction will be negligible, and at a quarter wave-guide wavelength spacing the interaction will usually be small, but at an eighth wavelength spacing, it may be considerable. The extent of the interaction will increase as the susceptance of the windows increases.

Asymmetrical Inductive Windows.—When the window opening in a thin metal diaphragm extends completely across a wave guide with the sides parallel to the electric field, and one side of the window coincides with one edge of the guide (Fig. 9-2), the equivalent circuit is again a shunt inductive susceptance. A theoretical expression has been calculated giving this equivalent susceptance, and the results are presented graphically in Fig. 9-2. Some experimental results are compared with this theory.[1] These experimental results were taken with diaphragms $\frac{1}{32}$ in. thick, and the experimental susceptances are therefore somewhat higher than predicted by theory.

The asymmetrical inductive window is sometimes preferred to the

[1] Theoretical formula and curves are given in "Wave Guide Handbook," 1st rev. ed., M.I.T. Radiation Laboratory, Rept. 43, Feb. 7, 1944 (not an official report). Experimental data from Sperry Gyroscope Company, Inc.

NOTE: footnotes are numbered by chapter.

symmetrical window because of its greater mechanical simplicity, but its susceptance is a more rapidly changing function of frequency when the guide is near cutoff for the $TE_{2,0}$ mode.

Inductive Strip.—When the obstacle is a thin strip of metal extending across the wave guide and is centered in the guide with its sides

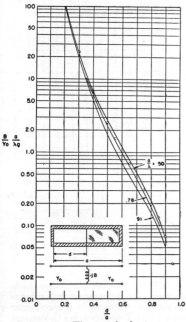

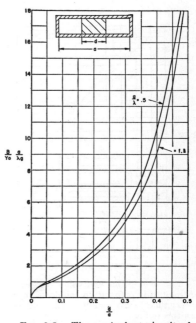

Fig. 9-2.—The equivalent susceptance of a thin, asymmetrical inductive window in a rectangular wave guide. The curves are theoretical, and experimental points are given for $a/\lambda = 0.80$, $\lambda = 6.0$ cm, and thickness of $\frac{1}{32}$ in.

Fig. 9-3.—The equivalent circuit of a thin inductive strip in a rectangular wave guide. The curves are theoretical.

parallel to the electric field, its equivalent circuit is again an inductive susceptance shunted across the guide. The results of a theoretical calculation are given in Fig. 9-3.[2]

Symmetrical Capacitive Windows.—When the window opening in a thin diaphragm extends completely across the guide and is symmetrically located with the sides perpendicular to the electric field (Fig. 9-4), the equivalent circuit is a capacitive reactance shunted across the guide. The results of a theoretical calculation for the susceptance are plotted in Fig. 9-4.[2]

[2] Theoretical formula and curves are given in "Wave Guide Handbook," 1st rev. ed., M.I.T. Radiation Laboratory, Rept. 43, Feb. 7, 1944 (not an official report).

Asymmetrical Capacitive Windows.—If the window opening in a thin metal diaphragm extends completely across the guide with one edge of the window coinciding with an edge of the guide that is perpendicular to the electric field (Fig. 9-4), the same theoretical curves may be used that apply to the symmetrical capacitive window, if λ_g is replaced by $\lambda_g/2$.

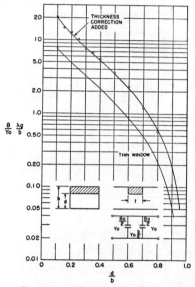

Fig. 9-5.—The effect of finite thickness upon the equivalent susceptance of capacitive windows in a rectangular wave guide. The curves are theoretical, and the experimental points are for $\lambda = 6.0$ cm, $b/\lambda g = 0.29$, and $t = 0.081$ cm.

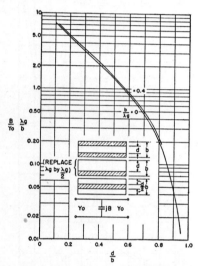

Fig. 9-4.—The equivalent susceptance of thin capacitive windows in a rectangular wave guide. The curves are theoretical.

Capacitive Strip.—If the thin diaphragm reduces to a metallic strip extending across the guide with its edges perpendicular to the electric field, and symmetrically located with respect to the side walls (Fig. 9-4), the same theoretical curves may be applied as for the symmetrical capacitive window.

Finite Thickness for Capacitive Windows.—Finite thickness of a capacitive window of the types illustrated in Fig. 9-4 may be taken into account by use of the equivalent circuit shown in Fig. 9-5. If the window thickness is finite but much less than a wavelength, the admittance at the input face of the window will be

$$\frac{Y}{Y_0} = 1 + \frac{G}{Y_0} + j\frac{B}{Y_0} \tag{9-2}$$

where

$$\frac{B}{Y_0} = \frac{B_0}{Y_0} + \frac{2\pi t}{\lambda_g}\left(\frac{b}{d} - \frac{d}{b}\right) \tag{9-3}$$

$$\frac{G}{Y_0} = \frac{2\pi t}{\lambda_g}\frac{B_0}{Y_0}\frac{d}{b} \tag{9-4}$$

The normalized susceptance of the infinitely thin window is B_0/Y_0, and t is the window thickness. This thickness correction must usually be made if theoretical results are to give good agreement with

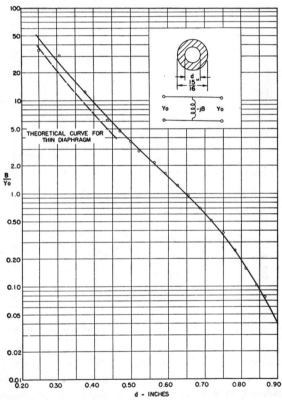

Fig. 9-6.—The equivalent susceptance of a circular aperture in a circular wave guide. The experimental points are for $\lambda = 3.20$ cm, $\lambda_g = 5.15$ cm, and window thickness of $\frac{1}{32}$ in.

experimental measurements. The measured susceptances at $\lambda = 6$ cm of asymmetrical capacitive windows of $\frac{1}{32}$ in. thickness are compared with the theoretical results with and without the correction for finite thickness in Fig. 9-5.

Circular Wave Guides. *Circular Aperture.*—The equivalent circuit of a thin metallic diaphragm with a circular aperture, in a circular wave guide that is above cutoff for the dominant ($TE_{1,1}$) mode only (Fig. 9-6), is an inductive susceptance shunted across the guide. Figure 9-6[3] shows experimental results for windows of $\frac{1}{32}$ in. thickness.

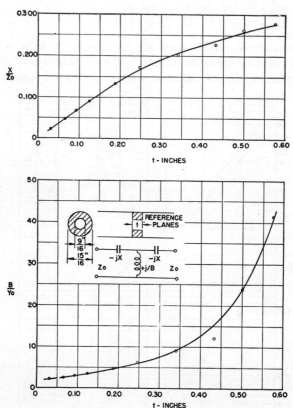

Fig. 9-7.—The effect of finite thickness upon the equivalent-circuit parameters of a circular window in a circular wave guide.

If the window is of finite thickness, and the reference planes are chosen at the faces of the window, the equivalent circuit will be a tee network, as shown in Fig. 9-7. In this figure, the parameters of the network are plotted as a function of the diaphragm thickness for a given aperture diameter, wavelength and guide size also being held constant.[3]

Circular Disk.—A thin circular metallic disk centrally located in a circular wave guide that is above cutoff for the dominant ($TE_{1,1}$)

[3] " Wave Guide Handbook," 1st rev. ed., M.I.T. Radiation Laboratory, Rept. 43, Feb. 7, 1944.

mode only has an equivalent circuit that consists of a capacitive susceptance shunted across the guide. Some experimental results that give this susceptance as a function of diameter are plotted in Fig. 9-8.[4]

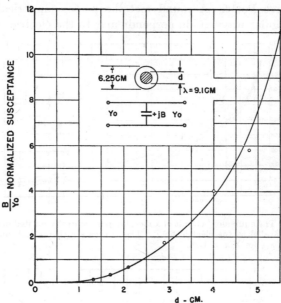

Fɪɢ. 9-8.—The equivalent susceptance of a thin circular disk centrally located in a circular wave guide.

3. Metallic Posts

Inductive Posts.—A round metallic post symmetrically located in a rectangular wave guide parallel to the electric field (Fig. 9-9) has an approximate equivalent circuit consisting of an inductive susceptance shunted across the guide. The reference plane is chosen at the center of the post.

To a better approximation, the equivalent circuit is a symmetrical tee network; this more complex representation is necessary because of the finite thickness of the post. The results of a calculation that give the parameters of this equivalent circuit as a function of the post diameter are given in Figs. 9-9 and 9-10. The magnitude of the reflection that will be set up in a matched line by an inductive post may be calculated with an error of a few per cent or less if only the shunt arm of the network is considered, but the series arms have an appreciable

[4] Data from Fʀᴀɴᴋ, N. H., M.I.T. Radiation Laboratory, Sec. T, Rept. 9, Sept. 24, 1942.

effect upon the phase of the reflection.   Theoretical and experimental results are compared in Fig. 9-9, the series arm being neglected in this comparison as only the magnitude of the reflection was measured.

Capacitive Posts.—A round metallic post symmetrically located in a rectangular wave guide perpendicular to the electric field has an

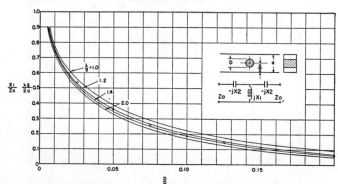

Fig. 9-9.—The equivalent circuit of a metallic post centrally located in a rectangular wave guide parallel to the electric field.   The curves are theoretical, and the experimental points are for $\lambda/a = 1.26$.

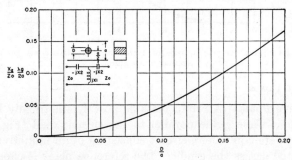

Fig. 9-10.—An additional parameter for the equivalent circuit of a metallic post centrally located in a rectangular wave guide parallel to the electric field (see Fig. 9-9). The curve is theoretical.

equivalent circuit consisting of a capacitive susceptance shunted across the guide.   Some experimental results that give the magnitude of this susceptance as a function of the post diameter are given in Fig. 9-11.[5]

4. Resonant Structures in Wave Guides

Certain structures, when placed in a wave guide, exhibit resonance phenomena.   If the axial dimensions of the structure are very small, the equivalent circuit at any frequency is a susceptance shunted across the guide.   But the frequency dependence of this susceptance is similar

[5] Experimental data from the Sperry Gyroscope Company, Inc.

to that of a resonant circuit shunting the guide, and the equivalent circuit is often drawn as a resonant circuit to indicate this frequency dependence.

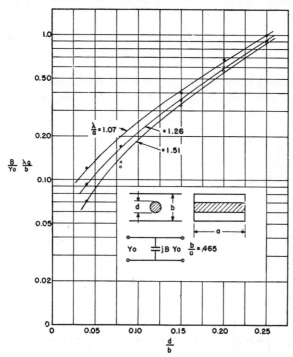

Fig. 9-11.—The equivalent susceptance of a metallic post centrally located in a rectangular wave guide perpendicular to the electric field. The curves and points are experimental, with $b/a = 0.465$.

These equivalent resonant circuits may be either series or parallel resonant, indicating that at some frequency the shunting susceptance passes through infinity or zero, respectively. The product of the equivalent circuit parameters may be determined from the resonant frequency f_0 of the structure.

$$\sqrt{LC} = \frac{1}{2\pi f_0} \qquad (9\text{-}5)$$

For the parallel resonant circuit, the normalized ratio of these parameters may be found by measuring the slope of the susceptance-frequency characteristic in the neighborhood of resonance.

$$\frac{B}{Y_0} = 2\frac{\Delta f}{f_0}\frac{\sqrt{\dfrac{C}{L}}}{Y_0} \qquad (9\text{-}6)$$

In these equations, f_0 is the resonant frequency and Δf the frequency deviation from resonance. For the series resonant circuit, the reactance passes through zero at resonance and in the vicinity of resonance is given by

$$\frac{X}{Z_0} = 2 \frac{\Delta f}{f_0} \frac{\sqrt{\frac{L}{C}}}{Z_0} \tag{9-7}$$

For the parallel resonant obstacle, which allows complete energy transmission past the obstacle at the resonant frequency, a loaded Q

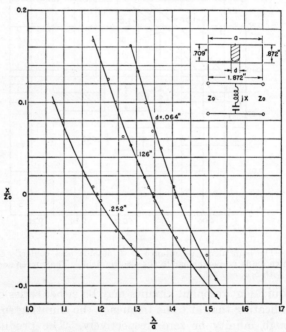

FIG. 9-12.—The reactance-wavelength characteristics of resonant posts in a rectangular wave guide. Curves and points are experimental.

is sometimes defined as the Q of the equivalent circuit when paralleled by the guide impedance. This loaded Q of a resonant circuit is equal to its normalized characteristic admittance $\sqrt{C/L}/Y_0$, and Eq. (9-6) may therefore be rewritten

$$\frac{B}{Y_0} = 2 \frac{\Delta f}{f_0} Q \tag{9-8}$$

Resonant Posts.—A metallic post centrally located in a wave guide and extending part way across the guide parallel to the electric field will exhibit resonance phenomena similar to a shunting series resonant circuit. For a given wave guide and post diameter, a length may be found that sets up an infinite reflection at any given frequency within the normal operating range of the guide. Usually this resonant length approximates a quarter wave in free space, if the height of the guide is appreciably greater.

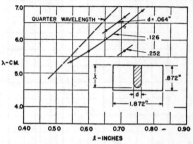

The reactance-wavelength characteristics of three typical resonant posts as determined experimentally are plotted in Fig. 9-12. Some experimentally determined resonant lengths for posts of various diameters are given in Fig. 9-13. The factors $\sqrt{L/C}$ for these same posts are given in Fig. 9-14. Some typical curves giving susceptance as a function of probe lengths are shown in Fig. 9-15. All these experimental data were taken with posts that ended in half spheres whose diameters were those of the posts. Cutting the ends of the posts off square would appreciably change these data.

Fig. 9-13.—The length for resonance for metallic posts with rounded ends centrally located in a rectangular wave guide.

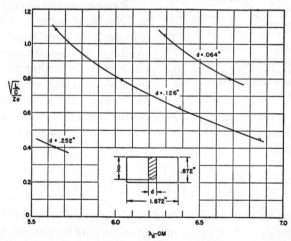

Fig. 9-14.—The normalized characteristic impedance $\sqrt{L/C}/Z_0$ of resonant posts in a rectangular wave guide, as a function of wavelength and post diameter.

Resonant Rings.—Another example of a series resonant structure in wave guide is the resonant ring. This is a conducting ring that exhibits resonance phenomena when placed perpendicular to the axis of a wave guide. No theoretical information is available.

The measured shunt susceptance of a circular ring of square cross section mounted centrally in a circular wave guide operating in the $TE_{1,1}$ mode is shown as a function of s/λ in Fig. 9-16. In this figure s is the mean circumference of the ring and λ the free-space wavelength. Resonance occurs when the mean circumference is somewhat longer than a free-space wavelength.

The measured susceptance of a rectangular resonant ring is plotted in Fig. 9-17 as a function of the mean perimeter of the ring. This parameter seems to be the resonance-determining factor more than does the shape of the ring. Here again the resonance occurs at a mean perimeter somewhat greater than a free-space wavelength.

Rectangular Resonant Windows in Thin Diaphragms.—A metal diaphragm with a rectangular opening exhibits a susceptance-frequency characteristic similar to that of a parallel resonant circuit shunting the guide. For a centrally located

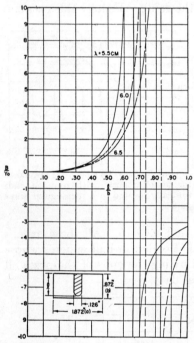

FIG. 9-15.—The normalized susceptance of resonant posts in a rectangular wave guide, as a function of post length and wavelength.

window in a rectangular guide operating in the dominant mode, it has been found empirically that the approximate dimensions for resonance are obtainable from the relation

$$\frac{a}{b}\sqrt{1-\left(\frac{\lambda}{2a}\right)^2} = \frac{a'}{b'}\sqrt{1-\left(\frac{\lambda}{2a'}\right)^2} \qquad (9\text{-}9)$$

where a and b are the guide dimensions, a' and b' are the dimensions of the opening, with a' being measured parallel to a and b' parallel to b. The free-space wavelength is λ. The results expressed in this equation can be represented by the following geometrical construction. In the center of the cross section of the guide, lay out a line of length $\lambda/2$, parallel to the larger dimension of the guide, and centered with respect to the walls. Draw hyperbolas whose axes are parallel to the guide walls passing through the ends of this line and also through

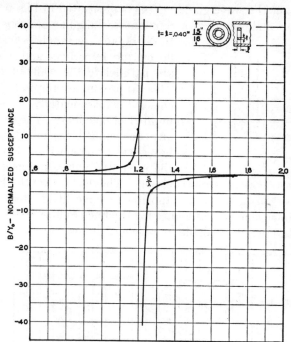

FIG. 9-16.—The normalized susceptance of a resonant ring in a circular wave guide, with *s* the mean perimeter of the ring and the free-space wavelength $\lambda = 3.20$ cm.

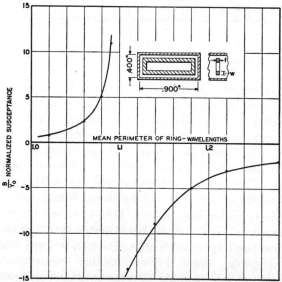

FIG. 9-17.—The normalized susceptance of a rectangular ring in a rectangular wave guide, with $w = t = 0.040$ in. and the free-space wavelength $\lambda = 3.20$ cm.

the corners of the wave guide.   This is illustrated in Fig. 9-18.   The approximate dimensions of a resonant rectangular opening are then

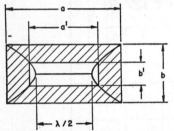

those of any rectangle whose corners lie on the hyperbola and whose sides are parallel to the walls of the guide. This approximate formula has been checked experimentally with a large number of openings. The experimentally determined resonant wavelength has always fallen within 5 per cent of the predicted value, and usually much closer.   The thickness of the diaphragm appears to have little effect upon the

Fig. 9-18.—Resonant rectangular window in a rectangular wave guide.

required dimensions for resonance for thicknesses up to 0.04 λ; experimental data are not available for thicker windows.

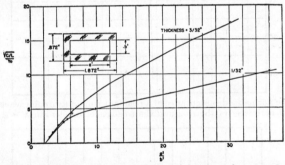

Fig. 9-19.—The normalized characteristic admittance of resonant windows in a rectangular wave guide. The resonant wavelength in all cases was approximately 5.8 cm.

A series of resonant diaphragms designed according to Eq. (9-9) will all have approximately the same resonant wavelengths, but the normalized characteristic admittance or loaded Q will increase with decreasing height of the window and will also increase with increasing thickness of the diaphragm. Some typical experimental data that give the normalized characteristic admittance of some typical windows as a function of the ratio a'/b' are shown in Fig. 9-19.

Equivalent Series and Parallel Resonant Structures.—A variety of apertures in thin diaphragms act as parallel resonant circuits shunting the wave guide. For each of these apertures, it is usually possible to find a corresponding obstacle that acts as a series resonant circuit shunting the guide. Some typical parallel resonant transmitting diaphragms in round wave guide carrying only the dominant mode are

TRANSMITTERS   **REFLECTORS**

FIG. 9-20.—Resonant structures in a circular wave guide. Electric field vertically polarized.

shown in Fig. 9-20, along with the corresponding series resonant reflecting obstacles.

5. Tee Junctions[6]

A junction of three wave guides is easily dealt with when an equivalent circuit can be set up. A variety of circuits may be developed in all cases experimentally and in some cases theoretically, the precise circuit depending upon what planes are chosen for reference. The

[6] ALLANSON, J. T., R. COOPER, and T. G. COWLING, The Theory and Experimental Behavior of Right-angled Junctions in Rectangular-section Wave Guides *J. Inst. Elect. Engrs.* (*London*), May, 1946, pp. 177–187.

circuits presented here have been developed from an approximate theory, but the results check very well with experimental measurements.   The form of the equivalent circuit has been chosen for greatest ease of application.

It is first necessary to introduce the concept of "characteristic planes" in the three guides.   The three guides are joined in an arbitrary manner, as illustrated in Fig. 9-21.   Energy is fed in one line

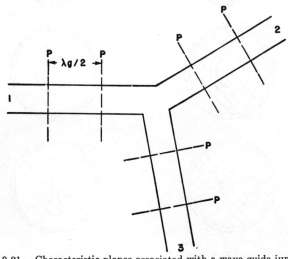

Fig. 9-21.—Characteristic planes associated with a wave-guide junction.

and extracted from a second, while the third is short-circuited.   It is found that there are a number of positions of the short circuit, placed a half wavelength apart, at which no power will flow into the second arm, and an infinite standing-wave ratio will be set up in the input guide.   These positions of the short are termed "characteristic planes" of the guide, and the voltage nodes of the standing waves will fall at the characteristic planes of the input line.

If characteristic planes in the three guides are chosen as reference planes, the equivalent circuit shown in Fig. 9-22 may be applied.   The three guides are coupled by an ideal transformer, and an additional susceptance is coupled to the transformer.   If, in addition to the location of the characteristic planes, the turns ratios of the equivalent transformer and the magnitude of the junction susceptance are known, the behavior of a wave-guide junction under all conditions is completely predictable at a distance far from the fringing fields.

For a symmetrical tee stub, as illustrated in Fig. 9-23, the turns ratios for arms 1 and 3 will be equal $(n_1 = n_3)$.   If the branching wave guide is shorted, there will be a normalized susceptance introduced at the junction of

$$-j\left(A \cot \frac{2\pi l}{\lambda_g} + \frac{B}{Y_0}\right)$$

where $A = (n_2/n_1)^2$ and $n_4 = n_1$.

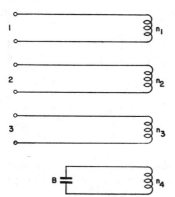

FIG. 9-22.—Equivalent circuit involving ideal transformers that may be used for a wave-guide junction referred to the characteristic planes.

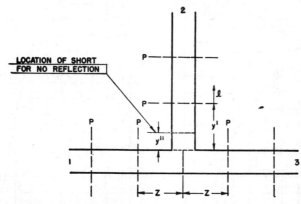

FIG. 9-23.—Notation used with the equivalent circuit of a tee junction in a wave guide.

In Fig. 9-23 and the curves of Figs. 9-25 through 9-28, the following terms are used:

(1) $A = (n_2/n_1)^2$.

(2) B/Y_0 = junction susceptance normalized to impedance of lines 1 and 3.

(3) z = distance from the stub center to the nearest characteristic points of arms 1 and 3.

(4) y' = distance from the stub entry to the nearest characteristic point of arm 2.

(5) y'' = distance from the stub entry at which a short must be placed in the stub to ensure no reflection at the junction of a wave incident from arm 1 or 3.

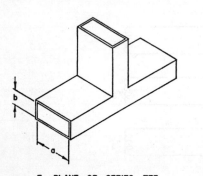   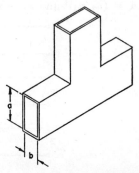

E - PLANE OR SERIES TEE   **H- PLANE OR SHUNT TEE**

FIG. 9-24.—Two types of tee junction commonly employed with a rectangular wave guide.

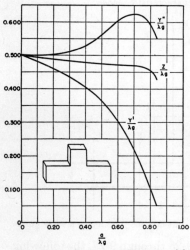   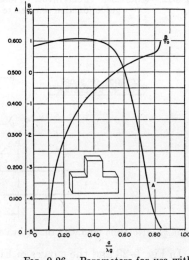

FIG. 9-25.—Parameters for use with the equivalent circuit of the *H*-plane tee.

FIG. 9-26.—Parameters for use with the equivalent circuit of the *H*-plane tee.

There are two kinds of rectangular wave-guide tee junctions to be considered. These are illustrated in Fig. 9-24.

1. *H*-plane tee or shunt tee. The branch guide is taken off the **narrow** side of the main guide in the plane of the magnetic field. This

is called a "shunt tee" because a signal fed in the branch guide will divide at the junction and be in phase in arms 1 and 3 at points equidistant from the junction. The parameters of the equivalent circuit for an H-plane tee are given in Figs. 9-25 and 9-26.

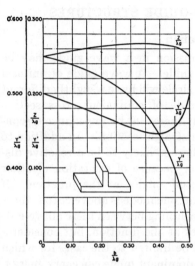

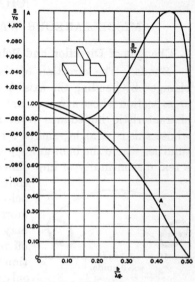

FIG. 9-27.—Parameters for use with the equivalent circuit of the E-plane tee.

FIG. 9-28.—Parameters for use with the equivalent circuit of the E-plane tee.

2. E-plane tee or series tee. The branch guide is taken off the wide side of the main guide in the plane of the electric field. This is called a "series tee" because a signal fed in the branch guide will divide at the junction and be out of phase in arms 1 and 3 at points equidistant from the junction. The parameters of the equivalent circuit for an E-plane tee are given in Figs. 9-27 and 9-28.

CHAPTER 10

MISCELLANEOUS WAVE-GUIDE STRUCTURES

1. Changes of Direction and Polarization

Bends.—The direction of transmission in a wave guide may be changed by bending the axis of the guide. A wave guide of uniform cross section whose axis is an arc of a circle will have a slightly different characteristic impedance from a guide of equivalent cross section whose axis is straight, and as a result there will be impedance discontinuities where the bent guide joins a straight section. In addition to a real discontinuity of impedance, there is likely to be a reactive dis-

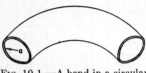

FIG. 10-1.—A bend in a circular wave guide.

continuity because of excitation of other below-cutoff modes at the junction. If more than one mode is above cutoff, there may be coupling between these above-cutoff modes at the junction, but consideration will be limited to the cases for which only the dominant mode can carry energy.

Circular Wave Guide.—A bend in circular wave guide (Fig. 10-1) carrying the dominant ($TE_{1,1}$) mode will, in general, cause elliptical polarization of the wave unless the bend is in one of the planes of mode symmetry. The amount of elliptical polarization increases with the sharpness of the bend, and the phase angle between the field vectors parallel and normal to the plane of the bend is, to a crude first approximation, proportional to the total angle of the bend and inversely proportional to the mean radius.

In theory, this elliptical polarization can be eliminated in a number of ways, such as by using two bends to compensate each other, by deforming the cross section during or following the bend, or by adding dielectric material; but successful results are difficult to obtain in practice.

If the plane of the bend is in one of the planes of mode symmetry, the mean radius of the bend can be appreciably less than the guide wavelength, and the reflection will be small if the cross section of the guide is not deformed.

Rectangular Wave Guide.—A bend in a rectangular wave guide may be in the plane of either the electric or magnetic field and is correspondingly called an *E*-plane or *H*-plane bend (Fig. 10-2). These bends are widely used to change the direction of transmission in a wave-guide system.

If the major impedance discontinuity at the end of a bend were the resistive mismatch of guide impedances, a mean bend length of $n\lambda_g/2$ would give optimum performance. But if the reactive discontinuity were of primary importance, the optimum length would be $\frac{\lambda_g}{4}(2n - 1)$.

Approximate theory indicates that the resistive discontinuity is the more important but that its effects are very small even for bends of short radius.

Experimental results indicate that a much more important practical consideration is to maintain the cross section of the guide in the bend. Results taken with carefully fabricated bends indicate that the optimum mean length for the bend is $n\lambda_g/2$. This figure is not at all critical, however, and the performance of a bend of small radius depends primarily upon the care with which it is fabricated and the accuracy with which the cross section has been maintained. If the inner radius of the bend is greater than a guide wavelength, λ_g, the standing-wave ratio introduced by the bend into a matched system will generally be less than 1.05 throughout the normal operating range of the guide. A much smaller radius, down to $\lambda_g/4$ or less, will introduce standing-wave ratios generally less than 1.1 and often much lower, but the bend must be fabricated with care to achieve this performance.

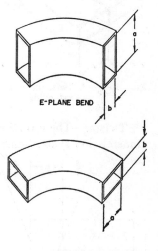

E-PLANE BEND

H-PLANE BEND

FIG. 10-2.—Two types of bend in a rectangular wave guide.

Several techniques of fabricating bends are widely used. If the wave guide is standard brass tubing, it may be filled with a low melting-point alloy and bent around the desired radius. For fairly large radii this gives sufficiently accurate inside dimensions, but for small radii the cross section will be distorted from a rectangular into a trapezoidal shape. It may then be necessary to force rollers through the guide to regain the rectangular cross section after the bend has been made.

Small radius bends may also be fabricated from sheet brass by silver-solder assembly, but this must be done with care, or irregularities will mar the inside surface. The required inside dimensions may also be obtained by machining the guide in halves from solid metal. The junction should preferably be in the center of the broad faces of the guide, if possible. Electroforming bends by plating copper on cast wax or metal forms is very satisfactory, giving a uniform rectangular cross section and a smooth inside surface.

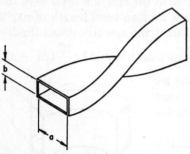

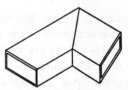

FIG. 10-3.—A twist in a rectangular wave guide.

FIG. 10-4.—A corner in a rectangular wave guide.

Twists.—The direction of polarization in a rectangular wave-guide transmission system may be changed by twisting the guide about its

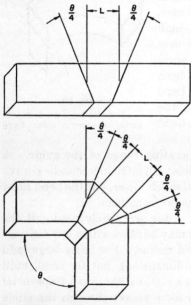

FIG. 10-5.—An *H*-plane double corner in a rectangular wave guide.

axis (Fig. 10-3). If these twists are fabricated carefully, they will introduce no large reflection into a matched wave-guide system. The optimum length of the twist is $n\lambda_g/2$, but is not critical. Twists that rotate the polarization 90 deg in a length of $2\lambda_g$ or more will generally introduce a standing-wave ratio below 1.1 into a matched system, and shorter twists are equally satisfactory if carefully made.

Corners. *Single Corner.*—Changing the direction of transmission in a wave guide by a simple abrupt corner (Fig. 10-4) is not satisfactory, except for small angles. For an angle of 45 deg, the standing-wave ratio introduced into a matched line by such a simple corner will be of the order of 1.2, and this standing-wave ratio will increase rapidly with increasing angle until a complete reflection is reached at an angle near 90 deg.

Double Corner.[1]—Satisfactory transmission around a corner up to 90 deg may be obtained by the use of two simple corners, which are spaced apart approximately $\lambda_g/4$ in order to cancel reflections. Bends

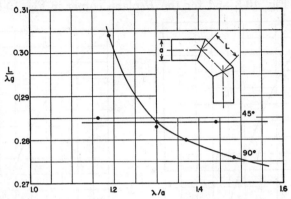

Fig. 10-6.—Dimensions for reflectionless transmission through an *H*-plane double corner in a rectangular wave guide.

are recommended for larger angles. The double corner is illustrated in Fig. 10-5, which also shows how this may easily be fabricated from a straight section of wave guide by two saw cuts and a soldering operation.

For a bend in the *E*-plane, the optimum spacing is given very closely by $L/\lambda_g = 0.25$ for all angles up to 90 deg. The band width (over which the standing-wave ratio introduced by such a corner is less than 1.05) decreases as the ratio λ/λ_c increases but usually falls in the range ± 3 to ± 10

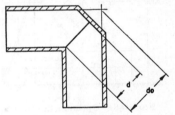

Fig. 10-7.—A mitered corner in a wave guide.

per cent of the design wavelength for a wave guide operated in the recommended range.

For a bend in the *H*-plane, the optimum value of L/λ_g is a function of the ratio λ/a and is plotted as a function of this ratio in Fig. 10-6 for angles of 45 and 90 deg. The band width of the 90-deg corner is similar to the *E*-plane corner. For smaller angles, the band width increases. For a 45-deg angle, with the corner designed for a center wavelength, the band width over which the standing-wave ratio is less than 1.05 is approximately equal to the recommended range of the wave guide.

[1] WALKER, R. M., Corners, Bends and Twists in Rectangular Waveguide, M.I.T. Radiation Laboratory, Rept. 585, July 6, 1944.

Mitered Corners.—The reflection at an abrupt corner may be eliminated by modifying the corner, as shown in Fig. 10-7. The dimension d/d_0 is plotted as a function of the angle for the E-plane corner in Fig. 10-8 and for the H-plane corner in Fig. 10-9.[2]   With

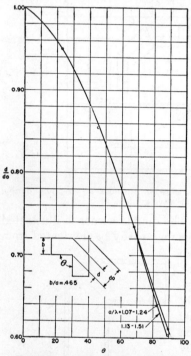

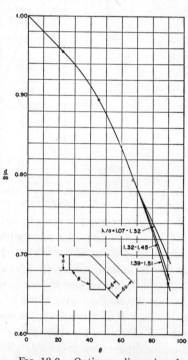

Fig. 10-8.—Optimum dimensions for a mitered E-plane corner in a rectangular wave guide. Experimental curves, with standing-wave ratio below 1.05 within limits indicated on the curves. $b/a = 0.465$.

Fig. 10-9.—Optimum dimensions for a mitered H-plane corner in a rectangular wave guide. Experimental curves, with standing-wave ratio below 1.05 within limits indicated on the curves.

these corners, the transmission band width is approximately equal to the band width of the double corner of Fig. 10-5, and an E-plane corner may give even better performance. Manufacturing tolerances must be held quite closely, however, or the performance will fall below the optimum figures. The double corner is more satisfactory in this respect.

2. Wave-guide Connectors

Butt Joints.—Two lengths of rectangular wave guide may be connected together by machining the two ends off square and clamping

[2] Experimental data obtained at the Sperry Gyroscope Company, Inc.

them together. This butt joint will be electrically smooth and free from loss if the guides are carefully aligned and tightly clamped together, and the major reflection will result from differences in the guide dimensions on either side of the joint. This effect is negligibly small for tubing of reasonable accuracy.

The efficiency of such a connection depends critically upon the tightness of the joint between the guides. If the ends of the guides are misaligned or not clamped tightly together, or if they are not finished off square and smooth, the loss and reflection may be relatively large. If there are mechanical imperfections, it is impossible to pre-

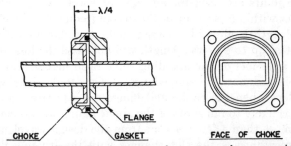

Fig. 10-10.—Choke-flange connector for a rectangular wave guide.

dict what the electrical performance will be, although losses as high as 1.0 db have been measured as a result of loose clamping. So while butt joints are very satisfactory when properly used, and are often preferred when accurate measurements are being performed, they must be assembled with care and mechanical accuracy to give the most satisfactory performance.

Choke Connectors.—The assembly of wave-guide components is often greatly facilitated with the use of choke couplings. A typical coupling is shown in Fig. 10-10. If properly designed, these couplings give only a small reflection and loss and offer advantages in flexibility and reliability.

The L-shaped cavity between the choke and flange of Fig. 10-10 may be considered a half-wave shorted transmission line in series with the wave guide, which presents a short circuit at the input and therefore introduces a minimum electrical discontinuity. The circular slot in the choke is made approximately a quarter wavelength deep at the design wavelength. The contact between the choke and flange is therefore at a point of zero current in the half-wave shorted line, and the contact does not have to be good to minimize losses. The distance from the slot to the wave guide must be determined experimentally, but it is electrically equivalent to a quarter wavelength.

For maximum band width, the width of the slot should be several times greater than the separation between choke and flange faces. A choke-flange connection of this type when properly designed for a center wavelength will introduce a standing-wave ratio below 1.05 over most of the recommended range of a wave guide (Sec. 7-7). The loss will usually be negligibly small, in the order of 0.001 to 0.01 db, increasing with decreasing guide size, and independent of the tightness with which the choke and flange are clamped together.

Transmission through a choke flange will be satisfactory if the choke and flange faces are separated and misaligned to a certain extent and these joints are used for nonrigid or "wobbly" couplings. For frequencies within 5 per cent of the design frequency, if a clearance of $\frac{1}{16}$ wavelength is allowed between choke and flange, a sidewise displacement of up to $\frac{1}{16}$ wavelength will not raise the loss above a few tenths of a decibel or the standing-wave ratio higher than 1.3. But the high-impedance—low-impedance design that gives good band width is lost when the choke and flange are separated, and the performance is likely to fall short of the above figures at wavelengths that differ by more than a few per cent from the design wavelength. The effective reactance of the slot changes with the fringing fields at its entry and therefore changes with separation.

Two choke couplings may be paired together and will generally form a satisfactory connection. At wavelengths different from the design wavelength, the standing-wave ratio will usually be somewhat higher than for the choke-flange combination, although the combination will give a standing-wave ratio less than 1.1 over most of the range of the wave guide. But with paired chokes there is usually a resonance encountered near the design wavelength, which is marked by a rise in the loss and standing-wave ratio.

When two chokes are used for a nonrigid or "wobbly" connection, the performance for large separations may be superior to the choke-flange combination, although for small separations there is little difference. The resonance wavelength depends critically upon the spacing between chokes. It is usually a good idea to check the performance of a two-choke nonrigid connection over the frequency range in which it is to be used. A resonance may also result if the axis of one guide is tilted with respect to the other.

Leakage at Connectors.—The energy in a wave guide is essentially perfectly shielded if the walls of the guide are of appreciable thickness, but there may be energy leakage at the connectors. This leakage may be greatly reduced by a number of expedients.

In most choke-flange connections, there is a groove that has been designed for the insertion of a rubber gasket, which will permit the line to be pressurized. If this gasket is made of conducting rubber of high conductivity, the leakage from the joint will be greatly reduced.

If it is not necessary that the line be pressurized, the gasket may be replaced by one made of fine metal wire that has been woven and compressed to form a feltlike material. This is very satisfactory for laboratory experiments.

Two simple flanges if faced off square and smooth and then clamped together will have appreciable leakage unless they are very carefully finished or lapped. Ordinary machining care is sufficient to minimize leakage if a thin gasket of soft copper foil is placed between the two flanges before they are clamped together.

3. Pressurizing Windows for Wave Guides

When a wave-guide transmission system is to be pressurized to prevent moisture condensation, it is necessary to use some sort of pressurizing window that will offer a minimum electrical discontinuity. Several designs have been tried and found satisfactory.

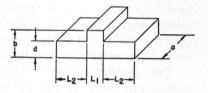

Dielectric Block.[3]—A block of dielectric material, as shown in Fig. 10-11, may be designed to introduce no reflection at a given wavelength and a small reflection over a considerable band. The central section, where the dielectric completely fills the guide, is electrically a quarter wave long at the design wavelength. It is matched to the air-filled guide by the dielectric steps on each end which are also a quarter wave long electrically. At wavelengths different from the design wavelength,

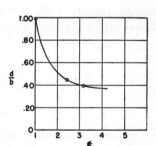

Fig. 10-11.—Dielectric block for pressurizing a wave guide.

the frequency sensitivity of the matching steps is compensated by the center section, and the complete structure therefore introduces only a small reflection.

The optimum length of the center section is given approximately by

[3] WALKER, R. M., Dielectric Windows in Wave Guides, M.I.T. Radiation Laboratory, Rept. 587, June 29, 1944.

$$L_1 = \frac{\lambda_{g(\text{diel.})}}{4} = \frac{1}{4} \frac{\lambda}{\sqrt{\epsilon - \left(\dfrac{\lambda}{\lambda_c}\right)^2}} \qquad (10\text{-}1)$$

where ϵ is the dielectric constant of the material forming the block, and the length of the matching sections by

$$L_2 = \tfrac{1}{4} \sqrt{\lambda_{g(\text{air})}\lambda_{g(\text{diel.})}} \qquad (10\text{-}2)$$

In Eqs. (10-1) and (10-2) $\lambda_{g(\text{air})}$ and $\lambda_{g(\text{diel.})}$ are the wavelengths in the air-filled and dielectric-filled wave guides, respectively. The proper height of the matching sections depends upon the dielectric constant, and experimental results are given in Fig. 10-11. A properly designed window will introduce a standing-wave ratio less than 1.05 throughout a frequency band exceeding 10 per cent.

The dielectric material should be chosen to have a temperature-expansion coefficient that matches the wave guide, or the seal may break when subjected to variations in temperature. Polyglass has been used for brass guide and Styraloy for aluminum. Any thin low-loss cement may be used for sealing; Vinylseal thinned with acetone has been recommended. The power-handling capacity of the window depends upon the dielectric that has been used, but it is usually good.

Thin Dielectric Sheet.—Thin sheets of dielectric may be used for pressurizing windows and will introduce a small reflection that does not change rapidly with wavelength. The standing-wave ratio σ introduced into a matched guide by a dielectric sheet is given by

$$\sigma - 1 = \frac{2\pi d}{\lambda}\left[\frac{\sqrt{\epsilon - \left(\dfrac{\lambda}{\lambda_c}\right)^2}}{\sqrt{1 - \left(\dfrac{\lambda}{\lambda_c}\right)^2}} - 1\right] \qquad (10\text{-}3)$$

where d is the window thickness, ϵ is the dielectric constant, λ is the free-space wavelength, and λ_c is the cutoff wavelength in the air-filled guide ($\lambda_c = 2 \times$ guide width). This assumes that the sheet is mounted in a properly designed holder. If simply clamped between two flanges, the standing-wave ratio will be higher than expected because of the radiation resistance and reactance of the slot between the flanges. A properly designed holder should have a minimum discontinuity in the wall of the guide.

Resonant Windows.—A pressurizing window may be constructed by using a resonant aperture in a metallic diaphragm and sealing the aperture with a glass window. This design is generally more frequency sensitive than the two previously mentioned, and the power-handling capacity is lower. With a typical design, the standing-wave ratio will be less than 1.15 for frequencies within 6 per cent of the resonant frequency, and this band width can be increased if compensating devices are added.

Perhaps the most satisfactory design uses a round resonant aperture in a plate. The opening is filled with glass, and the resonant diameter will depend upon the dielectric constant of the glass. When

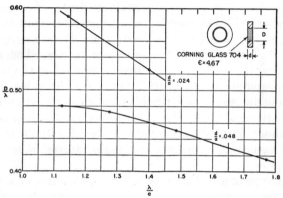

Fig. 10-12.—Dimensions for resonance of Kovar-glass windows used for pressurizing a wave guide. Experimental curves, with the window clamped between two chokes in a rectangular wave guide, with $a = 1.872$ in., and $b = 0.872$ in.

the window is of Corning No. 704 glass ($\epsilon = 4.67$) sealed in a Kovar plate, the diameter D for resonance is larger than the small dimension of the guide, and the resonant window must therefore be mounted between two chokes in order to give a continuous current path.

For a given aperture diameter the resonant wavelength will increase with increasing thickness (this is in contrast to air-filled rectangular windows, whose resonant dimensions do not change much with thickness). The band width will decrease with increasing thickness, and a compromise must be made between bandwidth and mechanical strength.

The results of some experimental determinations[4] of resonant wavelength are plotted in Fig. 10-12. These were all taken for a particular size of wave guide, as indicated, but it is believed that they may be extrapolated with fair accuracy to other sizes of guide, provided that the ratio of guide height to width is not greatly different.

[4] Experimental data obtained at the Sperry Gyroscope Company, Inc.

4. Flexible Wave Guides

It is sometimes desirable to use a transmission line that has the advantages offered by rectangular wave guides, but that is at the same time flexible. Several designs have been developed to a point where they may be used with satisfactory results.

One of the flexible wave guides is constructed by winding a continuous metal strip spirally about a rectangular form. The edges of the strip are interlocked and tightly crimped together to make good contact. This construction is illustrated in Fig. 10-13. When the

Fig. 10-13.—The construction of the wall of a flexible, metal wave guide.

guide is flexed, the contacts slide and, therefore, tend to loosen up with use. There is a consequent increase in the loss, which is normally little greater than the solid guide.

The performance is improved by encasing the guide in a tightly molded Neoprene gasket, which holds the convolutions tightly together and permits the guide to be pressurized. When the guide is protected in this manner, it may be extensively flexed with little change in properties, except at extremely low temperatures where the jacket may crack.

Another type of metal air hose that has been adapted to wave guide uses a similar interlocked spiral construction, but the convolutions are continuously soldered during fabrication. When the guide is flexed, the individual convolutions are distorted, and there is no sliding of the contacts. The metal strip is generally of thinner metal for this reason, but the guide may be pressurized without the addition of an outer covering, and its loss will not increase greatly with use. The

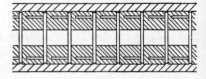

Fig. 10-14.—The construction of a vertabra-type flexible wave guide.

serviceability may be improved, however, by the addition of a protective Neoprene outer cover.

Metal bellows that are formed from a single piece of metal have been developed experimentally. In short lengths these are the most flexible guides and will handle much more compression and extension than other types of construction.

Another flexible guide uses a number of modified choke connectors, as illustrated in Fig. 10-14. This is called a "vertebra-type flexible guide." Each choke coupling is made approximately a quarter waveguide wavelength long. The back of each coupling is faced off as a plane perpendicular to the axis of the guide and is spaced from the face of the following choke by the outer protective jacket. This jacket also enables the guide to be pressurized. This type of guide

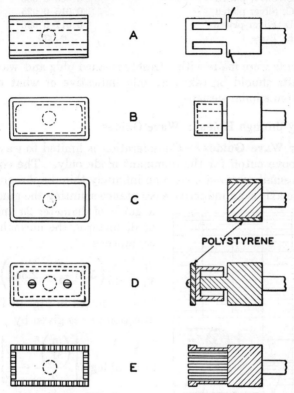

Fig. 10-15.—Miscellaneous wave-guide shorting plugs.

is very flexible, but the chokes must be carefully designed to avoid resonances when the guide is twisted or bent.

5. Shorting Plugs for Wave Guides

Various types of shorting plugs have been used for rectangular wave guides. Some of these are illustrated in Fig. 10-15. The ones shown were constructed and tested in 1 by ½ by 0.050-in. wall guide, and the losses were compared with the loss introduced by a brass plate soldered on the end of the wave guide. The results are given in Table 10-1.

The losses in types A to D do not vary greatly with age, but the losses introduced by type E have been observed to increase markedly with age and depend upon the stiffness of the fingers. The preceding

TABLE 10-1

Type of Plug	Measured Loss, db
A. Silver plated	0.001
B. Silver plated	0.005–0.006
C. Silver plated	0.015–0.025
D. Silver plated	0.017–0.035
E. Brass	0.038

measurements were made with a freshly cleaned plug and wave guide. These results should be taken as only indicative of what might be expected from similar designs.

6. Coupling through Holes in Wave Guides

Circular Wave Guides.[5]—Consideration is limited to wave guides that are above cutoff for the dominant mode only. The equivalent circuit of a small centered hole in an infinitely thin diaphragm normal to the guide axis is an inductive susceptance shunting the guide. For

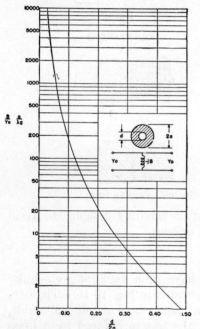

a guide of diameter $2a$ and a hole of diameter d, the normalized susceptance is

$$\frac{B}{Y_0} = \frac{\lambda_g}{4a}\left(5.71\frac{a^3}{d^3} - 2.344\right) \quad (10\text{-}4)$$

This is plotted in Fig. 10-16. The insertion loss is given by

$$\alpha_1 = 10 \log_{10}\left[\left(\frac{B}{Y_0}\right)^2 - 1\right] \quad \text{db} \quad (10\text{-}5)$$

or for large B/Y_0,

$$\alpha_1 \cong 20 \log_{10}\frac{\left(\frac{B}{Y_0}\right)}{2} \quad (10\text{-}6)$$

If the hole is of appreciable thickness t, the total insertion loss α_T will be given approximately by

$$\alpha_T = \alpha_1 + \alpha_2 \quad (10\text{-}7)$$

FIG. 10-16.—Theoretical susceptance of a small centered hole in a thin diaphragm in a circular wave guide.

where α_2 is the attenuation in a below cutoff wave guide given by

[5] "Waveguide Handbook Supplement," M.I.T. Radiation Laboratory, Rept. 41, Jan. 23, 1945 A.

$$\alpha_2 = 32.0 \sqrt{1 - \left(1.706 \frac{d}{\lambda}\right)^2} \frac{t}{d} \cong 32.0 \frac{t}{d} \quad \text{db} \quad (10\text{-}8)$$

Rectangular Wave Guides.—Consideration is limited to wave guides that are above cutoff for the dominant mode only. The equivalent circuit of a small centered hole in an infinitely thin diaphragm

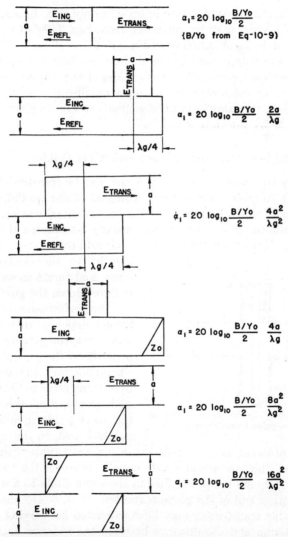

Fig. 10-17.—Miscellaneous arrangements of a small coupling hole between two rectangular wave guides, and the corresponding formulas to be used in calculating the attenuation through the hole.

normal to the guide axis is an inductive diaphragm shunting the guide. For a guide of larger dimension a and smaller dimension b and a hole of diameter d, the normalized susceptance is

$$\frac{B}{Y_0} \cong \frac{3}{2\pi} \frac{ab\lambda_g}{d^3} \tag{10-9}$$

The insertion loss of a hole in an infinitely thin diaphragm or one of finite thickness may be calculated from Eqs. (10-5) to (10-8), with the value of B/Y_0 obtained from Eq. (10-9).

When the hole is used to couple between two wave guides whose axes are not coincident, the insertion loss of the coupling hole may in many cases be calculated by a simple modification of the term α_1, of Eq. (10-6). Examples of arrangements where simple modifications are possible are shown in Fig. 10-17.

7. Coupling between Coaxial Lines and Wave Guides

Energy traveling down a coaxial line may be transferred to a wave guide by a suitable transformer. The axis of the coaxial line is generally normal to the broad face of the (rectangular) wave guide. The outer conductor of the coaxial line usually terminates at the wall of the guide. The center conductor extends into the interior of the guide, parallel to the electric lines of force, and forms an antenna that radiates down the guide.

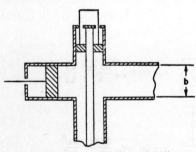

The performance of this transformer depends upon the impedance that the probe antenna presents to the coaxial line. For a traveling wave in the coaxial line to be transferred to the wave guide without reflection, this antenna in the wave guide should present a matched load to the coaxial line.

Fig. 10-18.—A tunable coaxial line to wave-guide transformers.

If the probe antenna is radiating into a wave guide with both ends terminated, the power will divide equally between the two terminations. To confine the power flow in the wave guide to a single direction, the other end of the guide is shorted.

A tunable transformer may be constructed by varying the length of the antenna and the distance between the antenna and the short circuit, as both of these parameters will affect the input impedance to the antenna. It is sometimes more convenient to extend the center conductor through the opposite wall of the wave guide, where it forms the center conductor of an additional length of shorted coaxial line. The position of the short on this line is then one of the variables. A tunable transformer of this type is illustrated in Fig. 10-18.

For probe antennas whose length is much less than a quarter wavelength, and whose diameter is small, it is possible to make some general remarks about the variation of input impedance with changing conditions. Although this particular antenna is of little practical interest, the general conclusions that are drawn indicate trends that may be extended with some validity to the more interesting case of the longer antennas of larger diameter.

The input impedance to the short small-diameter antenna is a large capacitive reactance in series with a small radiation resistance. The resistance varies with the following parameters:

$$R \cong l^2 \cos^2 \frac{\pi x_0}{a} \sin^2 \frac{2\pi x_1}{\lambda_g} \tag{10-10}$$

where l is the length of the antenna, x_0 is the displacement from the guide center, and x_1 is the distance from antenna to short. The maximum radiation resistance with varying x_1 is twice what would be found if both ends of the wave guide were terminated in its characteristic impedance. These relationships are predicted by theory and for the most part have been experimentally verified.

It is possible to find a length of antenna and a distance from antenna to short that will enable the antenna to present a matched load to the input coaxial line, and a fixed tuned transformer may be constructed in this manner, as illustrated in Fig. 10-19A. The optimum dimensions must be found experimentally. For example, the dimensions of a transformer of this type between $1\frac{5}{8}$-in. 50-ohm coaxial line and $1\frac{1}{2}$ by 3-in. wave guide at $\lambda = 10.2$ cm were antenna length $= 0.18\lambda$ and distance from antenna axis to short $= 0.16\lambda_g$. These dimensions will vary with different sizes of coaxial line and wave guide, and the preceding figures are only indicative.

The band width over which the transformer is satisfactory is made greater by increasing the size of the coaxial line and the diameter of the antenna, and also by rounding the end of the antenna. It is still further increased by modifying the probe, as shown in Fig. 10-19B, to end in a metal sphere, and by flaring the outer conductor of the coaxial line into the inner wall of the wave guide. A transformer of this type can be designed to introduce a standing-wave ratio less than 1.2 throughout most of the recommended range of a wave guide.

Two additional designs of fixed-tuned broad-band transformers are shown in Fig. 10-19C and 19-19D. Type C is called a "doorknob transformer" and has been designed to handle high powers without breakdown. Both C and D provide a support for the center conductor of the coaxial line, which is an advantage for some applications, and

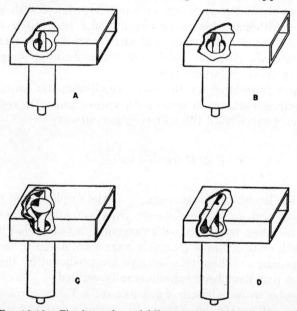

Fig. 10-19.—Fixed-tuned coaxial line to wave-guide transformers.

also provide a direct-current return. Both of these designs have good band width, but again the optimum dimensions must be determined experimentally for different sizes of coaxial line and wave guide.

8. Wave-guide Bridge Circuits

A variety of wave-guide structures may be built whose electrical properties are similar to those of various low-frequency bridge circuits. To understand their behavior, it is necessary to keep in mind the properties of the two types of wave-guide tee connections that are discussed in some detail in Sec. 9-5. The properties of these connections that are important to their application in bridge circuits will be briefly reviewed here.

A branch arm in the E-plane (Fig. 10-20) may be considered as connected in series with the collinear guides. If a signal is fed in the branch guide, as shown, the energy will divide equally between the two collinear arms, if both are terminated in matched loads, and the electric field in the two arms will be 180 deg out of phase at points equidistant from the center of the junction. In addition, there will in general

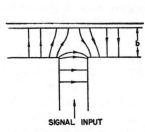

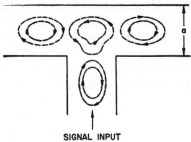

FIG. 10-20.—Electric-field distribution in an *E*-plane tee with signal fed in the branch arm.

FIG. 10-21.—Magnetic-field distribution in an *H*-plane tee with signal fed in the branch arm.

be a reflected wave in the input guide because of the impedance discontinuity at the junction.

A branch arm in the *H*-plane (Fig. 10-21) may be considered as connected in parallel with the collinear guides. If a signal is fed in the branch guide, the energy will divide equally between the collinear arms, if both are terminated in matched loads, but the electric field in the two arms will be in phase at points equidistant from the junction, in contrast to the series connection. But there will also be a reflected wave in the input guide because of the impedance discontinuity at the junction.

The "Magic Tee."—The so-called "magic tee" or "hybrid tee" is constructed by connecting wave guides in shunt and in series with a

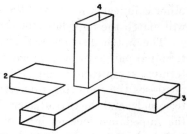

FIG. 10-22.—The wave-guide "magic tee" or "hybrid tee."

collinear guide at the same point. This is illustrated in Fig. 10-22. This structure now possesses many of the qualities of a bridge circuit.

If a signal is fed in the shunt arm, and the two collinear arms are terminated in matched loads, the power will still divide equally between the two collinear arms. Because of the symmetry of the structure, there will be no coupling between the series and shunt arms, as there is no net electric vector developed across the entrance to the series arm. Therefore no signal will be fed into the series arm.

If the load impedances of the two collinear arms are unequal, the symmetry of the structure will be destroyed, and there will then be energy transfer between the series and shunt arms. But for any two impedances that are equal, there will be no coupling between these arms. It is apparent that the behavior of the structure is similar to a bridge circuit, which compares the load impedances of the collinear arms with the signal fed in one branch arm and the detector on the other.

The impedances looking into the two branch arms with properly matched loads on the two collinear arms are not matched loads for the input wave guides. If, by the addition of some sort of matching structure, these impedances are made to match the waveguide impedance, the structure will possess additional qualities of balance. As before, a signal fed into one of the branch arms will divide equally between the two collinear arms, if they are matched, and will not couple energy into the other branch arm. But in addition, if a signal is fed in one of the collinear arms, it will divide equally between the two branch arms, if they are matched, and no signal will appear in the other collinear arm. Also, the input impedance to the collinear arms will match the impedance of the wave guide.

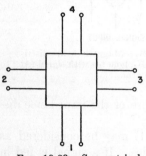

Fig. 10-23.—Symmetrical four-terminal-pair network, equivalent to the matched "magic tee."

The matched structure is often represented schematically as a four-terminal-pair network, as shown in Fig. 10-23, in which each pair of terminals represents one of the input wave guides. This network possesses the following properties: if a signal is fed into any pair of terminals, and the two adjacent are each terminated in a matched load, the impedance looking into the input terminals will also present a matched load to the input line. In addition, the power will divide equally between the two load impedances, and no signal will appear across the fourth pair of terminals. If there is a mismatched load on one of the adjacent pairs of terminals, the circuit may be analyzed by considering the arm as matched, but with a signal that is equal in strength to the reflected wave that results from the mismatch being fed into that arm by an additional signal generator. The low-frequency equivalent of this wave-guide structure is the hybrid coil, shown schematically in Fig. 10-24. The resemblance between the two circuits is apparent.

The matching of the two branch arms may be accomplished by the usual addition of metallic diaphragms. As the standing-wave ratio that must be matched is usually rather high, the band width is very small. To improve the band width, it is necessary to place the matching structure at the heart of the junction. One typical design is shown in Fig. 10-25. The impedance looking in the *H*-plane arm has been matched by the addition of the metallic post which is centrally located. The optimum length and position of this post must be determined experimentally,

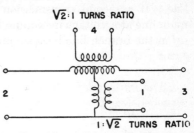

Fig. 10-24.—Schematic diagram of the hybrid coil, equivalent at low frequencies to the "magic tee."

but the optimum length is usually close to a half wavelength. The *E*-plane branch has been matched by the addition of the asymmetrical inductive window shown, whose dimensions and location are found by the usual techniques after the post has been added. Addition of this window has little effect upon the match of the *H*-plane tee, in spite of the proximity of the post to the window.

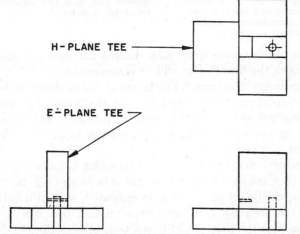

Fig. 10-25.—Wave-guide "magic tee," with added matching structure.

"Ring" or "Rat-race" Bridges.—A variety of other wave-guide structures may be built that have the same properties as the four-terminal-pair network shown in Fig. 10-23. A method by which these may be developed is outlined below.

Consider a transmission line on which there are traveling waves of identical frequency and equal amplitude fed in opposite directions. The standing-wave ratio will be infinite, and the voltage and current will alternately pass through zero at quarter-wave intervals along the line. If a second transmission line is connected in series with the main line at a voltage maximum (current zero), no signal will be picked up in the branch line because no current flows through the line input.

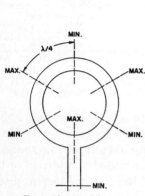

Fig. 10-26.—Ring transmission line fed by a series connection, with the positions of the standing-wave maxima and minima indicated.

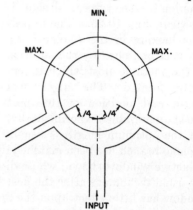

Fig. 10-27.—Series-fed ring transmission line, with two additional lines connected in series.

But if the connection is made at a current maximum (voltage node), the pickup in the branch line will be a maximum.

Contrastingly, if a branch line is connected in shunt with the main line at a current maximum, the pickup in the branch line will be zero, because the voltage across the input terminals of the branch line is zero. If the connection is made at a voltage loop, the pickup in the branch line will be a maximum.

If a transmission line $1\frac{1}{2}$ wavelengths long is formed into a closed ring, and then fed by a branch line that is in series (Fig. 10-26), standing waves will be set on the ring as indicated, and an infinite impedance will be seen by the input transmission line where it makes connection with the ring. Additional transmission lines could be connected in series with the ring at any of the indicated voltage maximums; these would not disturb the standing-wave pattern because they would extract no energy from the system. Or additional lines could be connected in shunt with the ring at any of the voltage minimums; these would also have no effect.

If transmission lines were connected in series with the rings at the voltage minimums, they would extract a maximum amount of energy from the system. If two such lines are connected at the two voltage minimums nearest the input line, and present an equal impedance at their input terminals, they will extract equal amounts of energy from the system. The symmetry of the system will not have been disturbed, and the standing-wave pattern on the section of the ring between the two branch arms will be unchanged (Fig. 10-27). There are two voltage maximums on this sector of the circle, and it is possible to connect an additional line in series with the ring at either of these points without disturbing the pattern and without any signal being picked up by this additional line.

The complete structure is now indicated in Fig. 10-28. This is a bridge structure similar in its properties to that pictured in Fig. 10-22, for a wave guide may be used as the transmission line. If a signal is fed in arm 1 of the bridge shown in Fig. 10-28, no signal will be detected in arm 4 if there are equal impedances attached to arms 2 and 3.

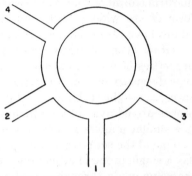

Fig. 10-28.—Ring transmission line with four arms connected in series, forming a bridge structure equivalent to the "magic tee."

A number of possible modifications of this structure are apparent. For example, the length of line or guide between any two adjacent arms of the bridge may be increased by any desired number of multiple half wavelengths without affecting the behavior of the bridge at the design frequency. Or the fourth arm, instead of being connected in series with the line at a voltage maximum, could be connected in shunt at a voltage minimum. If this latter course is followed, the structure will be symmetrical, and the bridge will be balanced at any frequency in the range of the wave guide.

For the structure of Fig. 10-28 to have the additional impedance matching and balanced properties of the network shown in Fig. 10-23, some attention must be paid to the relative impedance of the input guides and the guide that forms the ring. It can be shown that these additional properties will be gained if the characteristic impedance of the guide forming the ring is made less than that of the four incoming guides by a factor $\sqrt{2}$. In practice this may be accomplished by leaving unchanged the larger dimension of this guide and by reducing the height by approximately the factor $\sqrt{2}$. This will give this structure the same properties as the matched "magic tee" of the previous section. The band width will be reduced as compared with this "magic tee," but the power-handling capacity without breakdown is greater.

9. Tunable Wave-guide Impedance Transformers

Probe Transformers.—It is possible to construct wave-guide impedance transformers that are analogous to the various coaxial-line transformers that are discussed in Chap. 6. Double-slug transformers are widely used, and transformers employing tunable-stub guides have also been extensively employed.

Other types of transformers have been designed to utilize special properties of wave guides and wave-guide structures. Probes of the type discussed in Sec. 9-4, page 152, are equivalent to shunting reactances, as are the stub lines used in coaxial-line transformers. Tunable probes are equivalent to adjustable stub lines and may be employed in a similar manner in adjustable transformers.

One of the simplest and most satisfactory transformers of this type has a single probe of adjustable penetration. This probe extends into the wave guide through a centered slot in one of the broad faces and rides on a carriage that shifts its position. This transformer is capable of matching any two impedances, neither of which is purely reactive.

Other transformers employ two or three probes, fixed in position but adjustable in depth. Two fixed probes have a limited range of impedances that may be matched. Three fixed probes are required to provide the range of the single movable probe.

Phase Shifters.—A need sometimes arises for a device that will change the electrical length of a wave guide without introducing impedance discontinuities. Two such devices have been developed.

In one of these, the broad faces of the rectangular guide are slotted for a distance of several wavelengths. The width of the guide may then be changed by squeezing the slotted section. This changes the phase velocity in the guide and correspondingly affects the electrical length.

The other type of phase shifter employs a cylinder of dielectric that partially fills the guide. This cylinder is tapered at the ends to minimize reflections. When moved from a region of weak field at the edge of the guide into the strong field at the center, the dielectric will effect a greater reduction in the guide wavelength and give the desired change in electrical length.

CHAPTER 11

WAVE GUIDES FILLED WITH DIELECTRIC MATERIAL[1]

The electric and magnetic fields in a wave guide vary in the axial direction as $e^{-\gamma z} = e^{-(\alpha+j\beta)z}$, where γ is the propagation constant, α is the attenuation constant, and β is the phase constant. If the wave guide is partially or completely filled with some dielectric material of dielectric constant $\epsilon = \epsilon' - j\epsilon''$, the propagation constant of the guide will be affected, and its wave impedance and cutoff wavelength will also change.

In this chapter, the dielectric losses will be considered, but conductor losses in the guide will be assumed to be zero.

1. Wave Guides Completely Filled with Dielectric

Propagation Constant.—If the guide is completely filled with a dielectric, the propagation constant is

$$\gamma = \frac{2\pi}{\lambda} \sqrt{\left(\frac{\lambda}{\lambda_c}\right)^2 - \epsilon' + j\epsilon''} \tag{11-1}$$

where λ is the wavelength in air and λ_c the cutoff wavelength in the guide when air-filled. If the losses in the dielectric are small ($\epsilon''/\epsilon' \ll 1$), this formula reduces to

$$\gamma = \frac{\pi}{\lambda} \frac{\epsilon'' + 2j\left[\epsilon' - \left(\frac{\lambda}{\lambda_c}\right)^2\right]}{\sqrt{\epsilon' - \left(\frac{\lambda}{\lambda_c}\right)^2}} \tag{11-2}$$

and for a perfect dielectric

$$\gamma = j\frac{2\pi}{\lambda} \sqrt{\epsilon' - \left(\frac{\lambda}{\lambda_c}\right)^2} \tag{11-3}$$

Wave-guide Impedance.—The characteristic wave impedance Z_0 of a wave guide has been defined in Sec. 3-1 as the ratio of trans-

---

[1] The information in this chapter is largely a summary of a section of a report of N. H. Frank, "Wave Guide Handbook," M.I.T. Radiation Laboratory, Sec. T, Rept. 9, Sept. 24, 1942.

verse electric to transverse magnetic field strengths. The "normalized wave impedance" Z of the dielectric-filled guide is now defined as the ratio of its characteristic wave impedance to the characteristic wave impedance of the same guide when filled with air dielectric. The following formulas may then be applied:

For all *TE* waves:

For all *TE* waves in wave guides, the normalized wave impedance Z_{TE} of a dielectric-filled guide is

$$Z_{TE} = \frac{\gamma_0}{\gamma} \qquad (11\text{-}4)$$

where γ_0 is the propagation constant in the air-filled guide and γ the propagation constant in the dielectric-filled guide. This formula may be written

$$Z_{TE} = \sqrt{\frac{\left(\frac{\lambda}{\lambda_c}\right)^2 - 1}{\left(\frac{\lambda}{\lambda_c}\right)^2 - \epsilon' + j\epsilon''}} \qquad (11\text{-}5)$$

When the dielectric has a low power factor, this may be rewritten

$$Z_{TE} = \frac{\lambda_g}{\lambda_{g0}} \left[1 + \frac{j}{2} \frac{\epsilon''}{\epsilon' - \left(\frac{\lambda}{\lambda_c}\right)^2} \right] \qquad (11\text{-}6)$$

where λ_{g0} is the guide wavelength in the air-filled guide and λ_g the guide wavelength in the dielectric-filled guide. For an ideal dielectric

$$Z_{TE} = \frac{\lambda_g}{\lambda_{g0}} = \sqrt{\frac{1 - \left(\frac{\lambda}{\lambda_c}\right)^2}{\epsilon' - \left(\frac{\lambda}{\lambda_c}\right)^2}} \qquad (11\text{-}7)$$

The normalized wave impedance of a wave guide operating in a *TE* mode and filled with a dielectric is always less than unity and decreases with increasing dielectric constant.

For all *TM* waves:

For all *TM* waves in wave guides, the normalized wave impedance Z_{TM} of a dielectric-filled guide is

$$Z_{TM} = \frac{\gamma}{\epsilon \gamma_0} \qquad (11\text{-}8)$$

This may be written

$$Z_{TM} = \frac{1}{\epsilon' - j\epsilon''} \sqrt{\frac{\left(\frac{\lambda}{\lambda_c}\right)^2 - \epsilon' + j\epsilon''}{\left(\frac{\lambda}{\lambda_c}\right)^2 - 1}} \tag{11-9}$$

For a low-loss dielectric this becomes

$$Z_{TM} = \frac{\lambda_{g0}}{\epsilon'\lambda_g} \left\{ 1 + j\frac{\epsilon''}{\epsilon'} \left[1 - \frac{\frac{\epsilon'}{2}}{\epsilon' - \left(\frac{\lambda}{\lambda_c}\right)^2} \right] \right\} \tag{11-10}$$

and for a perfect dielectric

$$Z_{TM} = \frac{1}{\epsilon'} \sqrt{\frac{\epsilon' - \left(\frac{\lambda}{\lambda_c}\right)^2}{1 - \left(\frac{\lambda}{\lambda_c}\right)^2}} \tag{11-11}$$

The normalized wave impedance of a *TM* wave in a wave guide will be always less than unity if $(\lambda/\lambda_c)^2 < \frac{1}{2}$ and will decrease continuously with increasing dielectric constant. If $(\lambda/\lambda_c)^2 > \frac{1}{2}$, the normalized wave impedance will first increase to a value greater than unity and then decrease toward zero with increasing dielectric constant. It will pass through the value unity at a value of ϵ' given by

$$\epsilon' = \frac{\left(\frac{\lambda}{\lambda_c}\right)^2}{1 - \left(\frac{\lambda}{\lambda_c}\right)^2} \tag{11-12}$$

2. Reflection from Dielectric Plugs in Wave Guides

If there is a sudden change in the dielectric material inside a wave guide, a wave that is incident upon the boundary will be partially reflected because of the discontinuity in the medium of propagation. If the interface between dielectrics is normal to the axis of the guide, the effective impedance d scontinuity is simply the discontinuity in the characteristic wave impedance, and the reflection may be calculated accordingly. The reflection at the boundary will be

$$\rho = \frac{E_2}{E_1} = \frac{Z - 1}{Z + 1} \tag{11-13}$$

and the standing-wave ratio σ input to the interface, if the dielectric-filled section is terminated in its characteristic impedance, will be

$$\sigma = \frac{1 + |\rho|}{1 - |\rho|} \qquad (11\text{-}14)$$

or

$$\sigma = Z \quad \text{if} \quad Z > 1, \qquad \sigma = \frac{1}{Z} \quad \text{if} \quad Z < 1 \qquad (11\text{-}15)$$

and the losses in the dielectric are small.

If the portion of wave guide that is filled with dielectric material is finite in length, there will be a reflection at both the incoming and outgoing faces of the dielectric-filled region. The net reflection as measured in the input line will depend upon the length of the dielectric-filled section, which determines the phase relationship between the two components that contribute to the net reflection, and also upon the attenuation in the dielectric-filled section. If this attenuation is high enough so that the reflection from the far end of the dielectric section is negligibly small at the input, the net reflection as measured in the input line will be essentially independent of the length of the dielectric section.

The problem may be treated by considering the dielectric-filled section a length of transmission line of different characteristic impedance from the air-filled guide. Calculations based upon this approach yield a net reflection coefficient in the input line of

$$\rho = \frac{E_2}{E_1} = -\frac{\sinh \gamma l}{\sinh (\gamma l + \phi)} \qquad (11\text{-}16)$$

where l is the length of the dielectric section, γ is the propagation constant of the dielectric section, and

$$\phi = \ln \left(\frac{\dfrac{1}{Z} + 1}{\dfrac{1}{Z} - 1} \right) \qquad (11\text{-}17)$$

The net wave transmitted, E_3, will be related to the incident wave E_1 by

$$\frac{E_3}{E_1} = \frac{e^{\gamma l} \sinh \phi}{\sinh (\gamma l + \phi)} \qquad (11\text{-}18)$$

The difference is accounted for partially by the wave that is reflected and partially by the energy that is absorbed in the dielectric. For a rectangular air-filled guide operating in the dominant, or $TE_{1,0}$, mode with a plug of perfect dielectric, the fractions of the input power that will be reflected and transmitted are given by

$$P_{\text{refl.}} = \frac{\dfrac{1}{4}\left(\dfrac{\lambda_{g0}}{\lambda_g} - \dfrac{\lambda_g}{\lambda_{g0}}\right)^2 \sin^2 \dfrac{2\pi l}{\lambda_g}}{1 + \dfrac{1}{4}\left(\dfrac{\lambda_{g0}}{\lambda_g} - \dfrac{\lambda_g}{\lambda_{g0}}\right)^2 \sin^2 \dfrac{2\pi l}{\lambda_g}} \tag{11-19}$$

$$P_{\text{trans.}} = \frac{1}{1 + \dfrac{1}{4}\left(\dfrac{\lambda_{g0}}{\lambda_g} - \dfrac{\lambda_g}{\lambda_{g0}}\right)^2 \sin^2 \dfrac{2\pi l}{\lambda_g}} \tag{11-20}$$

where λ_{g0} is the wavelength in the air-filled guide and λ_g the wavelength in the dielectric-filled guide. These formulas have been checked

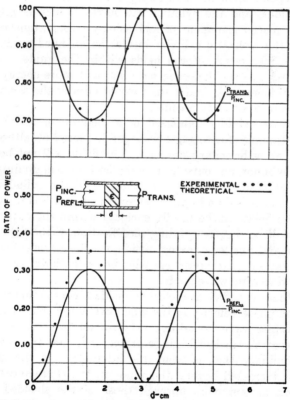

Fig. 11-1.—Reflection from and transmission through a section of a polystyrene-filled wave guide.

experimentally for polystyrene at $\lambda = 9.0$ cm, with the results shown in Fig. 11-1. The discrepancy can be accounted for largely by experimental error, as the measured total power transmitted and reflected sometimes exceeds 100 per cent of the input power.

3. Wave Guides Partially Filled with Dielectric

In this section will be considered wave guides that contain dielectric cylinders whose axes are parallel to the guide axis and which only partially fill the guide. The effect of inserting such a structure into an air-filled wave guide will be to reduce the wavelength and the phase velocity to a value intermediate between the values of the air-filled guide and the same guide when completely filled with dielectric. The cutoff wavelength will also be increased.

The magnitude of the effect of a cylinder of given cross-sectional area will depend upon the field strength in the guide at the location of the cylinder, and the cylinder will have an increasingly greater effect when placed in regions of increasingly strong transverse fields.

Placing the dielectric cylinder inside the air-filled guide will also affect the configuration of the fields within the guide. The fields will be pulled into the dielectric material, and more energy will flow through the dielectric cylinder than would occupy the same region if the guide were completely air-filled.

A dielectric cylinder immersed in a medium of lower dielectric constant is capable of acting as a wave guide (Sec. 7-6), although there is no conducting boundary present. The fields will not be confined within the cylinder, but outside the cylinder they will diminish toward zero with increasing distance from the axis of the cylinder. If the dielectric cylinder is then totally enclosed in a larger hollow conducting cylinder, the fields will be totally enclosed within the outer cylinder, and there will be a corresponding modification of the field structure external to, and to a lesser extent inside, the dielectric cylinder. But the propagation characteristics will be essentially those of the unshielded dielectric wave guide.

When there is sufficient dielectric inside a conducting wave guide to bring the phase velocity in the guide below the free-space velocity of the traveling wave, something very similar to complete reflection takes place at the dielectric-air interface, modified only by the conducting boundary that is near this interface. As the amount of dielectric is increased beyond this amount, the characteristics of the transmission system will approach those of the shielded dielectric guide.

The amount of dielectric required to approach this condition will be less if the air-filled guide is far from cutoff. The similarity to the shielded dielectric guide will also be greater, as the conducting boundaries will be farther from the boundaries of the dielectric cylinder and will have correspondingly less effect.

Case 1.—If a rectangular wave guide operating in the $TE_{1,0}$ mode is
partially filled with some perfect
dielectric material in the manner
indicated in Fig. 11-2, the field configuration will depend upon the
ratio λ/λ_g, which in turn will depend
upon the size of the wave guide and
the amount of wave guide that is
filled with dielectric. Three cases
are illustrated in Fig. 11-2, which
are drawn for a typical wave guide
and low-loss dielectric. The dielectric constant is assumed in this
and subsequent cases to be 2.45.
In the first case, $\lambda_g > \lambda$ and the
presence of the dielectric somewhat
modifies the fields that are present
in the air-filled guide. In the sec-
ond, $\lambda_g = \lambda$; this is the point at
which total internal reflection in
the dielectric is reached. In the
third, $\lambda_g < \lambda$, and this is similar to
the shielded dielectric guide. The
cutoff wavelength of the wave guide
will also be a function of the percentage of the wave guide that is
filled with dielectric, and in Fig.
11-3, a/λ_c is plotted as a function of

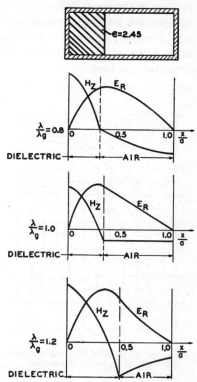

Fig. 11-2.—Field intensities in a
rectangular wave guide partially filled
with a dielectric.

d/a, where a is the width of the wave guide and d the width of the
dielectric, as illustrated. Also shown on this figure is the variation of

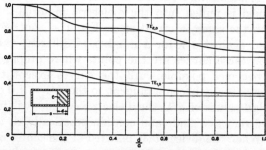

Fig. 11-3.—Properties of a wave guide partially filled with a dielectric.

a/λ_c as a function of d/a for the next higher, or $TE_{2,0}$, mode. The maxima in the slope of these curves will occur when the transverse field maxima are passing through the interface between the dielectric and air. For the $TE_{1,0}$ mode, the maximum slope is at a value of $d/a < 0.5$, indicating that the field is being pulled into the material with the higher dielectric constant.

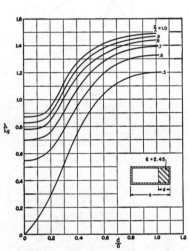

Fig. 11-4.—Properties of a wave guide partially filled with a dielectric.

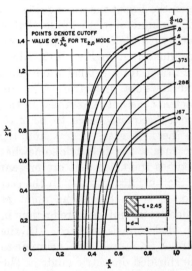

Fig. 11-5.—Properties of a wave guide partially filled with a dielectric.

In Fig. 11-4, the ratio λ/λ_g is plotted as a function of d/a for the various values of a/λ; these curves illustrate the effect of the dielectric upon the guide wavelength. The maxima in the slope of these curves will occur when the increment of d/a is in a region of maximum transverse field strength, as the effect of the dielectric will then be greatest. Here again, the maximum slope is at a value $d/a < 0.5$, also illustrative of how the field is pulled into the dielectric material. Figure 11-5 contains much the same information as Fig. 11-4, but here the ratio λ/λ_g is plotted against a/λ for a number of different values of d/a. Also shown on these curves are the points where propagation of the $TE_{2,0}$ mode becomes possible. All the curves except that labeled $d/a = 0$ will eventually become tangent to the $d/a = 1.0$ curve, for at sufficiently high values of a/λ, the dielectric cylinder will in every case act as a dielectric wave guide and contain practically all the energy.

Case 2.—When the dielectric is inserted at the center of the guide, instead of at the edges, the effect upon cutoff wavelength for the

$TE_{1,0}$ and $TE_{2,0}$ modes will be as illustrated in Fig. 11-6. For the $TE_{1,0}$ mode the maximum slope is at a value of $d/a = 0$; this is because the dielectric is being inserted in a region of maximum field strength

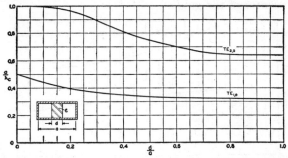

Fig. 11-6.—Properties of a wave guide partially filled with a dielectric.

when it is placed in the center of the guide. A similarity will be observed between the curve for the $TE_{2,0}$ mode in Fig. 11-6 and the curve for the $TE_{1,0}$ mode in Fig. 11-3. This arises from the fact that

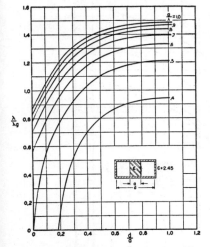

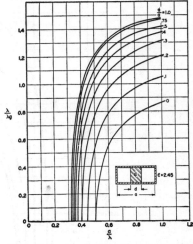

Fig. 11-7.—Properties of a wave guide partially filled with a dielectric.

Fig. 11-8.—Properties of a wave guide partially filled with a dielectric.

the dielectric is inserted in corresponding regions of field in the two cases.

In Fig. 11-7, the ratio λ/λ_g is plotted against the ratio d/a for various values of a/λ. This figure should be compared with Fig. 11-4, which is the corresponding figure for Case 1. Maxima of slope occur at $d/a = 0$, for the same reason as in Fig. 11-6. Figure 11-8 is comparable to Fig. 11-5 for Case 1. In this case it will be noted that the curves are crowded more toward the curve labeled $d/a = 1.0$, illustrating the greater effect of the dielectric when placed in the strong fields at the center of the guide.

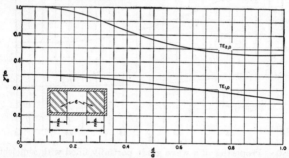

FIG. 11-9.—Properties of a wave guide partially filled with a dielectric

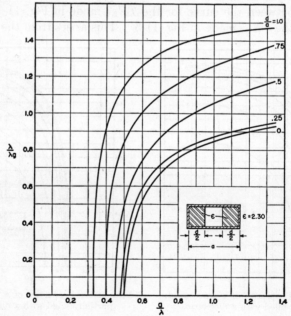

FIG. 11-10.—Properties of a wave guide partially filled with a dielectric.

Case 3.—When the dielectric is against both side walls of the wave guide, as illustrated in Fig. 11-9, the effect of a given amount of dielectric will be even less than in Case 1, because here the dielectric is concentrated even more in a region of low field. The variation of cutoff wavelength with increasing d/a is shown in Fig. 11-9 for the

$TE_{1,0}$ and $TE_{2,0}$ modes. The curve for the $TE_{2,0}$ mode is similar to the curve for the $TE_{1,0}$ mode in Fig. 11-3, except for a scale factor.

The variation in λ/λ_g as a function of a/λ is given in Fig. 11-10 for a number of values of d/a. In this case the curves are crowded more toward the curve for $d/a = 0$, which indicates the relative ineffectiveness of the dielectric when concentrated in a region of low field.

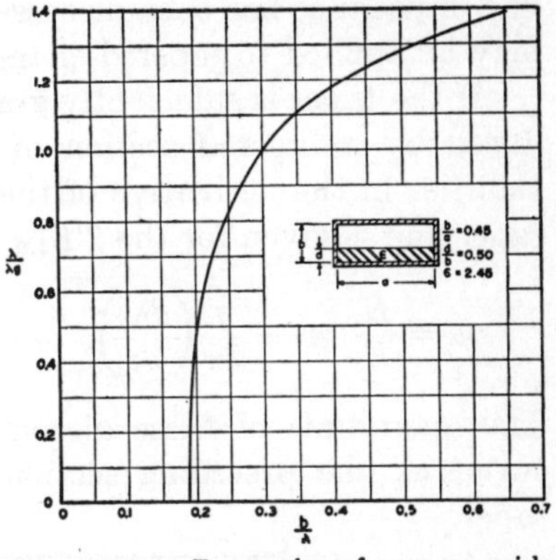

Case 4.—When the dielectric partially fills the wave guide in the manner indicated in Fig. 11-11, the situation is more complicated than in the preceding cases. The field structure that goes continuously into the $TE_{1,0}$ mode as the dielectric

Fig. 11-11.—Properties of a wave guide partially filled with a dielectric.

thickness approaches zero has five nonvanishing field components E_x, E_y, E_z, H_x, and H_z. This field has both electric and magnetic components along the axis of the guide and is transverse magnetic to the direction normal to the interface between the air and the dielectric. As the thickness of the dielectric approaches zero, the E_z and E_x components will vanish, leaving only the E_y, H_x, and H_z components that are found in an air-filled guide propagating the $TE_{1,0}$ mode.

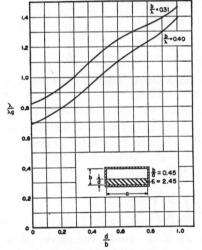

Fig. 11-12.—Properties of a wave guide partially filled with a dielectric.

In this case the properties of the guide are a function of an additional parameter, the ratio of the guide cross-section dimensions. Therefore no single family of curves can be applied to show the variation of λ/λ_g with increasing values of dielectric thickness d. For this reason, only a single typical curve of λ/λ_g vs. b/λ is shown in Fig. 11-11 for a wave guide in which $b/a = 0.45$ and $d/b = 0.50$. In Fig. 11-12 are given two curves of λ/λ_g vs. d/b for two typical values of b/λ. These are for wave guides in which $b/a = 0.45$.

4. Reflections from Tapered Sections of Dielectric

The general problem of reflections from tapered discontinuities in line impedance has been discussed in Sec. 3-5. The general principles may be applied to tapered changes of impedance in wave guides.

If the taper is sufficiently gradual, the reflection that will be introduced by a tapered section of dielectric depends upon the discontinuities in the derivative of the guide wavelength at the ends of the taper and is given for the $TE_{1,0}$ mode in rectangular guide by

$$\rho = \frac{E_2}{E_1} = -\frac{j}{8\pi}\left(\frac{d\lambda_g}{dz}\right)_{z=0} - \left(\frac{d\lambda_g}{dz}\right)_{z=l} \exp\left(-4\pi j \int_0^l \frac{dz}{\lambda_g}\right) \quad (11\text{-}21)$$

The magnitude of these discontinuities may be estimated from the curves of the preceding section for a number of different kinds of taper.

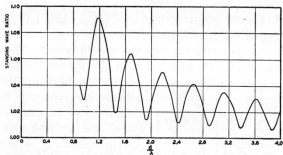

Fig. 11-13.—Standing-wave ratio introduced by a tapered junction of air-filled and dielectric-filled wave guides.

A taper that starts at one side of the wave guide and ends at the other should then be very good, as the rate of change of wavelength at the ends of the taper will be small. But there will be oscillations in the curve of reflection as a function of the length of the taper, because of the variations with length of the term

$$\exp\left(-4\pi j \int_0^l \frac{dz}{\lambda_g}\right)$$

If the taper starts or ends in the center of the guide, the reflection is likely to be larger for a similar taper of the same length, but the curve of reflection vs. length of taper will have smaller percentage changes with changing length of taper. The standing-wave ratio introduced as a function of the length of taper is given in Fig. 11-13 for a taper that starts on the long dimension of the guide and extends to the other side. That is, a cross section in the tapered region would appear as

Case 4 of the partially filled guide. This curve has been calculated from Eq. (11-21) and has not been checked experimentally.

5. Effect of a Dielectric Post in a Wave Guide

A dielectric post that extends across the center of a rectangular wave guide operating in the $TE_{1,0}$ mode, parallel to the lesser dimen-

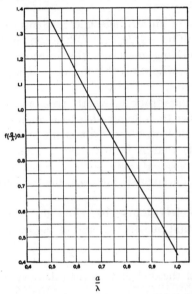

Fig. 11-14.—Function for calculating admittance of a dielectric post in a wave guide.

sion of the guide, will act as a shunt admittance provided that the diameter of the post is small compared with a wavelength, *i.e.*, if

$$\left(\frac{2\pi R}{\lambda}\right)^2 \ll 1 \qquad (11\text{-}22)$$

where R is the radius of the post. If this assumption is valid, the normalized admittance of the post will be given by

$$\frac{Y}{Y_0} = j\,\frac{a}{2\lambda_g}\left[\log_e \frac{\lambda}{R} - f\left(\frac{a}{\lambda}\right) - \frac{1}{2\epsilon}\left(\frac{\lambda}{\pi R}\right)^2 - 1.47\right] \qquad (11\text{-}23)$$

where a is the width of the guide, λ_g is the guide wavelength, λ is the wavelength in free space, ϵ is the complex dielectric constant of the substance forming the post, and $f(a/\lambda)$ is as given in Fig. 11-14.

CHAPTER 12

DIELECTRIC MATERIALS[1]

If the capacity of an air-dielectric condenser is C_0, its impedance at a frequency f will be $-j/2\pi f C_0$. When the air dielectric is replaced with another insulating material, the impedance of the condenser becomes $-j/2\pi f \epsilon C_0$, where ϵ is the dielectric constant of the insulating material.

The preceding paragraph is strictly true only for a vacuum-dielectric condenser rather than an air-dielectric condenser. But the difference between the dielectric constant of air and unity is so small (in the order of 0.001) that it is usually negligible and will be ignored here. Only in exceptional cases, such as those considered in Sec. 13-4 is it necessary to distinguish between the dielectric constant of air and a vacuum.

Losses in the dielectric may be taken into account by considering the dielectric constant as complex and of the form

$$\epsilon = \epsilon' - j\epsilon''$$

The loss tangent of the dielectric is then defined as

$$\tan \delta = \frac{\epsilon''}{\epsilon'}$$

Usually δ is a small angle and nearly equal to the power factor p. The true power factor is

$$p = \frac{\epsilon''}{\epsilon}$$
$$= \sin \delta$$

The Q of a dielectric material is closely equal to $1/\tan \delta$, where $\tan \delta$ is small compared with unity.

The dielectric constant of a material is the result of contributions of three molecular mechanisms:

[1] The material in this chapter is a summary of part of the information contained in the extensive reports by the Laboratory for Insulation Research, M.I.T., entitled Tables of Dielectric Materials, Vols. 1 and 2, produced under contract with the National Defense Research Committee.

1. Electronic and atomic polarization.
2. Orientation of permanent dipoles.
3. Ionic or electronic conduction.

The first of these effects contributes no loss but contributes a frequency-independent factor to the dielectric constant. The contribution of the other two mechanisms is frequently dependent and affects both dielectric constant and power factor. As a result, these

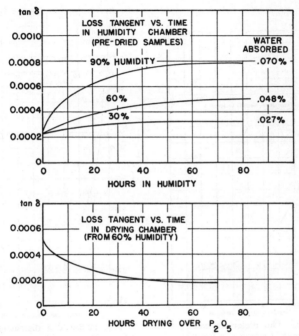

FIG. 12-1.—The effect of humidity upon the loss tangent of polystyrene at a frequency of 3,000 mc.

quantities will often have values at microwave frequencies that are different from their low-frequency values, values that may also be temperature sensitive.

Measured values of dielectric constant for a number of different materials are listed in Table 12-1 for two frequencies in the microwave region. These values were taken at a temperature of approximately 25°C, and the samples had been kept in a dehydrator for a considerable period of time prior to measurement.

The dielectric properties of a material may be considerably affected by moisture absorption. Water is a high dielectric constant high-loss material in the microwave region, and only a small amount need be absorbed by a dielectric material to alter its properties appreciably. The greatest effect that will usually be observed is an increase in power factor.   Increases by a factor of two or more in the power factor of already lossy dielectrics such as bakelite or wood have been observed as the result of exposure to a humid atmosphere for a period of a few days.   More quantitative information for the case of polystyrene is

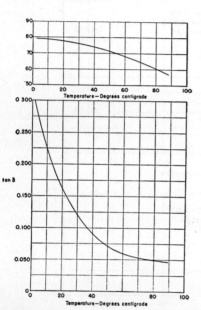

Fig. 12-2.—The dielectric constant and loss tangent of water at a frequency of 3,000 mc.

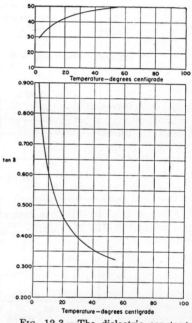

Fig. 12-3.—The dielectric constant and loss tangent of water at a frequency of 9,500 mc.

given in Fig. 12-1, where moisture absorption of only 0.070 per cent is seen to have increased the loss tangent from 0.0002 to 0.0008.

The dielectric properties of water at microwave frequencies are often of special interest.   Values of dielectric constant and loss tangent are plotted as a function of temperature in Figs. 12-2 and 12-3 for frequencies of 3,000 and 9,500 mc, and the results of some additional measurements at 24,000 mc are given in Table 12-2.   For frequencies between 300 and 3,000 mc, the power factor at any temperature is linearly proportional to the frequency, while the dielectric constant is slightly higher at the lower frequencies.

TABLE 12-1
DIELECTRIC CONSTANT AND LOSS
(Samples measured at approximately 25°C and zero humidity)

Substance	Frequency (cycles/sec)			
	3×10^9		1×10^{10}	
	ϵ'/ϵ_0	tan δ	ϵ'/ϵ_0	tan δ
1. Ceramic and other inorganic materials				
a. Steatite bodies:				
AlSiMag A-35	5.50	0.0035		
AlSiMag A-196	5.42	0.0018	5.24	0.0026
AlSiMag 211	....	....	5.90	0.0014
AlSiMag 228	5.97	0.0013	5.93	0.00195
AlSiMag 243	5.75	0.002	5.40	0.0002
Steatite Ceramic F-66	6.25	0.00055		
Crolite No. 29	6.86	0.0024	5.86	0.0027
b. Titania bodies:				
TI-Pure R-200	....	....	86.5	0.0033
Tam Ticon T-J, T-L, T-M	96.	0.00034		
c. Mixtures of ceramics and polymers:				
Experimental titanium dioxide and polystrene	24.3	0.0032		
Titanium dioxide (41.9%) and polydichlorostyrene (58.1%)	5.30	0.00060	5.30	0.00085
Titanium dioxide (65.3%) and polydichlorostyrene (34.7%)	....	....	10.2	0.00132
Titanium dioxide (81.4%) and polydichlorostyrene (18.6%)	....	....	23.0	0.00157
Strontium titanate (37.0%) and polydichlorostyrene (63.0%)	4.97	0.00117	4.90	0.00141
Strontium titanate (59.5%) and polydichlorostyrene (40.5%)	....	....	9.36	0.0023
Strontium titanate (74.8%) and polydichlorostyrene (25.2%)	....	....	15.2	0.0064
Strontium titanate (80.6%) and polydichlorostyrene (19.4%)	....	....	19.5	0.0050
Barium titanate (33.4%) and polydichlorostyrene (66.6%)	4.02	0.0017	4.02	0.0038
Barium titanate (67.2%) and polydichlorostyrene (32.8%)	....	....	9.7	0.0143
Barium titanate (76.5%) and polydichlorostyrene (23.5%)	....	....	15.5	0.0214
Barium titanate (79.0%) and polydichlorostyrene (21.0%)	....	....	18.4	0.0314
Magnesium titanate (61.8%) and polydichlorostyrene (38.2%)	5.91	0.00089		

TABLE 12-1.—(*Continued*)

Substance	Frequency (cycles/sec)			
	3×10^9		1×10^{10}	
	ϵ'/ϵ_0	tan δ	ϵ'/ϵ_0	tan δ
d. Other inorganic materials:				
Ruby mica	5.4	0.0003		
Fused quartz	3.80	0.0001	3.80	0.0001
Mycalex No. 1364	6.91	0.0036		
Mycalex K10	11.3*	0.0040	11.3*	0.0040
Turx No. 52	....	....	6.69	0.0066
Turx No. 160	....	....	6.85	0.0049
AlSiMag 393	....	....	4.95	0.00097
2. Glasses and mixtures with glasses				
a. Glasses:				
Corning Glass No. 001	5.95	0.0060		
Corning Glass No. 008	6.71	0.0126	6.71	0.0170
Corning Glass No. 009	8.67	0.0054		
Corning Glass No. 010	7.00	0.0044	6.95	0.0063
Corning Glass No. 012	6.64	0.0041	6.60	0.0063
Corning Glass No. 171	5.95	0.0056	5.83	0.0084
Corning Glass No. 704	4.67	0.0044	4.67	0.0057
Corning Glass No. 705	4.72	0.0052	4.71	0.0061
Corning Glass No. 706	4.70	0.0054		
Corning Glass No. 707	4.00	0.0019	3.99	0.0021
Corning Glass No. 723	3.76	0.0022		
Corning Glass No. 772	4.59	0.0038	4.59	0.0043
Corning Glass No. 774	4.89	0.0089		
Corning Glass No. 775	4.38	0.0043	4.38	0.0050
Corning Glass No. 790	3.84	0.00068	3.82	0.00094
Corning Glass No. 3320	4.72	0.0062	4.72	0.0073
Corning Glass No. 7052	5.04	0.0058	4.93	0.0081
Corning Glass No. 8460	9.0	0.01		
Corning Glass (C. Lab. No. 7141M)	4.00	0.0010	4.00	0.0016
Corning Glass No. 8871	8.34	0.0026	8.05	0.0049
Corning Glass No. 1990	7.99	0.00199	7.94	0.0042
Corning Glass No. 199-1	7.84	0.0038	7.83	0.0051
Foamglass	....	....	5.49	0.0455
G.E. Glass R-3	7.65	0.0024	7.62	0.0045
b. Mixtures with glasses:				
Polyglas P (M.I.T.)	2.91	0.00069		
Polyglas P (M.I.T.)	3.37	0.00076		
Polyglas P+(M.I.T.)	3.35	0.00078	3.32	0.00084
Polyglas D+ (Monsanto)	3.22	0.00120	3.22	0.0013
Polyglas D+ (M.I.T.)	3.22	0.00079	3.22	0.00085

TABLE 12-1.—(*Continued*)

Substance	Frequency (cycles/sec)			
	3×10^9		1×10^{10}	
	ϵ'/ϵ_0	tan δ	ϵ'/ϵ_0	tan δ
Polyglas M (Hood Rubber Co.)........	4.86	0.0339	5.22	0.0660
Polyglass S (M.I.T.).................	3.55	0.0040	3.53	0.0048
3. Liquids				
Water, conductivity....................	77.	0.15		
Sodium chloride solution.................	70.8	0.29		
Ethyl polychlorobenzene.................	2.72	0.129		
Hexachlorbutadiene.....................	2.51	0.0249		
Styrene monomer, unpurified.............	2.40	0.0020	2.36	0.0058
Styrene monomer, purified..............	2.39	0.00136	2.39	0.00368
2, 5-dichlorostyrene....................	2.58	0.0114		
Fractol A.............................	2.15	0.00072		
Primol D.............................	2.15	0.00077		
Marcol...............................	2.14	0.00097		
Bayol-16.............................	2.15	0.00099		
Bayol D.............................	2.06	0.00133		
Cable Oil No. 5314....................	2.23	0.0018		
Pyranol No. 1476.....................	2.72	0.0026		
Transil Oil No. 10C...................	2.18	0.0028		
Halowax Oil No. 1000..................	3.62	0.266		
Dow Corning No. 200, 3.87 cp..........	2.48	0.0048		
Dow Corning No. 200, 300 cp..........	2.69	0.010		
Dow Corning No. 200, 7600 cs.........	2.71	0.0103		
Dow Corning No. 500, 0.65 cs..........	2.20	0.00145		
Ignition Sealing Compound No. 4........	2.77	0.010		
4. Polymers				
a. Phenolics:				
Bakelite BM 120.....................	3.70	0.0438	3.68	0.0390
Bakelite BM 250.....................	5.19	0.046	4.93	0.025
Bakelite BM 262.....................	.....	....	4.41	0.0105
Bakelite BM 1895....................	4.44	0.0091	4.44	0.0096
Prystal (Catalin), 700 Base...........	4.74	0.153		
Catalin, 200 Base....................	4.89	0.108		
Catalin, 500 Base (yellow)............	4.72	0.087		
Catalin, 500 Base (orange)............	4.63	0.131		
Durez 11863.........................	4.45	0.0069	4.42	0.0076
Resinox 7013........................	4.27	0.0123	4.25	0.0124
Resinox 7934........................	4.04	0.0084	4.04	0.0083
Resinox L-8241......................	4.60	0.0042	4.60	0.0040
Durite No. 221X.....................	3.65	0.035		
Bakelite BT-48-306..................	3.64	0.0519	3.52	0.0366

TABLE 12-1.—(*Continued*)

Substance	Frequency (cycles/sec)			
	3×10^9		1×10^{10}	
	ϵ'/ϵ_0	tan δ	ϵ'/ϵ_0	tan δ
b. Aniline-formaldehyde resins:				
Cibanite E..........................	3.47	0.0053	3.47	0.0075
Dilectene No. 100...................	3.44	0.0039		
Formica Grade MF-66 Fiberglas........	3.90	0.026	3.88	0.029
c. Melamine-formaldehyde resins:				
Melmac Resin 592...................	4.67	0.041	4.58	0.0434
Plaskon melamine molding				
compound.........................	4.93	0.1028	4.60	0.110
Resimene 803-A....................	4.53	0.0820	4.23	0.076
d. Urea-formaldehyde resins:				
Beetle resin........................	4.57	0.0555	4.47	0.057
Plaskon urea molding compound........	4.79	0.0694	4.65	0.0782
e. Cellulose derivatives:				
Cellulose acetate type LL-1...........	3.24	0.029	3.24	0.040
Tenite I 008A H_4...................	3.25	0.031		
Tenite II 205A H_4..................	2.91	0.028		
Pyralin............................	3.74	0.165	3.32	0.131
Methocel...........................	3.35	0.055		
Ethocle Q-180......................	2.72	0.0169		
Ethocel Q-181......................	2.62	0.0183		
Ethocel sheet PC 368................	2.72	0.0175		
Ethocel plastic A-2144..............	2.76	0.0160	2.73	0.0217
Lumarith EC Formula No. 22361.......	2.74	0.0196	2.67	0.0256
Ethyl cellulose 449-70A..............	2.73	0.0176	2.70	0.0246
f. Acrylic resins:				
Lucite HM-102......................	2.57	0.00811		
Lucite HM-119......................	2.57	0.00513	2.56	0.0049
Plexiglas..........................	2.60	0.0057	2.59	0.0067
Polyethyl methacrylate A-3159.	2.45	0.0075	2.49	0.0097
Polyethyl methacrylate A-3160...:....	2.38	0.0044	2.36	0.0046
Polyisobutyl methacrylate A-3161......	2.40	0.0110	2.38	0.0035
Polycyclohexyl methacrylate..........	2.46	0.00349		
g. Vinyl resins:				
(1) Acetate:				
Polyvinyl acetate RH-838..........	2.88	0.0028		
(2) Alcohols:				
Polyvinyl alcohol RH-623..........	3.74	0.055	3.50	0.0502
Polyvinyl alcohol RH-403..........	3.75	0.0715		
Polyvinyl alcohol RH-393..........	4.12	0.084		
Polyvinyl alcohol RH-391N.	3.89	0.064	3.74	0.0636

TABLE 12-1.—(*Continued*)

Substance	Frequency (cycles/sec)			
	3×10^9		1×10^{10}	
	ϵ'/ϵ_0	tan δ	ϵ'/ϵ_0	tan δ
(3) Acetals:				
Formvar, type E..................	2.76	0.0113		
Alvar 11/90.....................	2.73	0.0136	2.65	0.0175
Butvar Low OH...................	2.51	0.0111	2.48	0.0107
Butvar D20.....................	2.68	0.037		
Butvar D22.....................	2.68	0.0517		
Monsanto vinyl butyral compound...	2.90	0.041	2.86	0.0419
(4) Polyvinyl chloride and polyvinylidene chloride:				
Vinylite QYNA..................	2.84	0.0055		
Vinylite VYHH..................	2.79	0.0076		
Vinylite VU1900.................	2.65	0.0131	2.59	0.0104
Chlorovinyl Resin DV200...........	2.70	0.0069	2.70	0.0065
Chlorovinyl Resin RH654...........	2.69	0.0067	2.69	0.0067
Geon 2046......................	2.89	0.0116	2.83	0.0116
Saran Sheets B-115 (Acadia)........	2.71	0.0072	2.70	0.00510
Saran Sheet B-115 (Dow)...........	2.78	0.0056		
Supercooled Saran.................	....	....	2.67	0.0059
(5) Polyvinyl benzene and related polymers:				
Polystyrene XMS 10023............	2.55	0.0005		
Loalin (molding powder)............	2.49	0.00022		
Loalin, cast.....................	2.51	0.00251		
Styron C-176....................	2.55	0.00026	2.54	0.0003
Polystyrene Foam.................	1.05	<0.00003		
Polystyrene Fibers Q-107...........	2.11	0.00063		
Lustron D-276...................	2.51	0.00041		
Polystyrene D-334................	2.54	0.00024		
Polystyrene (Polaroid).............	2.52	0.0025		
Polystyrene (in vacuo).............	2.51	0.00024		
Polystyrene (in air)...............	2.48	0.00128		
Styramic.......................	2.65	0.00022	2.62	0.00023
Polystyrene, completely hydrogenated.	2.25	0.00016	2.25	0.00041
Polystyrene + 20% vinyl cyanide....	2.76	0.0045		
Styraloy 22.....................	2.40	0.0032	2.40	0.0024
Dow Exp. Plastic Q-127............	2.45	0.00213		
G.E. No. 1421 Resin..............	2.53	0.0005	2.52	0.00056
Dow Exp. Plastic Q-166............	2.71	0.0315	2.62	0.0249
Dow Exp. Plastic Q-200.5..........	2.52	0.00044		

TABLE 12-1.—(*Continued*)

Substance	Frequency (cycles/sec)			
	3×10^9		1×10^{10}	
	ϵ'/ϵ_0	tan δ	ϵ'/ϵ_0	tan δ
Dow Exp. Plastic Q-200.7...........	2.50	0.00054		
Dow Exp. Plastic Q-247.............	2.52	0.00031	2.51	0.00037
Dow Exp. Plastic Q-344.............	2.34	0.00090	2.31	0.00086
Dow Exp. Plastic Q-385.5...........	2.50	0.00063	2.49	0.0008
Dow Exp. Plastic Q-409.............	2.60	0.00087	2.60	0.0012
Polyparachloro-styrene..............	2.61	0.00079		
Poly 2, 5-dichlorostyrene D-1385.....	2.62	0.00023	2.60	0.00023
Poly 2, 5-dichlorostyrene F-1891......	2.55	0.00038	2.55	0.00040
Mathieson Plastic CY-8.............	2.60	0.00031		
Mathieson Plastic CZ-12............	2.65	0.0039		
Mathieson Plastic CQ-10DM........	2.64	0.00108		
Poly 3, 4-dichlorostyrene...........	2.71	0.00170		
Exp. 2, 5-dichlorostyrene and isoprene copolymer......................	.....	....	2.63	0.0014
Thalid X-526-S....................	2.93	0.0163	2.93	0.0159
(6) Polyvinyl carbazole:				
Polymer 80 vinyl carbazole +20 styrene...........................	2.80	0.00081		
Polectron No. 24..................	2.88	0.00093		
Polectron No. 5...................	2.86	0.0005		
h. Polyethylene:				
Polyethylene......................	2.26	0.00040		
Polyethylene M702-R...............	2.21	0.00019		
Polyethylene KLW A-3305...........	2.25	0.00022		
Polyethylene Lot 122A..............	2.25	0.00058	2.24	0.00066
Polyethylene Lot 122B.............	2.25	0.00117	2.25	0.00119
Polyethylene Lot 122C..............	2.32	0.0050	2.31	0.0044
i. Rubbers:				
(1) Natural and modifications:				
Pale crepe........................	2.15	0.0030		
Pale crepe, vulcanized..............	2.36	0.0047		
Pale crepe, moderate amount of carbon black...........................	3.25	0.0148		
Pale crepe, large amount of carbon black...........................	6.29	0.0234		
Marbon B........................	2.37	0.0029	2.36	0.0045
Marbon S........................	2.56	0.0023	2.54	0.0022
Marbon S-1......................	2.50	0.00176	2.50	0.0019
(2) Synthetic:				
GR-S (Buna S) uncured.............	2.45	0.0044		

TABLE 12-1.—(*Continued*)

Substance	Frequency (cycles/sec)			
	3×10^9		1×10^{10}	
	ϵ'/ϵ_0	tan δ	ϵ'/ϵ_0	tan δ
GR-S (Buna S) compound...........	2.49	0.0056	2.44	0.0050
GR-S (Buna S) compound, large amount of carbon black..........	6.3	0.027	6.3	0.019
Rubber GR-S BXG-117G compound.	2.75	0.0057	2.74	0.0048
Polyisobutylene Run 5047-2..........	2.21	0.00047		
Polystyrene-polyisobutylene D-957...	2.30	0.00014		
Polystyrene-polyisobutylene D-955...	2.30	0.00035		
GR-I (Butyl rubber) uncured........	2.35	0.0009	2.35	0.0008
GR-I (Butyl rubber) cured..........	2.38	0.00093	2.38	0.00099
Neoprene GN......................	2.84	0.0480		
Neoprene GRM-10 loaded compound.	4.06	0.0339	4.02	0.0261
Neoprene loaded compound..........	4.10	0.035	4.10	0.0358
Pliobond M-190 C..................	3.76	0.074		
Gilsonite..........................	.....	....	2.55	0.00093
Millimar..........................	2.64	0.0011	2.64	0.0012
Shellacs:				
XL shellac (natural)................	2.86	0.0254		
Zinfo shellac (natural).............	2.86	0.029		
C Pure garnet shellac..............	2.94	0.027		
Dewaxed garnet shellac.............	2.75	0.0267		
Miscellaneous:				
Bakelite Resin XRS 16631..........	2.80	0.0161	2.70	0.0150
Celltite...........................	1.38	0.0039	1.37	0.0038
Cerex X-214.......................	2.65	0.0018	2.62	0.0029
Columbia Resin CR-38..............	2.87	0.0088		
Columbia Resin CR-39..............	2.88	0.0203		
Columbia Resin CR-149.............	3.03	0.0076	3.01	0.0070
Dihydronaphthalene, tetramer of.......	.....	....	2.63	0.00046
Dow Polyfiber Plastic...............	2.03	0.00045		
E Resin...........................	2.43	0.0006	2.42	0.0005
Fiberglas laminate BK-164..........	3.88	0.0120	3.99	0.0131
Fibreglas laminated with Q-166........	3.78	0.0241	3.70	0.0231
Hycar Hardboard...................	1.55	0.0093	1.52	0.0076
Insl-X A-110-5.....................	2.44	0.020		
Laminac No. 4122..................	3.03	0.037	2.88	0.031
Laminate of ECC-11-162 Fiberglas + Bakelite BRS-16631 Resin...........	3.60	0.0135	3.63	0.0123
Laminate of Knit Fiber A + Bakelite BRS-16631 Resin...................	2.75	0.0117		
Laminte Fiberglas ECC-11-148........	3.78	0.0140		

TABLE 12-1.—(*Concluded*)

Substance	Frequency (cycles/sec)			
	3×10^9		1×10^{10}	
	ϵ'/ϵ_0	tan δ	ϵ'/ϵ_0	tan δ
Marbon S Board..................	1.28	0.0017	1.27	0.0016
Marco Resin MR-1-C..............	2.99	0.0185		
Marco Resin MR-20-C.............	2.81	0.016		
Micarta No. 254..................	3.43	0.0505	3.25	0.041
Micarta No. 259..................	5.30	0.033	5.19	0.0385
Micarta No. 299..................	4.63	0.022	4.59	0.0230
Micarta No. 496..................	3.78	0.055	3.62	0.057
Nylon No. 610...................	2.84	0.0117		
Permafil........................	....	....	3.08	0.0276
Plaskon 911.....................	3.07	0.0175	3.02	0.0158
Plasticeramic...................	2.61	0.00086	2.60	0.00070
"Teflon," Poly F-1114...........	2.1	0.00015	2.08	0.00037
5. Waxes				
Acrawax C.......................	2.48	0.0015	2.45	0.0019
Apiezon W.......................	2.62	0.0016		
Beeswax (white).................	2.35	0.0050	2.35	0.0048
Beeswax (yellow)................	2.38	0.010		
Cerese Wax AA..................	2.29	0.00088	2.26	0.0007
Cerese Wax AA + phenyl mercuric stearate	2.29	0.00046	2.27	0.00050
Cerese Wax (brown)..............	2.25	0.00028		
Ceresin (yellow)................	2.26	0.0006		
Opalwax........................	2.55	0.0167	2.51	0.0160
Ozokerite......................	2.26	0.0006		
Paraffin wax (132° ASTM)........	2.25	0.00020	2.24	0.00021
Parowax........................	2.25	0.0002	2.25	0.00025
6. Miscellaneous				
Amber..........................	2.59	0.0090		
Cenco Sealstix..................	2.96	0.0210		
Plicene cement.................	2.40	0.00078	2.35	0.00068
Sealing wax....................	2.97	0.0119		
Halowax No. 1001...............	2.73	0.044		
Halowax No. 1013...............	3.09	0.043	2.85	0.0186
Halowax No. 1014...............	3.12	0.0345	2.95	0.0160
Halowax No. 11-314.............	2.89	0.0037	2.87	0.00095
Sulfur.........................	3.44	0.0007	3.44	0.0014
Ice (−12°C)....................	3.20	0.0009	3.17	0.0007
Paper (70%) and paraffin (30%)........	2.69	0.0362	2.64	0.0288
Mahogany.......................	1.96	0.034	1.86	0.035
Balsawood......................	1.21	0.010	1.21	0.0083

TABLE 12-2
PROPERTIES OF WATER AT 24,000 MC

	Temp., °C	ϵ'/ϵ_0	tan δ
Water..............................	3	27	1.00
	25	35	0.06
	60	44	0.33
Ice..	−15	3.3	0.003

CHAPTER 13

CAVITY RESONATORS

1. General Discussion[1]

At ordinary radio frequencies, a resonant circuit usually consists of a coil and a condenser. Associated with these circuit elements

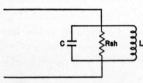

FIG. 13-1.—A parallel resonant circuit formed from conventional circuit elements.

are losses that are often lumped together into an equivalent resistance, as indicated in Fig. 13-1. In this figure L is the inductance, C the capacitance, and R_{sh} the equivalent resistance that accounts for the circuit losses. A knowledge of these three parameters permits a complete description of the behavior of the circuit in response to an impressed voltage.

The resonant frequency f_0 of the circuit of Fig. 13-1 is given by

$$f_0 = \frac{1}{2\pi \sqrt{LC}} \tag{13-1}$$

The input impedance Z to the circuit at a frequency f different from f_0 is

$$Z = \frac{1}{R_{sh}} + j \left(\frac{f}{f_0} - \frac{f_0}{f} \right) \sqrt{\frac{C}{L}} \tag{13-2}$$

The characteristic impedance R_0 of the circuit may be defined by

$$R_0 = \sqrt{\frac{L}{C}} \tag{13-3}$$

[1] HANSEN, W. W., A Type of Electrical Resonator, *J. Applied Phys.*, **9**, 654–663 (1938). Additional references that include general and specific information are the following:

RAMO, S., and J. R. WHINNERY, "Fields and Waves in Modern Radio," John Wiley & Sons, Inc., New York, 1944. SARBACHER, R. I., and W. A. EDSON, "Hyper and Ultrahigh Frequency Engineering," John Wiley & Sons, Inc., New York, 1943. SCHELKUNOFF, S. A., "Electromagnetic Waves," D. Van Nostrand Company, Inc., New York, 1943. M. I. T. RADAR SCHOOL STAFF, "Principles of Radar," McGraw-Hill Book Company, Inc., New York, 1946.

The customary definition of Q is

$$Q = \frac{R_{sh}}{2\pi f L} \tag{13-4}$$

Ordinary resonant circuits are usually discussed in terms of the quantities L, C, and R_{sh}, and the equations that describe the circuit behavior are usually written with these terms involved. But the behavior of the circuit could be described equally well in terms of the parameters R_0, Q, and f_0, and for circuits that are used at high frequencies, it is often more convenient to deal with these latter parameters, for reasons that are explained below.

At microwave frequencies, the components of an ordinary resonant circuit become so small that they are physically not practical to use, and cavity resonators are preferred because they are physically large and highly efficient. Any closed cavity with conducting walls has associated with it an infinite number of discrete resonant frequencies, each corresponding to a different configuration of electromagnetic fields in the interior of the cavity. For any one of these resonant modes, the cavity is like an ordinary resonant circuit in many ways, and its behavior may be described in terms of the three parameters R_0, Q, and f_0. But for each of the possible resonant modes, these parameters will in general have different values.

It is sometimes difficult to define for a cavity resonator the parameters of the equivalent coil and condenser circuit. The inductance L of a lumped constant resonant circuit may be defined in a number of ways:

(1)
$$L = 2\left(\frac{1}{2}\frac{LI^2}{I^2}\right) = 2 \times \frac{\text{energy stored}}{\text{current}^2} \tag{13-5}$$

(2)
$$L = \frac{n\phi}{I} = \frac{\text{flux linkages}}{\text{current}} \tag{13-6}$$

(3) Calculate L from the equation $f_0 = \dfrac{1}{2\pi\sqrt{LC}}$ with

$$C = 2 \times \frac{\text{energy stored}}{\text{voltage}^2}$$

In an ordinary resonant circuit each of these definitions leads to the same calculated value of inductance. This is not true for a cavity resonator, where in the general case a different answer will be obtained by each method of calculation.

But for any cavity resonator, there is a unique value of resonant frequency for each mode of resonance. For a given mode and given cavity shape, this resonant frequency depends only upon the size of the cavity.

The Q of a cavity may also be uniquely defined for each mode. We have previously defined Q by

$$Q = \frac{R_{sh}}{2\pi fL} \tag{13-7}$$

and it might be assumed that, because of the difficulty in determining a unique value of L, a similar difficulty would be encountered in attempting to define Q. But Q may be defined by

$$Q = 2\pi \frac{\text{energy stored}}{\text{energy lost/cycle}} \tag{13-8}$$

and the value given by this definition is a unique quantity for a given mode of resonance.

Characteristic impedance may also be uniquely defined except for a scale factor that depends upon what value of voltage or current is chosen as reference. This is a fundamental shortcoming and in general cannot be circumvented by a good choice of definition. The losses may be expressed either in terms of an equivalent series resistance R_{se}, defined by the relation

$$\text{Average energy lost/sec} = \frac{I^2 R_{se}}{2} \tag{13-9}$$

or in terms of an equivalent shunt resistance R_{sh}, defined by the relation

$$\text{Average energy lost/sec} = \frac{V^2}{2R_{sh}} \tag{13-10}$$

If these definitions were unique, the ratio of shunt to series resistance would be Q^2, as in ordinary resonant circuits. But in general, this ratio is not equal to Q^2 for cavity resonators. The choices of V and I are in a sense arbitrary, and even if the most "reasonable" choices are made, they will not necessarily lead to answers that agree. But if a single value of voltage or of current is chosen as reference, the circuit parameters may be uniquely defined with respect to the arbitrarily chosen voltage or current.

The shunt resistance and series resistance are quantities that are often more directly applicable to problems than is the characteristic impedance. When a resonator is to be driven by an electron beam, for example, it is important to know what impedance will be encountered by the current in the beam as it passes through the resonator. This shunt impedance R_{sh} is related to the characteristic impedance R_0 by

$$R_{sh} = R_0 Q \tag{13-11}$$

when the voltage across the path traversed by the electron beam is used as the basis of calculation.

In the remainder of this chapter, the shunt impedance of resonators will be calculated rather than their characteristic impedance. The path along which the electric field will be integrated to give the reference voltage will be that path along which the maximum voltage is developed. The fact that shunt impedance is used rather than series impedance in no way makes less valid the definition of series impedance; there is just an inherent ambiguity, and a choice is made for convenience.

2. Methods by Which Resonator Parameters Are Calculated[2]

Resonant Frequency.—To obtain the resonant frequency of a cavity resonator, solutions to Maxwell's equations must be found which satisfy the boundary conditions imposed by the resonator. It is nearly always assumed that the cavity is made of a perfect conductor, which means that, for calculations of resonant frequency, penetration of the fields into the walls of the resonator is neglected. The boundary conditions which must then be met are that no tangential electric field and no normal magnetic field exist at the surface of the cavity walls.

The electric and magnetic fields are derivable from some sort of a potential that satisfies a wave equation, and the calculation usually leads to an attempt to find a suitable potential function that is applicable to the problem in hand. An analytical solution is only possible for a limited number of cavity shapes, shapes that can be simply defined in terms of one of the standard coordinate systems. A number of approximate methods of calculation have been developed which give more or less accurate answers for many cavity shapes that cannot be solved by analytical methods.

For example, a complex resonator may be divided into two or more regions of simpler shape. Functions may then be found that are solutions to the wave equation and that satisfy the boundary conditions in each region. If the fields in each region may be made to be equal over the surface that is common to both regions, and to give a continuous derivative at that surface, the frequency will be determined.

A principle of similitude may be applied to cavity resonators, as follows: If all the linear dimensions of a cavity resonator are changed by a constant factor (and the resistivity of the walls changed by the same factor), the resonant wavelengths of all the normal modes in the

[2] The material in this section follows some unpublished notes of W. W. Hansen.

cavity will be scaled by the same factor.   The correction indicated in the parentheses is usually negligibly small.

Q.—The Q of a resonator has previously been defined by

$$Q = 2\pi \frac{\text{energy stored}}{\text{energy lost/cycle}} \qquad (13\text{-}12)$$

This is a unique definition for a given mode in a given cavity.   The quantity Q is sometimes used as a figure of merit for a resonant circuit, for it is a measure of the damping of a freely oscillating circuit, although shunt impedance is sometimes a more useful figure of merit.   It can be shown that the total field energy in a freely oscillating circuit varies with time according to the equation

$$W = W_0 e^{-\frac{\omega t}{Q}} \qquad (13\text{-}13)$$

where W is the energy at a time t and W_0 is the initial energy at $t = 0$. The Q of a resonator is also a measure of the sharpness of resonance, being inversely proportional to the band width between the frequencies where the impedance (or admittance) has fallen to 70.7 per cent of its resonant value.   This band width Δf is related to the resonant frequency f_0 by

$$\frac{\Delta f}{f_0} = \frac{1}{Q} \qquad (13\text{-}14)$$

To calculate the Q of a resonator, the relation must be found between energy stored in the cavity and losses in the cavity.   If dielectric losses are neglected, and only losses resulting from conduction currents in the resonator walls considered, these losses are

$$\text{Energy lost/cycle} = \frac{\delta}{8} \int B^2 |d\sigma| \qquad (13\text{-}15)$$

where δ is the skin depth, B is the magnetic field at the wall of the cavity, and $d\sigma$ is an element of area in the cavity wall.   The integral is carried out over the interior surface of the cavity.   The energy stored in the cavity is

$$\text{Energy stored} = \frac{1}{8\pi} \int B^2 \, d\tau \qquad (13\text{-}16)$$

with $d\tau$ an element of volume, and the integral carried out over the volume of the cavity.   The Q of the cavity is then

$$Q = \frac{2 \int B^2 \, d\tau}{\delta \int B^2 |d\sigma|} \qquad (13\text{-}17)$$

It will be seen that Q is a dimensionless quantity. This equation may be written as

$$Q\frac{\delta}{\lambda} = \frac{2\int B^2\, d\tau}{\lambda\int B^2|d\sigma|} \tag{13-18}$$

where δ is the skin depth, given in Eq. (2-7). The term on the right-hand side is independent of the wavelength and depends only upon the shape and mode of the cavity. It is therefore sometimes known as the "form factor" of the cavity (for the given mode).

To a first approximation, the form factor is given by

$$Q\frac{\delta}{\lambda} \sim \frac{2}{\lambda}\frac{\int d\tau}{\int|d\sigma|} \tag{13-19}$$

for it is not a rapidly varying function of the flux distribution. Also, because the magnetic field is a maximum at or near the surface of the resonator, the mean surface value of B^2 will be twice the mean value throughout the volume, and it can be said approximately that

$$Q\frac{\delta}{\lambda} \cong \frac{1}{\lambda}\frac{V}{S} \tag{13-20}$$

where V is the volume and S the area of the bounding surface of the resonator. A substitution of typical values shows that Q's greater than 1,000 are easily obtainable at microwave frequencies.

The form factor increases with increasing volume to surface ratio. Large cavities that operate on one of the higher modes of oscillation will therefore have higher Q's in general than will smaller cavities that resonate with simpler modes at the same wavelength.

Cavities that are reentrant have a low volume to surface ratio and are likely to have Q's that are lower than simpler shapes will give.

Two cavities of the same shape and same material but of different size will have Q's that are proportional to the square root of the resonant wavelength.

Shunt Impedance.—The shunt impedance, or shunt resistance, of an ordinary resonant circuit may be defined by

$$R_{sh} = \frac{\text{voltage}^2}{2\times\text{energy lost/sec}} \tag{13-21}$$

This definition is in many ways the most useful one that can be applied to a cavity resonator, as it is a factor of the resonator which tells the amount of input power that must be supplied to the resonator to maintain a given voltage across whatever path may be chosen. The path usually chosen is the one across which the maximum voltage is developed. If the resonator is being driven by a beam of electrons, the path that is chosen is the path followed by the electron beam.

The shunt impedance may be calculated by the following technique. The energy lost per second is given by

$$\text{Energy lost/sec} = \frac{\delta f}{8} \int B^2 |d\sigma| \qquad (13\text{-}22)$$

where δ is the skin depth given in Eq. (2-7), f is the frequency, B is the magnetic field at the surface, and $d\sigma$ is an element of surface in the cavity. The integration is carried out over the enclosing area of the cavity.

The voltage is defined as the line integral of the electric field, which by Stokes's theorem may be set equal to

$$\int E \, dS_1 = -\frac{1}{c} \int \dot{B} \, d\sigma_1 \qquad (13\text{-}23)$$

where c is the velocity of light, dS_1 is an element of length, and $d\sigma_1$

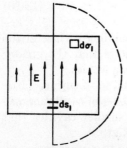

is an element of area. The value of the integral will obviously depend upon the chosen path of integration.

For example, in the resonator illustrated in Fig. 13-2, a circular cylindrical resonator operating in the $TM_{0,1,0}$ mode, the path of integration is chosen along the axis of the resonator to give the maximum voltage and is closed outside the cavity. The element of length dS_1 is along the axis of the resonator, as indicated. The element of area $d\sigma_1$ lies in a cross section containing the axis, and the integration is carried out over the portion of that cross section enclosed by the path of the line integral.

Fig. 13-2.—Illustrating the calculation of shunt impedance in a cavity resonator.

The shunt resistance obtained by this method of calculation is then given by

$$R = 16\pi^2 \frac{\left(\int \dot{B} \, d\sigma_1\right)^2}{\lambda^2 \int B^2 |d\sigma|} \frac{\lambda c}{\delta} \qquad \text{emu} \qquad (13\text{-}24)$$

where c is the velocity of light and δ the skin depth.
The factor

$$16\pi^2 \frac{\left(\int \dot{B} \, d\sigma_1\right)^2}{\lambda^2 \int B^2 |d\sigma|}$$

is independent of the resonant frequency of the cavity and has to do only with the shape and mode of the resonator. It then follows that for two resonators of the same shape but of different size the shunt impedance is proportional to the square root of the resonant wavelength.

To get some idea of the magnitudes involved, for copper at $\lambda = 10$ cm

$$\frac{\lambda c}{\delta} = 2.5 \times 10^6 \qquad \text{ohms} \qquad (13\text{-}25)$$

as c, the velocity of light, is equal to 30 ohms when converted to practical units The shape factor of a cavity is of the order unity, so the shunt resistance is of the order of a megohm.

If the Q of a cavity is increased by increasing the conductivity of the walls, the shunt impedance will increase by the same factor. It is possible to build resonators with high shunt impedances and low Q's, however, or conversely with high Q's and low shunt impedances. For example, as the height of the cylindrical resonator of Fig. 13-2 is increased, the shunt impedance will increase without limit, while the Q will approach a constant value. On the other hand, with a highly reentrant resonator of the type discussed in Sec. 13-3, page 227, the voltage developed across the gap may be small while the Q is large.

3. Characteristics of Various Cavity Resonators

Rectangular Resonators.—The characteristics of a rectangular prism resonator, such as illustrated in Fig. 13-3, are readily calculated by analytical methods.

A resonant wavelength λ_0 will be found in such a resonator when

$$\lambda_0 = \frac{4}{\sqrt{\left(\frac{l}{a}\right)^2 + \left(\frac{m}{b}\right)^2 + \left(\frac{n}{z_0}\right)^2}} \qquad (13\text{-}26)$$

where l is the number of half-wave variations of field along the x-axis m is the number of half-wave variations of field along the y-axis, n

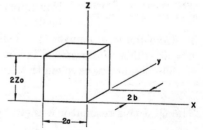

Fig. 13-3.—A rectangular cavity resonator, illustrating the notation used.

is the number of half-wave variations of field along the z-axis, and $l, m, n = 0, 1, 2, 3, \ldots$ but not more than one may equal zero for fields to exist.

For large resonators of this type, the number of modes dN in a range of wavelength $d\lambda$ is

$$dN = 8\pi \frac{V}{\lambda_1^4} d\lambda \qquad (13\text{-}27)$$

where V is the volume of the resonator and λ_1 is the center of the wavelength band $d\lambda$. If the three dimensions of the prism are equal, and the resonator is a perfect cube, there will be a twelvefold symmetry degeneracy. For example, the following modes will have identical resonant frequencies:

$$
\begin{array}{ll}
TE_{3,4,5} & TM_{3,4,5} \\
TE_{3,5,4} & TM_{3,5,4} \\
TE_{4,3,5} & TM_{4,3,5} \\
TE_{4,5,3} & TM_{4,5,3} \\
TE_{5,3,4} & TM_{5,3,4} \\
TE_{5,4,3} & TM_{5,4,3}
\end{array}
$$

If only two sides of the prism are equal, there will be a fourfold degeneracy. If all sides are unequal, there will be a twofold degeneracy, *i.e.*, TE and TM modes of the same subscripts will have the same resonant frequency. In practice, this twofold symmetry will usually be destroyed by irregularities in manufacture.

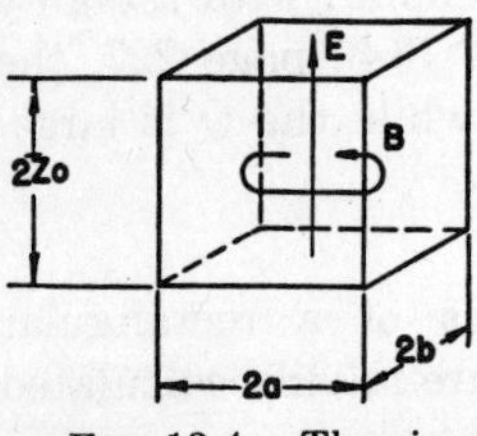

FIG. 13-4.—The simplest mode in a rectangular cavity resonator.

The number of resonant states N in a large rectangular prism resonator with resonant wavelengths greater than some minimum wavelength λ_2 is given approximately by

$$N = \frac{8\pi}{3} \frac{V}{\lambda_2^3} \qquad (13\text{-}28)$$

This approximate formula is quite accurate even for low N.

Consider a resonator in which $a = b$, and where $l = m = 1$ and $n = 0$. This is illustrated in Fig. 13-4.

The resonant wavelength of such a resonator is

$$\lambda_0 = 2 \sqrt{2}\, a \qquad (13\text{-}29)$$

The Q of this resonator is given by

$$Q \frac{\delta}{\lambda_0} = 0.353 \frac{1}{1 + \dfrac{a}{2z_0}} \qquad (13\text{-}30)$$

and the shunt impedance by

$$R \frac{\delta}{\lambda_0} = 120 \frac{z_0}{a} \frac{1}{1 + \dfrac{a}{2z_0}} \qquad (13\text{-}31)$$

where δ is the skin depth, given in Eq. (2-7).

For large cubical resonators, in which $a = b = z_0$, resonators operating in a high mode of oscillation, the Q is approximately given by

$$Q \frac{\delta}{\lambda_0} = \frac{a}{2\lambda_0} \qquad (13\text{-}32)$$

Cylindrical Resonators.—The infinite number of resonant modes that may exist in a simple circular cylindrical resonator may be divided into two classes: (1) those in which the electric field is everywhere transverse to the axis of the cylinder, and (2) those in which the magnetic field is everywhere transverse to the axis of the cylinder. The notation that will be applied to cylindrical resonators is illustrated in Fig. 13-5.

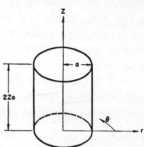

Fig. 13-5.—A circular cylindrical cavity resonator, illustrating the notation used.

TE Modes.—Considering first those modes in which the electric field has no component parallel to the axis, the resonant wavelength λ_0 is given by

$$\lambda_0 = \frac{4}{\sqrt{\left(\dfrac{l}{z_0}\right)^2 + \left(\dfrac{2u'_{m,n}}{\pi a}\right)^2}} \qquad (13\text{-}33)$$

Each of these modes occurs when the resonator is effectively a section of a circular wave guide that is an integral number of half wavelengths long for some TE mode of transmission in the wave guide. The term l gives the number of half wavelengths along the axis contained in the resonator and must, therefore, be an integral number, *i.e.*, 1, 2, 3, ... No mode exists in which $l = 0$. If the $TE_{m,n}$ mode in a wave guide is the mode being excited in the resonator $u'_{m,n}$ is the nth root of the equation

$$J_m'(u') = 0 \qquad (13\text{-}34)$$

Some of the lower roots of this equation are listed in Table 13-1.

The Q of the resonator when a half wave long is

$$Q \frac{\delta}{\lambda_0} = \frac{1}{\lambda_0} \frac{z_0 \left[(u'_{m,n})^2 + \left(\dfrac{\pi a}{2z_0}\right)^2 \right]\left[1 - \left(\dfrac{n}{u'_{m,n}}\right)^2 \right]}{\left[\dfrac{z_0}{a} (u'_{m,n})^2 + \dfrac{a^2\pi^2}{4z_0^2} + \dfrac{a(z_0 - a)}{4z_0^2} \dfrac{\pi^2 n^2}{(u'_{m,n})^2} \right]} \qquad (13\text{-}35)$$

where δ is the skin depth, given in Eq. (2-7). The Q is seen to decrease with increasing order of excitation. For a particularly interesting case that occurs when $n = 0$, and $l = m = 1$, the Q is given approximately by

$$Q \frac{\delta}{\lambda_0} = 0.610 \sqrt{1 + \left(0.410 \frac{a}{z_0}\right)^2} \frac{1 + 0.168 \left(\frac{a}{z_0}\right)^2}{1 + 0.168 \left(\frac{a}{z_0}\right)^3} \qquad (13\text{-}36)$$

Resonators operating in this mode of oscillation, which corresponds to the $TE_{0,1}$ mode in a wave guide, have an exceptionally high Q and are ideal for precision wavemeters except that some sort of damping system must be used to eliminate the other modes unless the tuning range is small.

TM Modes.—For the other class of resonant modes, in which the magnetic field has no component parallel to the axis, the resonant wavelengths are given by

$$\lambda_0 = \frac{4}{\sqrt{\left(\frac{l}{z_0}\right)^2 + \left(\frac{2u_{m,n}}{\pi a}\right)^2}} \qquad (13\text{-}37)$$

As before, each of these modes occurs when the resonator is effectively a section of circular wave guide that is an integral number of half wavelengths long, this time for a TM mode of propagation   As before, l is an integer that gives the number of half waves along the axis of the resonator. In addition, modes exist when $l = 0$; these modes have an electric field that is everywhere parallel to the axis and do not represent possible modes of transmission in a wave guide.

If the $TM_{m,n}$ mode in a wave guide is the mode excited in the resonator, $u_{m,n}$ is the nth root of the equation

$$J_m(u) = 0 \qquad (13\text{-}38)$$

When $l = 0$, the axial electric field will still be given by an mth order Bessel function, which will have its nth root at the radius a. As before, the term $u_{m,n}$ will be the nth root of an mth order Bessel function which determines the axial field. A tabulation of some of the lower roots of this equation are given in Table 13-1.

The Q of the TM modes for a resonator a half wave in length when $m \neq 0$ is given by

$$Q \frac{\delta}{\lambda_0} = \frac{a}{\lambda_0} \frac{1}{1 + \frac{a}{z_0}} \qquad (13\text{-}39)$$

If $m = 0$, the Q is given by

$$Q \frac{\delta}{\lambda_0} = \frac{a}{\lambda_0} \frac{a}{1 + \frac{a}{2z_0}} \qquad (13\text{-}40)$$

where δ is the skin depth, given in Eq. (2-7). With this exception, for these modes the Q is not a function of the order of excitation; this is in contrast to the other class of modes.

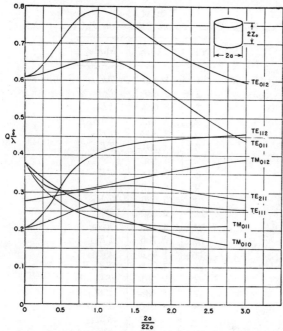

FIG. 13-6.—The form factor $\left(Q \dfrac{\delta}{\lambda}\right)$ of some of the lower modes in circular cylindrical resonators.

The shunt resistance in ohms of the mode in which $l = n = 0$ and $m = 1$, *i.e.*, the lowest mode in which the electric field is everywhere axial, is given by

$$R \frac{\delta}{\lambda_0} = 144 \frac{z_0}{a} \frac{1}{1 + \dfrac{a}{2z_0}} \qquad (13\text{-}41)$$

and the resonant wavelength λ_0 by

$$\lambda_0 = 2.61a \qquad (13\text{-}42)$$

The form factor of a cylindrical cavity, $Q \dfrac{\delta}{\lambda}$, is plotted as a function of the ratio z_0/a in Fig. 13-6 for some of the lowest modes of oscillation in a cylindrical cavity.[3] These modes are identified by subscripts

[3] WILSON, I. G., C. W. SCHRAMM, and J. P. KINZER, High Q Resonant Cavities for Microwave Testing, *Bell System Tech. J.*, Vol. 25, No. 3 (1946).

of the form $TE_{m,n,l}$. For example, the $TE_{0,1,2}$ mode corresponds to a section of wave guide operating in the $TE_{0,1}$ mode and two half wavelengths long.

TABLE 13-1
THE FIRST TWENTY-FIVE ZEROS OF $J_m(x)$ AND $J_m'(x)$

No.	Value	Mode
1	1.841	TE_{11}
2	2.405	TM_{01}
3	3.054	TE_{21}
4	3.832	TM_{11}
5	3.832	TE_{01}
6	4.201	TE_{31}
7	5.136	TM_{21}
8	5.318	TE_{41}
9	5.332	TE_{12}
10	5.520	TM_{02}
11	6.380	TM_{31}
12	6.416	TE_{51}
13	6.706	TE_{22}
14	7.016	TM_{12}
15	7.016	TE_{02}
16	7.501	TE_{61}
17	7.588	TM_{41}
18	8.016	TE_{32}
19	8.417	TM_{22}
20	8.536	TE_{13}
21	8.578	TE_{71}
22	8.654	TM_{03}
23	8.771	TM_{51}
24	9.283	TE_{42}
25	9.647	TE_{81}

Equations (13-27) and (13-28) are approximately true for large circular cylindrical cavities. If the cross section is circular, there exists a twofold degeneracy for most modes, which have two possible polarizations. This degeneracy will be removed if the cross section is elliptical.

Spherical Resonators.—The first resonance will occur in a spherical cavity of radius a when

$$\lambda_0 = 2.28a \qquad (13\text{-}43)$$

and the second resonance when

$$\lambda_0 = 1.4a \qquad (13\text{-}44)$$

The field configuration for these first two modes is shown in Fig. 13-7.

The Q of a spherical cavity operating in the dominant mode is given by

$$Q \frac{\delta}{\lambda_0} = 0.318 \qquad (13\text{-}45)$$

and the shunt impedance given by

$$R \frac{\delta}{\lambda_0} = 104.4 \qquad (13\text{-}46)$$

Spherical Resonators with Reentrant Cones.[4]—A resonator that can be solved by analytical methods consists of part of a sphere of

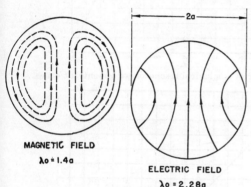

MAGNETIC FIELD
$\lambda_0 = 1.4a$

ELECTRIC FIELD
$\lambda_0 = 2.28a$

FIG. 13-7.—Spherical cavity resonators with the two lowest modes.

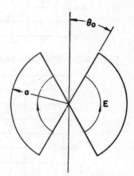

FIG. 13-8.—Spherical resonator with reentrant cones.

radius a and two cones whose apex is at the center of the sphere and whose half angle is θ_0. Such a resonator is sketched in Fig. 13-8, and the field corresponding to the fundamental mode of oscillation is illustrated.

The resonant wavelength of this cavity is

$$\lambda_0 = 4a \qquad (13\text{-}47)$$

and is not a function of the angle θ_0. The Q of the resonator does vary with the angle θ_0, and in Fig. 13-9, $Q \frac{\delta}{\lambda_0}$ is plotted as a function of θ_0. The maximum value of Q is found at an angle of $\theta_0 = 34$ deg and is given by

$$Q \frac{\delta}{\lambda_0} = 0.1095 \qquad (13\text{-}48)$$

[4] HANSEN, W. W., and R. D. RICHTMYER, On Resonators Suitable for Klystron Oscillators, *J. Applied Phys.*, **10**, 189–199 (1939).

The shunt impedance is also a function of the angle θ_0, and Fig. 13-10 gives the variation of $R\dfrac{\delta}{\lambda_0}$ with θ_0. The maximum value of R is

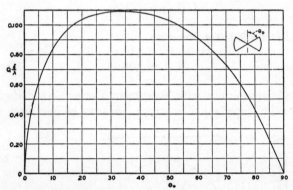

Fig. 13-9.—The form factor of a spherical resonator with reentrant cones.

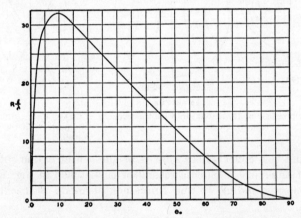

Fig. 13-10.—The shunt impedance of a spherical resonator with reentrant cones.

reached at an angle of $\theta_0 = 9$ deg. At this angle R in ohms is given by

$$R\frac{\delta}{\lambda_0} = 32.04 \qquad (13\text{-}49)$$

Ellipsoid-hyperboloid Resonators.[5]—Another type of resonator that has been solved analytically is the ellipsoid-hyperboloid shown in Fig. 13-11. The resonator is a figure of revolution about an axis passing through the foci. The resonant wavelength of this resonator may be determined from Fig. 13-12. In this figure, the distance a

[5] Hansen and Richtmyer, *loc. cit.*

between the foci is held constant and also the hyperboloid that determines part of the resonator. The equatorial radius x_0 is varied, and λ_0/x_0 is plotted as a function of the shape factor, σ_0, defined by $\sigma_0 = 2x_0/a$. Also shown on the curve are the resonator shapes that correspond to various values of σ_0; these resonators are scaled in the drawing so as to maintain constant the resonant wavelength λ_0.

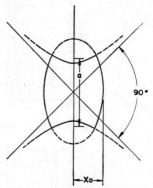

Fig. 13-11.—Ellipsoid-hyperboloid resonator.

The Q of the resonator is also a function of the shape factor σ_0, and in Fig. 13-13, $Q\dfrac{\delta}{\lambda_0}$ is plotted against σ_0. The variation in shunt impedance with the shape can be obtained from Fig. 13-14, where $R\dfrac{\delta}{\lambda_0}$ is plotted against σ_0.

Coaxial-line Resonators.[6]—One type of coaxial-line resonator is that shown in Fig. 13-15. The lowest *TEM* resonance in this cavity will be found when the cavity is a half wavelength long. This resonant

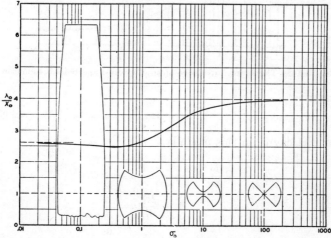

Fig. 13-12.—The resonant wavelength of an ellipsoid-hyperboloid resonator with equatorial radius x_0.

[6] BARROW, W. L., and W. W. MIEHER, Natural Oscillations of Electrical Cavity Resonators, *Proc. Inst. Radio Engrs.*, **28**, 184–191 (1940). Some slightly misleading aspects of this paper are clarified in R. A. KIRKMAN, and M. KLINE, The Transverse Electric Modes in Coaxial Cavities, *Proc. Inst. Radio Engrs.*, **34**, 14P–17P (1946).

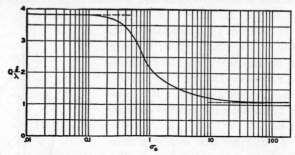

Fig. 13-13.—The form factor of an ellipsoid-hyperboloid resonator.

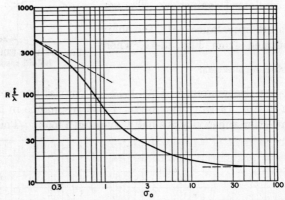

Fig. 13-14.—The shunt impedance of an ellipsoid-hyperboloid resonator.

wavelength is

$$\lambda_0 = 4z_0 \tag{13-50}$$

The Q of the cavity in this mode is

$$Q\frac{\delta}{\lambda_0} = \frac{1}{4 + \dfrac{2z_0}{b}\dfrac{1 + \dfrac{b}{a}}{\log_e \dfrac{b}{a}}} \tag{13-51}$$

where δ is the skin depth, given in Eq. (2-7). The optimum diametric ratio for lowest losses is $b/a = 3.6$; this leads to a formula for Q of

$$Q\frac{\delta}{\lambda_0} = \frac{1}{4 + 7.2\dfrac{z_0}{b}} \tag{13-52}$$

The shunt impedance of this resonator is

$$R\frac{\delta}{\lambda_0} = \frac{60}{\pi}\frac{b}{z_0}\frac{\log_e^2\frac{b}{a}}{1+\frac{b}{a}}\frac{1}{1+2\frac{b}{z_0}\frac{\log_e\frac{b}{a}}{1+\frac{b}{a}}} \qquad (13\text{-}53)$$

When $b \ll \lambda$, the maximum R is found when $b/a = 9.2$. For this value, the preceding formula reduces to

$$R\frac{\delta}{\lambda_0} = 30\frac{1}{1.41 + 3.24\frac{z_0}{b}} \qquad (13\text{-}54)$$

and for large z_0/b

$$R\frac{\delta}{\lambda_0} \cong 9.25\frac{b}{z_0} \qquad (13\text{-}55)$$

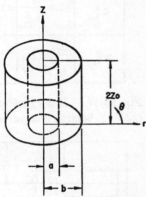

It will be observed that optimum Q occurs at $b/a = 3.6$ and optimum R at $b/a = 9.2$. But at $b/a = 3.6$, R has fallen only to 74 per cent of its maximum value, and at $b/a = 9.2$, Q has fallen only to 78 per cent of its maximum. So the values are not critical with diametric ratio.

Fig. 13-15.—A resonator formed of a section of coaxial line.

In addition to the lowest resonant mode, resonances will be found whenever the length of the cavity is an integral number of half wavelengths. Higher modes of propagation can also exist on a coaxial line; their properties are discussed in Sec. 4-8. It is characteristic of these modes that the wavelength along the line always exceeds the wavelength of the principal mode. Additional resonances will be found whenever the cavity is an integral number of half wavelengths for any of these higher modes. There are also higher modes in which the electric field is only axial; these modes correspond to no mode of propagation on a coaxial line.

Some of the more important results of the preceding sections are compared in Table 13-2.

Capacity-loaded Coaxial-line Resonators.[7]—One widely used form of resonator is the capacity-loaded coaxial-line resonator shown in

[7] HANSEN, W. W., On the Resonant Frequency of Closed Concentric Lines, *J. Applied Phys.*, **10**, 38–45 (1939). Also HAHN, W. C., A New Method for the Calculation of Cavity Resonators, *Jour. Applied Phys.*, **12**, 62–68 (1941).

TABLE 13-2

CHARACTERISTICS OF RESONATORS

Type of resonator	Rectangular prism	Cylinder	Sphere	Dimpled sphere	Ellipsoid hyperboloid	Coaxial
λ_0	2 828a	2.61a	2.28a	4a	1.3a	4Z₀
$Q\,\dfrac{\delta}{\lambda_0}$	$0.353\,\dfrac{1}{1+\dfrac{a}{2Z_0}}$	$0.383\,\dfrac{1}{1+\dfrac{a}{2Z_0}}$	0.318	0.1095 for $\theta_0=34°$	0.22	$\dfrac{1}{4.2+7.2\dfrac{Z_0}{b}}$ for $b/a=3.6$
$R\,\dfrac{\delta}{\lambda_0}$	$120\dfrac{Z_0}{a}\,\dfrac{1}{1+\dfrac{a}{2Z_0}}$	$144\dfrac{Z_0}{a}\,\dfrac{1}{1+\dfrac{a}{2Z_0}}$	104.4	32 04 for $\theta_0=9°$	76.4	$30\dfrac{1}{1.41+3.24\dfrac{Z_0}{b}}$ for $b/a=9.2$

Fig. 13-16. If the gap length δ is large, and the center conductor length $(z_0 - \delta)$ is large compared with the outer radius ρ_2, resonance will occur when the center conductor length is approximately a quarter wave $[\lambda_0 = 4(z_0 - \delta)]$. More accurate calculations will take into account the fringing fields at the open end of the plunger. The effect of these is equivalent to a lumped capacity between inner and outer conductors of the coaxial line, located at the open end of the reentrant part. This capacity may be approximately calculated from the principles and curves given in Sec. 6-1, page 96. The resonant frequency will then be found to a second approximation when the susceptance of this equivalent capacity is equal and of opposite sign to the susceptance of the length of coaxial transmission line formed by the center conductor and the outer cyclinder.

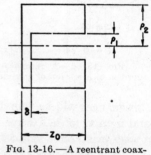

FIG. 13-16.—A reentrant coaxial cavity resonator.

As the reentrant post length becomes small, the resonant wavelength of the cavity does not approach zero, but approaches instead the resonant wavelength of the $TM_{0,1,0}$ mode in a cylindrical cavity. This limiting value is given by ($\lambda_0 = 2.61\rho_2$).

If the dimension δ is small enough to introduce an appreciable capacity at the end of the coaxial transmission line, the resonant wavelength for given radial dimensions and plunger length will be correspondingly modified. To a first approximation the resonator may be considered a short length of coaxial line that is resonated by the large lumped capacity at the end of the center conductor and this capacity calculated from the gap spacing and area. This leads to a formula for resonant wavelength in terms of resonator dimensions of

$$\lambda_0 = 2\pi \left(\frac{z_0 \rho_1}{2\delta} \ln \frac{\rho_2}{\rho_1} \right)^{1\!\!/_2} \qquad (13\text{-}56)$$

This calculation neglects the additional equivalent capacity of the fringing fields at the end of the plunger and, hence, always gives a resonant wavelength that is smaller than the true value. The factor by which the wavelength given by Eq. (13-56) must be multiplied to give the true value is commonly of the order 1.25 to 1.75.

More accurate calculations have led to the results that are presented graphically in Fig. 13-17. These charts make it possible to determine within a few per cent the resonant wavelength of a cavity of given dimensions, provided that the gap is not too large. On all the charts, the ratio δ/ρ_1 is plotted against the ratio z_0/ρ_1. There are several families of curves, each family for a given ratio ρ_2/ρ_1. Each curve in the family is for a given value of $k\rho_1$, where k is related to the resonant wavelength λ_0 by the formula

$$k = \frac{2\pi}{\lambda_0} \qquad (13\text{-}57)$$

Two families of curves are plotted on each chart, to aid in interpolation.

The Q of a cavity of this type is given approximately by

$$Q \frac{\delta}{\lambda} = \frac{2z_0}{\lambda} \frac{\ln \dfrac{\rho_2}{\rho_1}}{2 \ln \dfrac{\rho_2}{\rho_1} + z_0 \left(\dfrac{1}{\rho_1} + \dfrac{1}{\rho_2} \right)} \qquad (13\text{-}58)$$

where δ is the skin depth, given in Eq. (2-7), rather than the gap spacing, and ρ_1, ρ_2, and z_0 are cavity dimensions.
The shunt impedance is given approximately by

$$R \frac{\delta}{\lambda} = 60\pi \left(\frac{2z_0}{\lambda} \right)^2 \frac{\ln^2 \dfrac{\rho_2}{\rho_1}}{2 \ln \dfrac{\rho_2}{\rho_1} + z_0 \left(\dfrac{1}{\rho_1} + \dfrac{1}{\rho_2} \right)} \qquad (13\text{-}59)$$

where as before δ is skin depth rather than gap spacing. More exact calculations show that a resonator with fixed gap spacing δ and inner radius ρ_1 will have its maximum shunt impedance when the toroidal cross section is approximately square, *i.e.*, when

$$z_0 - \delta \cong \rho_2 - \rho_1 \qquad (13\text{-}60)$$

4. Effect of Temperature and Humidity upon the Resonant Frequency of a Cavity

The resonant frequency of a cavity will vary with changing temperature because of dimensional variations. For a cavity constructed of a single metal, the percentage change in resonant wavelength will be equal to the percentage change in linear dimensions, which in turn depends upon the expansion coefficient of the material of which the cavity is built. Temperature coefficients of some typical materials are listed in Table 13-3. Temperature compensation is possible with the use of bimetal construction.

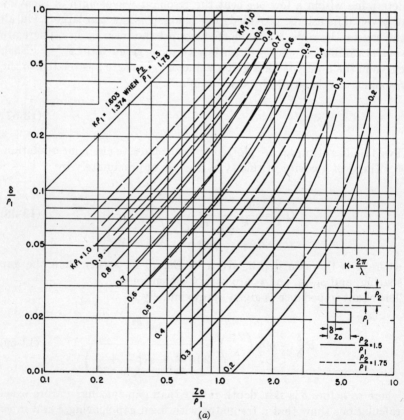

Fig. 13-17a and b.—Design curves for finding the reso-

In addition, if the cavity is not sealed, there will be a change in resonant frequency because of the varying dielectric constant of air with changing temperature and humidity. If the cavity has been calibrated at 25°C, 60 per cent humidity, and sea-level pressure, the change in resonant frequency to be expected under different atmospheric conditions may be determined from the nomograph of Fig. 13-18.

5. Coupling between Resonators and Transmission Lines

To utilize the characteristics of, or to extract power from, a cavity resonator, it is usually necessary to couple the resonator to a load, which is frequently a transmission line. This may be done in several ways. Coaxial transmission lines may be coupled to resonators either

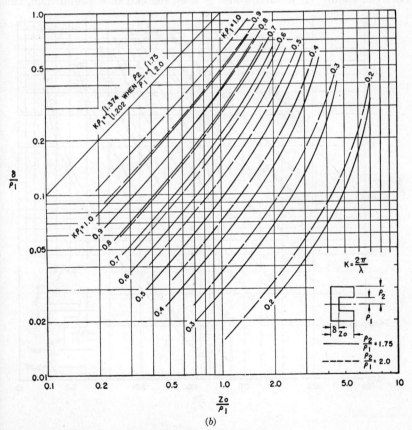

(b)

nant wavelength of a reentrant coaxial cavity resonator.

by electric or magnetic coupling. To provide electric coupling, the center conductor of the coaxial line is extended as a probe into the cavity and will couple to the cavity if the probe is in line with a component of the electric field within the cavity. Magnetic coupling may be provided by terminating the coaxial line in a loop that links magnetic flux within the cavity.

Cavities are usually coupled to wave guides by holes through the metal wall that separates guide from cavity and may be coupled to coaxial lines in the same manner. There will be magnetic coupling through a round hole if the magnetic field at the surface of the guide has a component parallel to the magnetic field at the adjoining surface of the cavity. There will be electric coupling if both cavity and guide have components of electric field normal to the common surface between them. If a narrow slot is used instead of a round hole, the

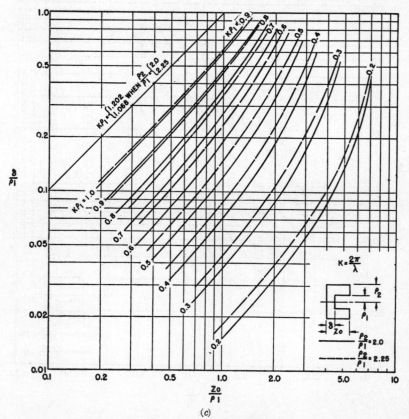

(c)

Fig. 13-17c and d.—Design curves for finding the reso-

electric coupling will be very small, and there will be appreciable
magnetic coupling only if the tangential magnetic field in both guide
and cavity have components parallel to the slot.

When a cavity is coupled to a transmission line, the resonant frequency and Q are modified by the coupling circuit, and there is some
question as to the precise resonant frequency of the cavity. This
arises from the difficulty of establishing exact lines of demarcation
between line, coupling circuit, and cavity. For many purposes, it is
convenient to regard the resonant frequency of the over-all cavity and
coupling circuit as the frequency at which a minimum standing-wave
ratio is seen on the input transmission line looking toward the cavity.
It is convenient to choose a reference plane as the location of a minimum
on the input line when the cavity is detuned. An equivalent circuit

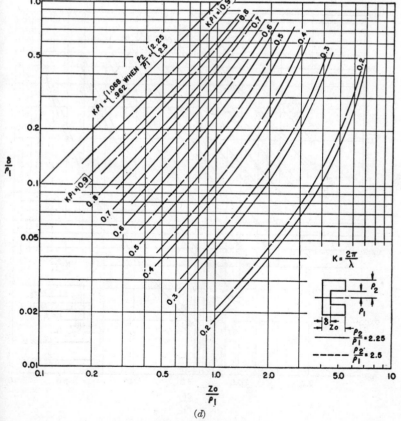

(d)

nant wavelength of a reentrant coaxial cavity resonator.

may then be set up for the cavity and coupling network, as shown in Fig. 13-19, consisting of a virtual resonant circuit located at the reference plane.

In actual operation, the cavity will be loaded by the input admittance of the coupled transmission line, which parallels the virtual resonant circuit. The input admittance to the cavity Y is given at resonance by

$$Y = G \tag{13-61}$$

where G is the shunt conductance of the virtual resonant circuit. A quantity β may be defined by

$$\beta = \frac{Y_0}{G} \tag{13-62}$$

where Y_0 is the characteristic admittance of the input line. The stand-

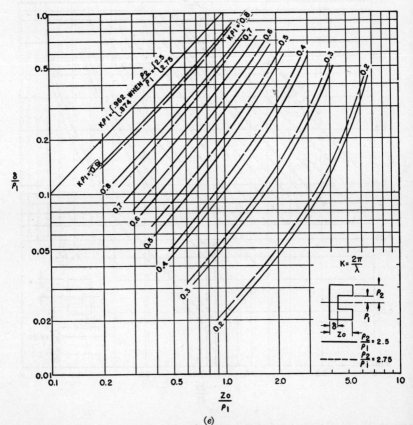

(e)

Fig. 13-17e and f.—Design curves for finding the resing-wave ratio looking toward the cavity at resonance will equal β if $\beta > 1$, or $1/\beta$ if $\beta < 1$. If $\beta > 1$, a voltage maximum will appear at the reference plane at resonance. If $\beta < 1$, a voltage minimum will be at the reference plane at resonance.

The following terms may be used to describe the cavity and its coupled load, when the transmission line is matched at its far end, so that its input admittance is Y_0.

$$\text{Unloaded } Q = Q_0 = \frac{2\pi f \times \text{energy stored in cavity}}{\text{power dissipated in cavity}} = \frac{\omega C}{G} \tag{13-63}$$

$$\text{External } Q = Q_E = \frac{2\pi f \times \text{energy stored in cavity}}{\text{power dissipated in load}} = \frac{\omega C}{Y_0} \tag{13-64}$$

$$\text{Loaded } Q = Q_L = \frac{2\pi f \times \text{energy stored in cavity}}{\text{power dissipated in load and cavity}} = \frac{\omega C}{G + Y_0} \tag{13-65}$$

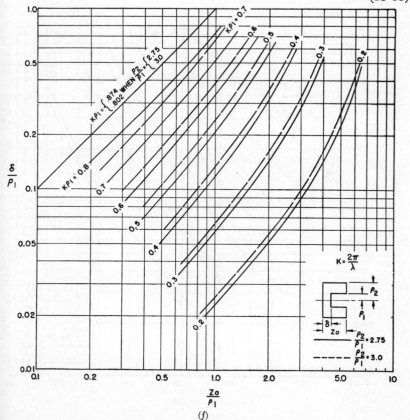

(*f*)

onant wavelength of a reentrant cavity resonator.

TABLE 13-3

COEFFICIENT OF THERMAL EXPANSION AT 20°C

Substance	Coefficient
Aluminum	24×10^{-6}
Brass	19
Phosphor bronze	17
Copper	16
Duraluminum	24
Glass, soft	8.5
Glass, hard	9.7
Steel	10
Magnesium	26
Molybdenum	5
Monel metal	14
Invar	0.9
Quartz, fused	0.42
Silver	19
Stainless steel	10

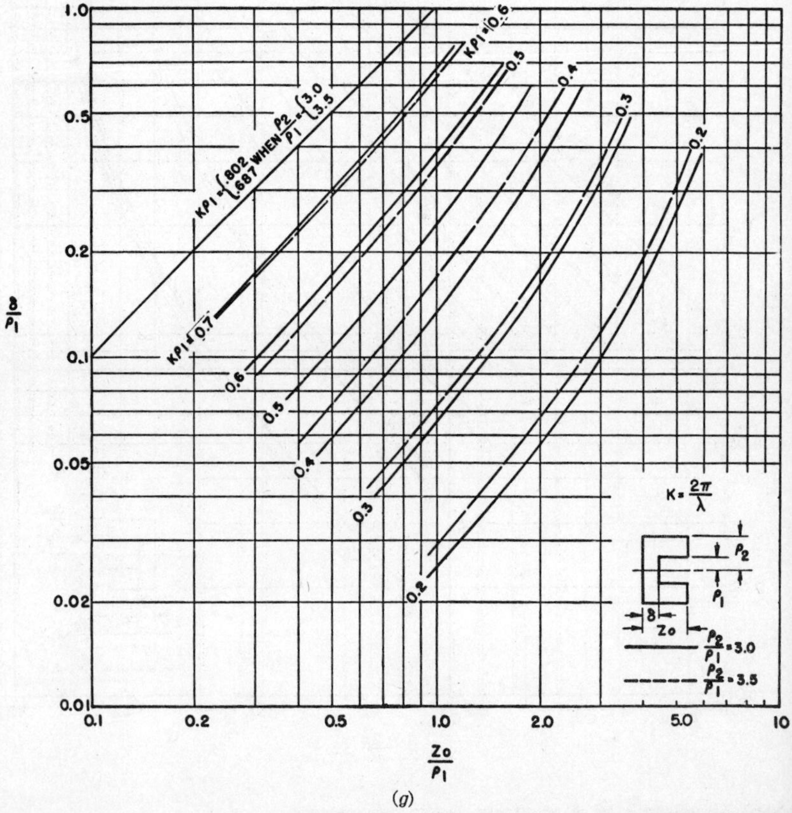

(*g*)

FIG. 13-17 *g* and *h*.—Design curves for finding the reso

The various terms are related by the equations:

$$\frac{Q_0}{Q_L} = 1 + \beta \qquad (13\text{-}66)$$

$$\frac{Q_0}{Q_E} = \beta \qquad (13\text{-}67)$$

$$\frac{Q_E}{Q_L} = 1 + \frac{1}{\beta} \qquad (13\text{-}68)$$

Frequently the cavity is loaded by an admittance other than Y_0, if the transmission line is not matched at its other end. If the load impedance at the far end of the line places an admittance $G_L + jB_L$ at the reference plane, the coupled Q will be

$$Q_c = \frac{\omega C}{G_L} \qquad (13\text{-}69)$$

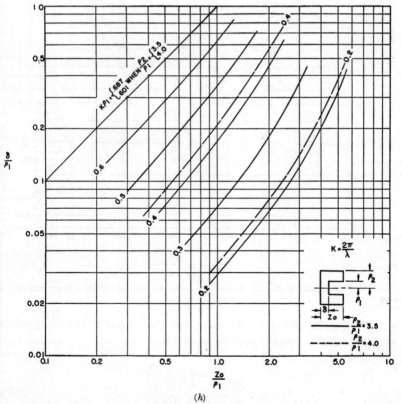

(h)

nant wavelength of a reentrant coaxial cavity resonator.

The resonant frequency of the tuned circuit will be changed an amount Δf by the susceptance of the coupled load, given by

$$\frac{\Delta f}{f_0} = -\frac{1}{2}\frac{B_L}{\omega C} \qquad (13\text{-}70)$$

If the resonant cavity is coupled to a load whose standing-wave ratio

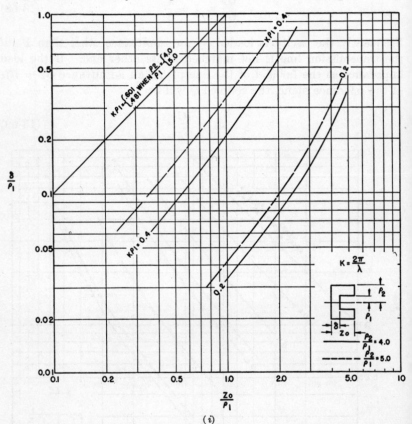

Fig. 13-17*i*.—Design curves for finding the resonant wavelength of a reentrant coaxial cavity resonator.

σ is known, the maximum amount that the resonant frequency will be changed by the coupled load is given by

$$\frac{\Delta f}{f_0} = \pm\frac{\left(\sigma - \dfrac{1}{\sigma}\right)}{4Q_c} \qquad (13\text{-}71)$$

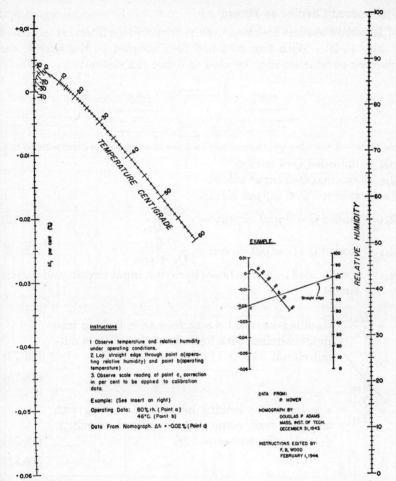

FIG. 13-18.—The effect of humidity and temperature on the frequency of coaxial and cavity resonators.

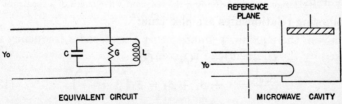

FIG. 13-19.—A microwave cavity coupled to a transmission line, and the approximate equivalent circuit that applies for any single resonant mode in the cavity.

6. Resonant Cavities as Filters[8]

Resonant cavities are often used as transmission filters, as indicated in Fig. 13-20. With two matched lines coupled to the cavity, the following parameters may be used to define the system:

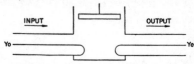

Fig. 13-20.—A tunable microwave cavity used as a filter, coupled to a transmission line.

Q_0 = unloaded Q of cavity

Q_{E1} = external Q of input circuit

Q_{E2} = external Q of output circuit

$$Q_{L1} = \text{loaded } Q \text{ of input circuit} = \frac{Q_0 Q_{E1}}{Q_0 + Q_{E1}} \tag{13-72}$$

$$Q_{L2} = \text{loaded } Q \text{ of output circuit} = \frac{Q_0 Q_{E2}}{Q_0 + Q_{E2}} \tag{13-73}$$

Q_{L12} = total loaded Q, due to losses in cavity, input circuit, and output circuit

Also

$$\beta_1 = \frac{Q_0}{Q_{E1}} = \text{standing-wave ratio } \sigma \text{ at resonance looking into input coupling with load disconnected from output circuit if } \beta_1 > 1; \text{ otherwise } \sigma = 1/\beta_1 \tag{13-74}$$

$$\beta_2 = \frac{Q_0}{Q_{E2}} \tag{13-75}$$

$$\gamma_1 = \frac{Q_{L2}}{Q_{E1}} = \sigma \text{ at resonance looking into input coupling with matched load connected to output circuit if } \gamma_1 > 1; \text{ otherwise } \sigma = 1/\gamma_1 \tag{13-76}$$

$$\gamma_1 = \frac{\beta_1}{1 + \beta_2} \tag{13-77}$$

$$\gamma_2 = \frac{Q_{L1}}{Q_{E2}} \tag{13-78}$$

$$\gamma_2 = \frac{\beta_2}{1 + \beta_1} \tag{13-79}$$

The following relationships are also true:

$$\frac{1}{Q_{L12}} = \frac{1}{Q_{E1}} + \frac{1}{Q_{E2}} + \frac{1}{Q_0} \tag{13-80}$$

$$\frac{Q_0}{Q_{L12}} = 1 + \beta_1 + \beta_2 = \beta_1\left(1 + \frac{1}{\gamma_1}\right) \tag{13-81}$$

[8] This follows an unpublished report of E. T. Jaynes, "Theory of Microwave Coupling Systems," Combined Research Group, Naval Research Laboratory, Washington, D.C., Aug. 29, 1945.

If a given band width Δf is required with matched loads on the transmission lines, this specifies that

$$Q_{L12} = \frac{f_0}{\Delta f} \tag{13-82}$$

The insertion loss of the filter depends upon two factors:
1. Reflection loss at the input
2. Absorption loss in the cavity

If the lines are matched, and

$$P_0 = \text{incident power on input line}$$
$$P_1 = P_0 - \text{reflection loss}$$
$$P_2 = P_1 - \text{absortpion loss in cavity}$$

the following relationships hold:

$$\frac{P_1}{P_0} = \frac{4\gamma_1}{(1 + \gamma_1)^2} \tag{13-83}$$

$$\frac{P_2}{P_1} = \frac{Q_{L2}}{Q_{E2}} = \frac{\beta_2}{1 + \beta_2} = \frac{\beta_1 - \gamma_1}{\beta_1} \tag{13-84}$$

$$\text{Efficiency} = \frac{P_2}{P_0} = \frac{4\gamma_1}{(1 + \gamma_1)^2} \frac{\beta_1 - \gamma_1}{\beta_1} \tag{13-85}$$

If, while maintaining constant band width, both β_1 and β_2 may be adjusted, minimum insertion loss will be when $\beta_1 = \beta_2$. And

$$\beta_1 = \frac{1}{2}\left(\frac{Q_0}{Q_{L12}} - 1\right) \tag{13-86}$$

$$\text{Efficiency} = \frac{Q_{L12}}{Q_0}\left(\frac{Q_0}{Q_{L12}} + \frac{Q_{L12}}{Q_0} - 2\right) = \left(\frac{2\beta_1}{1 + 2\beta_1}\right)^2 \tag{13-87}$$

If the output coupling β_2 is fixed, minimum insertion loss will be found when reflection loss is zero ($\gamma_1 = 1$). Then

$$\beta_1 = 1 + \beta_2 \tag{13-88}$$

$$\text{Efficiency} = \left(1 - \frac{1}{\beta_1}\right) \tag{13-89}$$

$$\text{Band width} = 2\beta_1 \frac{f_0}{Q_0} \tag{13-90}$$

If input coupling is fixed, efficiency will be maximized when $\gamma_2 = 1$. Then

$$\gamma_1 = \frac{\beta_1}{2 + \beta_1} \tag{13-91}$$

$$\beta_2 = 1 + \beta_1 \tag{13-92}$$

$$\text{Efficiency} = \frac{\beta_1}{1 + \beta_1} \frac{2\gamma_1}{1 + \gamma_1} \tag{13-93}$$

$$\text{Band width} = 2\beta \frac{f_0}{2Q_0} = 2(1 + \beta_1) \frac{f_0}{Q_0} \tag{13-94}$$

INDEX

DOVER BOOKS ON SCIENCE
BOOKS THAT EXPLAIN SCIENCE

CONCERNING THE NATURE OF THINGS, Sir William Bragg. Christmas lectures delivered at the Royal Society by Nobel laureate. Why a spinning ball travels in a curved track; how uranium is transmuted to lead, etc. Partial contents: atoms, gases, liquids, crystals, metals etc. No scientific background needed; wonderful for intelligent high school student. 32pp. of photos, 57 figures. xii + 232pp. 5⅜ x 8.   T31 Paperbound **$1.35**

THE NATURE OF LIGHT AND COLOUR IN THE OPEN AIR, M. Minnaert. Why is falling snow sometimes black? What causes mirages, the fata morgana, multiple suns and moons in the sky; how are shadows formed? Prof. Minnaert of the University of Utrecht answers these and similar questions in optics, light, colour, for non-specialists. Particularly valuable to nature, science students, painters, photographers. Translated by H. M. Kremer-Priest, K. Jay. 202 illustrations, including 42 photos. xvi + 362pp. 5⅜ x 8.   T196 Paperbound **$1.95**

THE RESTLESS UNIVERSE, Max Born. New enlarged version of this remarkably readable account by a Noble laureate. Moving from subatomic particles to universe, the author explains in very simple terms the latest theories of wave mechanics. Partial contents: air and its relatives, electrons & ions, waves & particles, electronic structure of the atom, nuclear physics. Nearly 600 illustrations, including 7 animated sequences. 325pp. 6 x 9.   T412 Paperbound **$2.00**

MATTER & LIGHT, THE NEW PHYSICS, L. de Broglie. Non-technical papers by a Nobel laureate explain electromagnetic theory, relativity, matter, light and radiation, wave mechanics, quantum physics, philosophy of science. Einstein, Planck, Bohr, others explained so easily that no mathematical training is needed for all but 2 of the 21 chapters. Unabridged. Index. 300pp. 5⅜ x 8.   T35 Paperbound **$1.75**

THE COMMON SENSE OF THE EXACT SCIENCES, W. K. Clifford. Introduction by James Newman, edited by Karl Pearson. For 70 years this has been a guide to classical scientific and mathematical thought. Explains with unusual clarity basic concepts, such as extension of meaning of symbols, characteristics of surface boundaries, properties of plane figures, vectors, Cartesian method of determining position, etc. Long preface by Bertrand Russell. Bibliography of Clifford. Corrected, 130 diagrams redrawn. 249pp. 5⅜ x 8.   T61 Paperbound **$1.60**

THE EVOLUTION OF SCIENTIFIC THOUGHT FROM NEWTON TO EINSTEIN, A. d'Abro. Einstein's special and general theories of relativity, with their historical implications, are analyzed in non-technical terms. Excellent accounts of the contributions of Newton, Riemann, Weyl, Planck, Eddington, Maxwell, Lorentz and others are treated in terms of space and time, equations of electromagnetics, finiteness of the universe, methodology of science. 21 diagrams. 482pp. 5⅜ x 8.   T2 Paperbound **$2.00**

WHAT IS SCIENCE, Norman Campbell. This excellent introduction explains scientific method, role of mathematics, types of scientific laws. Contents: 2 aspects of science, science & nature, laws of science, discovery of laws, explanation of laws, measurement & numerical laws, applications of science. 192pp. 5⅜ x 8.   S43 Paperbound **$1.25**

THE RISE OF THE NEW PHYSICS, A. d'Abro. A half-million word exposition, formerly titled THE DECLINE OF MECHANISM, for readers not versed in higher mathematics. The only thorough explanation, in everyday language, of the central core of modern mathematical physical theory, treating both classical and modern theoretical physics, and presenting in terms almost anyone can understand the equivalent of 5 years of study of mathematical physics. Scientifically impeccable coverage of mathematical-physical thought from the Newtonian system up through the electronic theories of Dirac and Heisenberg and Fermi's statistics. Combines both history and exposition; provides a broad yet unified and detailed view, with constant comparison of classical and modern views on phenomena and theories. "A must for anyone doing serious study in the physical sciences," JOURNAL OF THE FRANKLIN INSTITUTE. "Extraordinary faculty . . . to explain ideas and theories of theoretical physics in the language of daily life," ISIS. Indexed. 97 illustrations. ix + 982pp. 5⅜ x 8.

T3 Volume 1, Paperbound **$2.00**
T4 Volume 2, Paperbound **$2.00**

A HISTORY OF ASTRONOMY FROM THALES TO KEPLER, J. L. E. Dreyer. (Formerly A HISTORY OF PLANETARY SYSTEMS FROM THALES TO KEPLER.) This is the only work in English to give the complete history of man's cosmological views from prehistoric times to Kepler and Newton. Partial contents: Near Eastern astronomical systems, Early Greeks. Homocentric spheres of Eudoxus, Epicycles. Ptolemaic system, medieval cosmology. Copernicus. Kepler, etc. Revised, foreword by W. H. Stahl. New bibliography. xvii + 430pp. 5⅜ x 8.   S79 Paperbound **$1.98**

THE PSYCHOLOGY OF INVENTION IN THE MATHEMATICAL FIELD, J. Hadamard. Where do ideas come from? What role does the unconscious play? Are ideas best developed by mathematical reasoning, word reasoning, visualization? What are the methods used by Einstein, Poincaré, Galton, Riemann. How can these techniques be applied by others? Hadamard, one of the world's leading mathematicians, discusses these and other questions. xiii + 145pp. 5⅜ x 8.   T107 Paperbound **$1.25**

SPINNING TOPS AND GYROSCOPIC MOTION, John Perry. Well-known classic of science still unsurpassed for lucid, accurate, delightful exposition. How quasi-rigidity is induced in flexible and fluid bodies by rapid motion; why gyrostat falls; top rises; nature and effect on climatic conditions of earth's precessional movement; effect of internal fluidity on rotating bodies, etc. Appendixes describe practical uses to which gyroscopes have been put in ships, compasses, monorail transportation. 62 figures. 128pp. 5⅜ x 8.   T416 Paperbound **$1.00**

A CONCISE HISTORY OF MATHEMATICS, D. Struik. Lucid study of development of mathematical ideas, techniques, from Ancient Near East, Greece, Islamic science, Middle Ages, Renaissance, modern times. Important mathematicians are described in detail. Treatment is not anecdotal, but analytical development of ideas. "Rich in content, thoughtful in interpretation" U. S. QUARTERLY BOOKLIST. Non-technical; no mathematical training needed. Index. 60 illustrations, including Egyptian papyri, Greek mss., portraits of 31 eminent mathematicians. Bibliography. 2nd edition. xix + 299pp. 5⅜ x 8.   S255 Paperbound **$1.75**

FOUNDATIONS OF GEOMETRY, Bertrand Russell. Analyzing basic problems in the overlap area between mathematics and philosophy, Nobel laureate Russell examines the nature of geometrical knowledge, the nature of geometry, and the application of geometry to space. It covers the history of non-Euclidean geometry, philosophic interpretations of geometry—especially Kant—projective and metrical geometry. This is most interesting as the solution offered in 1897 by a great mind to a problem still current. New introduction by Prof. Morris Kline of N. Y. University. xii + 201pp. 5⅜ x 8.   S232 Clothbound **$3.25**
                     S233 Paperbound **$1.60**

THE NATURE OF PHYSICAL THEORY, P. W. Bridgman. Here is how modern physics looks to a highly unorthodox physicist—a Nobel laureate. Pointing out many absurdities of science, and demonstrating the inadequacies of various physical theories, Dr. Bridgman weighs and analyzes the contributions of Einstein, Bohr, Newton, Heisenberg, and many others. This is a non-technical consideration of the correlation of science and reality. Index. xi + 138pp. 5⅜ x 8.
                     S33 Paperbound **$1.25**

EXPERIMENT AND THEORY IN PHYSICS, Max Born. A Nobel laureate examines the nature and value of the counterclaims of experiment and theory in physics. Synthetic versus analytical scientific advances are analyzed in the work of Einstein, Bohr, Heisenberg, Planck, Eddington, Milne, and others by a fellow participant. 44pp. 5⅜ x 8.   S308 Paperbound **60c**

THE STUDY OF THE HISTORY OF MATHEMATICS & THE STUDY OF THE HISTORY OF SCIENCE, George Sarton. Scientific method & philosophy in 2 scholarly fields. Defines duty of historian of math provides especially useful bibliography with best available biographies of modern mathematicians, editions of their collected works, correspondence. Shows that combination of history & science will aid scholar in understanding science today. Bibliography includes best known treatises on historical methods. 200-item critically evaluated bibliography. Index. 10 illustrations. 2 volumes bound as one. 113pp. + 75pp. 5⅜ x 8.   T240 Paperbound **$1.25**

SCIENCE AND METHOD, Henri Poincaré. Procedure of scientific discovery, methodology, experiment, idea-germination—the intellectual processes by which discoveries come into being. Most significant and most interesting aspects of development, application of ideas. Chapters cover selection of facts, chance, mathematical reasoning, mathematics and logic; Whitehead, Russell, Cantor; the new mechanics, etc. 288pp. 5⅜ x 8.   S222 Paperbound **$1.25**

SCIENCE AND HYPOTHESIS, Henri Poincaré. Creative psychology in science. How such concepts as number, magnitude, space, force, classical mechanics were developed, and how the modern scientist uses them in his thought. Hypothesis in physics, theories of modern physics. Introduction by Sir James Larmor. "Few mathematicians have had the breadth of vision of Poincaré, and none is his superior in the gift of clear exposition," E. T. Bell. Index. 272pp. 5⅜ x 8.
                     S221 Paperbound **$1.25**

FOUNDATIONS OF PHYSICS, R. B. Lindsay & H. Margenau. Excellent bridge between semi-popular works & technical treatises. A discussion of methods of physical description, construction of theory; valuable for physicist with elementary calculus who is interested in ideas that give meaning to data, tools of modern physics. Contents include symbolism, mathematical equations; space & time; foundations of mechanics; probability; physics & continua; electron theory; special & general relativity; quantum mechanics; causality. "Thorough and yet not overdetailed. Unreservedly recommended," NATURE (London). Unabridged, corrected edition. List of recommended readings. 35 illustrations. xi + 537pp. 5⅜ x 8.   S377 Paperbound **$2.45**

CLASSICS OF SCIENCE

THE THIRTEEN BOOKS OF EUCLID'S ELEMENTS, edited by **Sir Thomas Heath.** Definitive edition of one of the very greatest classics of Western world. Complete English translation of Heiberg text, together with spurious Book XIV. Detailed 150-page introduction discussing aspects of Greek and medieval mathematics. Euclid, texts, commentators, etc. Paralleling the text is an elaborate critical apparatus analyzing each definition, proposition, postulate, covering textual matters, mathematical analysis, commentators of all times, refutations, supports, extrapolations, etc. This is the full EUCLID. Unabridged reproduction of Cambridge U. 2nd edition. 3 volumes. Total of 995 figures, 1426pp. 5⅜ x 8.   S88,89,90 3 volume set, paperbound **$6.00**

OPTICKS, Sir Isaac Newton. In its discussions of light, reflection, color, refraction, theories of wave and corpuscular theories of light, this work is packed with scores of insights and discoveries. In its precise and practical discussion of construction of optical apparatus, contemporary understandings of phenomena it is truly fascinating to modern physicists, astronomers, mathematicians. Foreword by Albert Einstein. Preface by I. B. Cohen of Harvard University. 7 pages of portraits, facsimile pages, letters, etc. cxvi + 414pp. 5⅜ x 8.   S205 Paperbound **$2.00**

THE PRINCIPLE OF RELATIVITY, A. Einstein, H. Lorentz, M. Minkowski, H. Weyl. These are the 11 basic papers that founded the general and special theories of relativity, all translated into English. Two papers by Lorentz on the Michelson experiment, electromagnetic phenomena. Minkowski's SPACE & TIME, and Weyl's GRAVITATION & ELECTRICITY. 7 epoch-making papers by Einstein: ELECTROMAGNETICS OF MOVING BODIES, INFLUENCE OF GRAVITATION IN PROPAGATION OF LIGHT, COSMOLOGICAL CONSIDERATIONS, GENERAL THEORY, and 3 others. 7 diagrams. Special notes by A. Sommerfeld. 224pp. 5⅜ x 8.   S81 Paperbound **$1.75**

THE ANALYTICAL THEORY OF HEAT, Joseph Fourier. This book, which revolutionized mathematical physics, is listed in the Great Books program, and many other listings of great books. It has been used with profit by generations of mathematicians and physicists who are interested in either heat or in the application of the Fourier integral. Covers cause and reflections of rays of heat, radiant heating, heating of closed spaces, use of trigonometric series in the theory of heat, Fourier integral, etc. Translated by Alexander Freeman. 20 figures. xxii + 466pp. 5⅜ x 8. S93 Paperbound **$2.00**

THE WORKS OF ARCHIMEDES, edited by T. L. Heath. All the known works of the great Greek mathematician are contained in this one volume, including the recently discovered Method of Archimedes. Contains: On Sphere & Cylinder, Measurement of a Circle, Spirals, Concids, Spheroids, etc. This is the definitive edition of the greatest mathematical intellect of the ancient world. 186-page study by Heath discusses Archimides and the history of Greek mathematics. Bibliography. 563pp. 5⅜ x 8. S9 Paperbound **$2.00**

A PHILOSOPHICAL ESSAY ON PROBABILITIES, Marquis de Laplace. This famous essay explains without recourse to mathematics the principle of probability, and the application of probability to games of chance, natural philosophy, astronomy, many other fields. Translated from the 6th French edition by F. W. Truscott, F. L. Emory, with new introduction for this edition by E. T. Bell. 204pp. 5⅜ x 8. S166 Paperbound **$1.25**

INVESTIGATIONS ON THE THEORY OF THE BROWNIAN MOVEMENT, Albert Einstein. Reprints from rare European journals. 5 basic papers, including the Elementary Theory of the Brownian Movement, written at the request of Lorentz to provide a simple explanation. Translated by A. D. Cowper. Annotated, edited by R. Fürth. 33pp. of notes elucidate, give history of previous investigations. Author, subject indexes. 62 footnotes. 124pp. 5⅜ x 8.
S304 Paperbound **$1.25**

THE GEOMETRY OF RENÉ DESCARTES. With this book Descartes founded analytical geometry. Original French text, with Descartes' own diagrams, and excellent Smith-Latham translation. Contains Problems the Construction of Which Requires Only Straight Lines and Circles; On the Nature of Curved Lines; On the Construction of Solid or Supersolid Problems. Notes. Diagrams. 258pp. 5⅜ x 8. S68 Paperbound **$1.50**

DIALOGUES CONCERNING TWO NEW SCIENCES, Galileo Galilei. This classic of experimental science, mechanics, engineering, is as enjoyable as it is important. Based on 30 years' experimentation and characterized by its author as "superior to everything else of mine," it offers a lively exposition of dynamics, elasticity, sound, ballistics, strength of materials, and the scientific method. Translated by H. Grew and A. de Salvio. 126 diagrams. Index. xxi + 288pp. 5⅜ x 8. S99 Paperbound **$1.65**

TREATISE ON ELECTRICITY AND MAGNETISM, James Clerk Maxwell. For more than 80 years a seemingly inexhaustible source of leads for physicists, mathematicians, engineers. Total of 1082pp. on such topics as Measurement of Quantities, Electrostatics, Elementary Mathematical Theory of Electricity, Electrical Work and Energy in a System of Conductors, General Theorems, Theory of Electrical Images, Electrolysis, Conduction, Polarization, Dielectrics, Resistance, etc. "The greatest mathematical physicist since Newton," Sir James Jeans. 3rd edition. 107 figures, 21 plates. 1082pp. 5⅜ x 8. S186 Clothbound **$4.95**

PRINCIPLES OF PHYSICAL OPTICS, Ernst Mach. This classical examination of the propagation of light, color, polarization etc. offers a historical and philosophical treatment that has never been surpassed for breadth and easy readability. Contents: Rectilinear propagation of light. Reflection, refraction. Early knowledge of vision. Dioptrics. Composition of light. Theory of color and dispersion. Periodicity. Theory of interference. Polarization. Mathematical representation of properties of light. Propagation of waves, etc. 279 illustrations, 10 portraits. Appendix. Indexes. 324pp. 5⅜ x 8. S178 Paperbound **$1.75**

THEORY OF ELECTRONS AND ITS APPLICATION TO THE PHENOMENA OF LIGHT AND RADIANT HEAT, H. Lorentz. Lectures delivered at Columbia University by Nobel laureate Lorentz. Unabridged, they form a historical coverage of the theory of free electrons, motion, absorption of heat, Zeeman effect, propagation of light in molecular bodies, inverse Zeeman effect, optical phenomena in moving bodies, etc. 109 pages of notes explain the more advanced sections. Index. 9 figures. 352pp. 5⅜ x 8. S173 Paperbound **$1.85**

MATTER & MOTION, James Clerk Maxwell. This excellent exposition begins with simple particles and proceeds gradually to physical systems beyond complete analysis: motion, force, properties of centre of mass of material system, work, energy, gravitation, etc. Written with all Maxwell's original insights and clarity! Notes by E. Larmor. 17 diagrams. 178pp. 5⅜ x 8.
S188 Paperbound **$1.25**

AN INTRODUCTION TO THE STUDY OF EXPERIMENTAL MEDICINE, Claude Bernard. 90-year-old classic of medical science, only major work of Bernard available in English, records his efforts to transform physiology into exact science. Principles of scientific research illustrated by specific case histories from his work; roles of chance, error, preliminary false conclusions, in leading eventually to scientific truth; use of hypothesis. Much of modern application of mathematics to biology rests on the foundation set down here. New foreword by Professor I. B. Cohen, Harvard Univ. xxv + 266pp. 5⅜ x 8. T400 Paperbound **$1.50**

PRINCIPLES OF MECHANICS, Heinrich Hertz. This last work by the great 19th century physicist is not only a classic, but of great interest in the logic of science. Creating a new system of mechanics based upon space, time, and mass, it returns to axiomatic analysis, to understanding of the formal or structural aspects of science, taking into account logic, observation, and a priori elements. Of great historical importance to Poincaré, Carnap, Einstein, Milne. A 20-page introduction by R. S. Cohen, Wesleyan University, analyzes the implications of Hertz's thought and the logic of science. Bibliography. 13-page introduction of Helmholtz. xiii + 274pp. 5⅜ x 8.

S316 Clothbound **$3.50**
S317 Paperbound **$1.75**

ANIMALS IN MOTION, Eadweard Muybridge. Largest, most comprehensive selection of Muybridge's famous action photos of animals, from his ANIMAL LOCOMOTION. 3919 high-speed shots of 34 different animals and birds in 123 different types of action: horses, mules, oxen, pigs, goats, camels, elephants, dogs, cats, guanacos, sloths, lions, tigers, jaguars, raccoons, baboons, deer, elk, gnus, kangaroos, many others, in different actions—walking, running, flying, leaping. Horse alone shown in more than 40 different ways. Photos taken against ruled backgrounds; most actions taken from 3 angles at once: 90°, 60°, rear. Most plates original size. Of considerable interest to scientists as a classic of biology, as a record of actual facts of natural history and physiology. "A really marvellous series of plates," NATURE (London). "A monumental work," Waldemar Kaempffert. Photographed by E. Muybridge. Edited by L. S. Brown, American Museum of Natural History. 74-page introduction on mechanics of motion. 340 pages of plates, 3919 photographs. 416pp. Deluxe binding, paper. (Weight 4½ lbs.) 7⅞ x 10⅝.

T203 Clothbound **$10.00**

THE HUMAN FIGURE IN MOTION, Eadweard Muybridge. This new edition of a great classic in the history of science and photography is the largest selection ever made from the original Muybridge photos of human action: 4789 photographs, illustrating 163 types of motion: walking, running, lifting, etc. in time-exposure sequence photos at speeds up to 1/6000th of a second. Men, women, children, mostly undraped, showing bone and muscle positions against ruled backgrounds, mostly taken at 3 angles at once. Not only was this a great work of photography, acclaimed by contemporary critics as a work of genius, it was also a great 19th century landmark in biological research. Historical introduction by Prof. Robert Taft, U. of Kansas. Plates original size, full detail. Over 500 action strips. 407pp. 7¾ x 10⅝.

T204 Clothbound **$10.00**

ON THE SENSATIONS OF TONE, Hermann Helmholtz. This is an unmatched coordination of such fields as acoustical physics, physiology, experiment, history of music. It covers the entire gamut of musical tone. Partial contents: relation of vibration, resonance, analysis of tones by sympathetic resonance, beats, chords, tonality, consonant chords, discords, progression of parts, etc. 33 appendixes discuss various aspects of sound, physics, acoustics, music, etc. Translated by A. J. Ellis. New introduction by Prof. Henry Margenau of Yale. 68 figures. 43 musical passages analyzed. Over 100 tables. Index. xix + 576pp. 6⅛ x 9¼.

S114 Clothbound **$4.95**

COLLECTED WORKS OF BERNHARD RIEMANN. This important source book is the first to contain the complete text of both 1892 Werke and the 1902 supplement, unabridged. It contains 31 monographs, 3 complete lecture courses, 15 miscellaneous papers, which have been of enormous importance in relativity, topology, theory of complex variables, and other areas of mathematics. Edited by R. Dedekind, H. Weber, M. Noether, W. Wirtinger. German text. English introduction by Hans Lewy. 690pp. 5⅜ x 8.

S226 Paperbound **$2.85**

CONTRIBUTIONS TO THE FOUNDING OF THE THEORY OF TRANSFINITE NUMBERS, Georg Cantor. These papers founded a new branch of mathematics. The famous articles of 1895-7 are translated with an 82-page introduction by P. E. B. Jourdain dealing with Cantor, the background of his discoveries, their results, future possibilities. Bibliography. Index. Notes. ix + 211pp. 5⅜ x 8.

S45 Paperbound **$1.25**

PRINCIPLES OF PSYCHOLOGY, William James. This is the complete "Long Course," which is not to be confused with abridged editions. It contains all the wonderful descriptions, deep insights that have caused it to be a permanent work in all psychological libraries. Partial contents: functions of the brain, automation theories, mind-stuff theories, relation of mind to other things, consciousness, times, space, thing perception, will, emotions, hypnotism, and dozens of other areas in descriptive psychology. "A permanent classic like Locke's ESSAYS, Hume's TREATISE," John Dewey. "The preeminence of James in American psychology is unquestioned," PERSONALIST. "The American classic in psychology—unequaled in breadth and scope in the entire psychological literature," PSYCHOANALYTICAL QUARTERLY. Index. 94 figures. 2 volumes bound as one. Total of 1408pp.

T381 Vol. 1. Paperbound **$2.00**
T382 Vol. 2. Paperbound **$2.00**

RECREATIONS

SEVEN SCIENCE FICTION NOVELS OF H. G. WELLS. This is the complete text, unabridged, of seven of Wells's greatest novels: War of the Worlds, The Invisible Man, The Island of Dr. Moreau, The Food of the Gods, The First Men in the Moon, In the Days of the Comet, The Time Machine. Still considered by many experts to be the best science-fiction ever written, they will offer amusement and instruction to the scientific-minded reader. 1015pp. 5⅜ x 8.

T264 Clothbound **$3.95**

28 SCIENCE FICTION STORIES OF H. G. WELLS. Unabridged! This enormous omnibus contains 2 full-length novels—Men Like Gods, Star Begotten—plus 26 short stories of space, time, invention, biology, etc. The Crystal Egg, The Country of the Blind, Empire of the Ants, The Man Who Could Work Miracles, Aepyornis Island, A Story of the Days to Come, and 22 others! 915pp. 5⅜ x 8. **T265 Clothbound $3.95**

FLATLAND, E. A. Abbott. This is a perennially popular science-fiction classic about life in a two-dimensioned world, and the impingement of higher dimensions. Political, satiric, humorous, moral overtones. Relativity, the fourth dimension, and other aspects of modern science are explained more clearly than in most texts. 7th edition. New introduction by Banesh Hoffmann. 128pp. 5⅜ x 8. **T1 Paperbound $1.00**

CRYPTANALYSIS, Helen F. Gaines. (Formerly ELEMENTARY CRYPTANALYSIS.) A standard elementary and intermediate text for serious students. It does not confine itself to old material, but contains much that is not generally known except to experts. Concealment, Transposition, Substitution ciphers; Vigenere, Kasiski, Playfair, multafid, dozens of other techniques. Appendix with sequence charts, letter frequencies in English, 5 other languages, English word frequencies. Bibliography. 167 codes. New to this edition: solutions to codes. vi + 230pp. 5⅜ x 8⅜. **T97 Paperbound $1.95**

FADS AND FALLACIES IN THE NAME OF SCIENCE, Martin Gardner. Examines various cults, quack systems, frauds, delusions which at various times have masqueraded as science. Accounts of hollow-earth fanatics like Symmes; Velikovsky and wandering planets; Hoerbiger; Bellamy and the theory of multiple moons; Charles Fort, dowsing, pseudoscientific methods for finding water, ores, oil. Sections on naturopathy, iridiagnosis, zone therapy, food fads, etc. Analytical accounts of Wilhelm Reich and orgone sex energy; L. Ron Hubbard and Dianetics; A. Korzybski and General Semantics; many others. Brought up to date to include Bridey Murphy, others. Not just a collection of anecdotes, but a fair, reasoned appraisal of eccentric theory. Formerly titled IN THE NAME OF SCIENCE. Preface. Index. x + 384pp. 5⅜ x 8. **T394 Paperbound $1.50**

REINFELD ON THE END GAME IN CHESS, Fred Reinfeld. Analyzes 62 end games by Alekhine, Flohr, Tarrasch, Morphy, Bogolyubov, Capablanca, Vidmar, Rubinstein, Lasker, Reshevsky, other masters. Only first-rate book with extensive coverage of error; of immense aid in pointing out errors you might have made. Centers around transitions from middle play to various types of end play. King & pawn endings, minor piece endings, queen endings, bad bishops, blockage, weak pawns, passed pawns, etc. Formerly titled PRACTICAL END PLAY. 62 figures. vi + 177pp. 5⅜ x 8. **T417 Paperbound $1.25**

PUZZLE QUIZ AND STUNT FUN, Jerome Meyer. 238 high-priority puzzles, stunts, and tricks—mathematical puzzles like The Clever Carpenter, Atom Bomb, Please Help Alice; mysteries and deductions like The Bridge of Sighs, Dog Logic, Secret Code; observation puzzlers like The American Flag, Playing Cards, Telephone Dial; more than 200 others involving magic squares, tongue twisters, puns, anagrams, word design. Answers included. Revised, enlarged edition of FUN-TO-DO. Over 100 illustrations. 238 puzzles, stunts, tricks. 256pp. 5⅜ x 8. **T337 Paperbound $1.00**

THE BOOK OF MODERN PUZZLES, G. L. Kaufman. More than 150 word puzzles, logic puzzles. No warmed-over fare but all new material based on same appeals that make crosswords and deduction puzzles popular, but with different principles, techniques. Two-minute teasers, involved word-labyrinths, design and pattern puzzles, puzzles calling for logic and observation, puzzles testing ability to apply general knowledge to peculiar situations, many others. Answers to all problems. 116 illustrations. 192pp. 5⅜ x 8. **T143 Paperbound $1.00**

101 PUZZLES IN THOUGHT AND LOGIC by C. R. Wylie, Jr. Designed for readers who enjoy the challenge and stimulation of logical puzzles without specialized mathematical or scientific knowledge. These problems are entirely new and range from relatively easy, to brainteasers that will afford hours of subtle entertainment. Detective problems, how to find the lying fisherman, how a blindman can identify color by logic, and many more. Easy-to-understand introduction to the logic of puzzle solving and general scientific method. 128pp. 5⅜ x 8. **T367 Paperbound $1.00**

MATHEMAGIC, MAGIC PUZZLES, AND GAMES WITH NUMBERS, Royal V. Heath. Over 60 new puzzles and stunts based on properties of numbers. Demonstrates easy techniques for multiplying large numbers mentally, identifying unknown numbers, determining date of any day in any year, dozens of similar useful, entertaining applications of mathematics. Entertainments like The Lost Digit, 3 Acrobats, Psychic Bridge, magic squares, triangles, cubes, circles, other material not easily found elsewhere. Edited by J. S. Meyer. 76 illustrations. 128pp. 5⅜ x 8. **T110 Paperbound $1.00**

LEARN CHESS FROM THE MASTERS, Fred Reinfeld. Improve your chess, rate your improvement, by playing against Marshall, Znosko-Borovsky, Bronstein, Najdorf, others. Formerly titled CHESS BY YOURSELF, this book contains 10 games in which you move against masters, and grade your moves by an easy system. Games selected for interest, clarity, easy principles; illustrate common openings, both classical and modern. Ratings for 114 extra playing situations that might have arisen. Full annotations. 91 diagrams. viii + 144pp. 5¾ x 8. **T362 Paperbound $1.00**

THE COMPLETE NONSENSE OF EDWARD LEAR. Original text & illustrations of all Lear's nonsense books: A BOOK OF NONSENSE, NONSENSE SONGS, MORE NONSENSE SONGS, LAUGHABLE LYRICS, NONSENSE SONGS AND STORIES. Only complete edition available at popular price. Old favorites such as The Dong With a Luminous Nose, hundreds of other delightful bits of nonsense for children & adults. 214 different limericks, each illustrated by Lear; 3 different sets of Nonsense Botany; 5 Nonsense Alphabets; many others. 546 illustrations. 320pp. 5⅜ x 8.
T167 Paperbound **$1.00**

CRYPTOGRAPHY, D. Smith. Excellent elementary introduction to enciphering, deciphering secret writing. Explains transposition, substitution ciphers; codes; solutions. Geometrical patterns, route transcription, columnar transposition, other methods. Mixed cipher systems; single-alphabet, polyalphabetical substitution; mechanical devices; Vigenere system, etc. Enciphering Japanese; explanation of Baconian Biliteral cipher frequency tables. More than 150 problems provide practical application. Bibliography. Index. 164pp. 5⅜ x 8.
T247 Paperbound **$1.00**

MATHEMATICAL EXCURSIONS, Helen A. Merrill. Fun, recreation, insights into elementary problem-solving. A mathematical expert guides you along by-paths not generally travelled in elementary math courses—how to divide by inspection, Russian peasant system of multiplication; memory systems for pi; building odd and even magic squares; dyadic systems; facts about 37; square roots by geometry; Tchebichev's machine; drawing five-sided figures; dozens more. Solutions to more difficult ones. 50 illustrations. 145pp. 5⅜ x 8.
T350 Paperbound **$1.00**

MATHEMATICAL RECREATIONS, M. Kraitchik. Some 250 puzzles, problems, demonstrations of recreational mathematics for beginners & advanced mathematicians. Unusual historical problems from Greek, Medieval, Arabic, Hindu sources; modern problems based on "mathematics without numbers," geometry, topology, arithmetic, etc. Pastimes derived from figurative numbers, Mersenne numbers, Fermat numbers; fairy chess; latruncles, reversi, many other topics. Full solutions. Excellent for insights into special fields of math. 181 illustrations. 330pp. 5⅜ x 8.
T163 Paperbound **$1.75**

MATHEMATICAL PUZZLES FOR BEGINNERS AND ENTHUSIASTS, G. Mott-Smith. 188 mathematical puzzles to test mental agility. Inference, interpretation, algebra, dissection of plane figures, geometry, properties of numbers, decimation, permutations, probability, all enter these delightful problems. Puzzles like the Odic Force, How to Draw an Ellipse, Spider's Cousin, more than 180 others. Detailed solutions. Appendix with square roots, triangular numbers, primes, etc. 135 illustrations. 2nd revised edition. 248pp. 5⅜ x 8.
T198 Paperbound **$1.00**

NEW WORD PUZZLES, Gerald L. Kaufman. Contains 100 brand new challenging puzzles based on words and their combinations, never published before in any form. Most are new types invented by the author—for beginners or experts. Chess word puzzles, addle letter anagrams, double word squares, double horizontals, alphagram puzzles, dual acrostigrams, linkogram lapwords—plus 8 other brand new types, all with solutions included. 196 figures. 100 brand new puzzles. vi + 122pp. 5⅜ x 8.
T344 Paperbound **$1.00**

MATHEMATICS, MAGIC AND MYSTERY, Martin Gardner. Card tricks, feats of mental mathematics, stage mind-reading, other "magic" explained as applications of probability, sets, theory of numbers, topology, various branches of mathematics. Creative examination of laws and their application, with sources of new tricks and insights. 115 sections discuss tricks with cards, dice, coins; geometrical vanishing tricks, dozens of others. No sleight of hand needed; mathematics guarantees success. 115 illustrations. xii + 174pp. 5⅜ x 8.   T335 Paperbound **$1.00**

MATHEMATICS ELEMENTARY TO INTERMEDIATE

HOW TO CALCULATE QUICKLY, Henry Sticker. This handy volume offers a tried and true method for helping you in the basic mathematics of daily life—addition, subtraction, multiplication, division, fractions, etc. It is designed to awaken your "number sense" or the ability to see relationships between numbers as whole quantities. It is not a collection of tricks working only on special numbers, but a serious course of over 9,000 problems and their solutions, teaching special techniques not taught in schools: left-to-right multiplication, new fast ways of division, etc. 5 or 10 minutes daily use will double or triple your calculation speed. Excellent for the scientific worker who is at home in higher math, but is not satisfied with his speed and accuracy in lower mathematics. 256pp. 5 x 7¼.
T295 Paperbound **$1.00**

FAMOUS PROBLEMS OF ELEMENTARY GEOMETRY, Felix Klein. Expanded version of the 1894 Easter lectures at Göttingen. 3 problems of classical geometry: squaring circle, trisecting angle, doubling cube, considered with full modern implications: transcendental numbers, pi, etc. Notes by R. Archibald. 16 figures. xi + 92pp. 5⅜ x 8.
T348 Clothbound **$1.50**
T298 Paperbound **$1.00**

HIGHER MATHEMATICS FOR STUDENTS OF CHEMISTRY AND PHYSICS, J. W. Mellor. Not abstract, but practical, building its problems out of familiar laboratory material, this covers differential calculus, coordinate, analytical geometry, functions, integral calculus, infinite series, numerical equations, differential equations, Fourier's theorem, probability, theory of errors, calculus of variations, determinants. "If the reader is not familiar with this book, it will repay him to examine it," CHEM. & ENGINEERING NEWS. 800 problems, 189 figures. Bibliography. xxi + 641pp. 5⅜ x 8.
S193 Paperbound **$2.00**

TRIGONOMETRY REFRESHER FOR TECHNICAL MEN, A. Albert Klaf. 913 detailed questions and answers cover the most important aspects of plane and spherical trigonometry. They will help you to brush up or to clear up difficulties in special areas.—The first portion of this book covers plane trigonometry, including angles, quadrants, trigonometrical functions, graphical representation, interpolation, equations, logarithms, solution of triangle, use of the slide rule and similar topics–188 pages then discuss application of plane trigonometry to special problems in navigation, surveying, elasticity, architecture, and various fields of engineering. Small angles, periodic functions, vectors, polar coordinates, De Moivre's theorem are fully examined—The third section of the book then discusses spherical trigonometry and the solution of spherical triangles, with their applications to terrestrial and astronomical problems. Methods of saving time with numerical calculations, simplification of principal functions of angle, much practical information make this a most useful book—913 questions answered. 1738 problems, answers to odd numbers. 494 figures. 24 pages of useful formulae, functions. Index. x + 629pp. 5⅜ x 8.
T371 Paperbound **$2.00**

CALCULUS REFRESHER FOR TECHNICAL MEN, A. Albert Klaf. This book is unique in English as a refresher for engineers, technicians, students who either wish to brush up their calculus or to clear up uncertainties. It is not an ordinary text, but an examination of most important aspects of integral and differential calculus in terms of the 756 questions most likely to occur to the technical reader. The first part of this book covers simple differential calculus, with constants, variables, functions, increments, derivatives, differentiation, logarithms, curvature of curves, and similar topics—The second part covers fundamental ideas of integration, inspection, substitution, transformation, reduction, areas and volumes, mean value, successive and partial integration, double and triple integration. Practical aspects are stressed rather than theoretical. A 50-page section illustrates the application of calculus to specific problems of civil and nautical engineering, electricity, stress and strain, elasticity, industrial engineering, and similar fields.—756 questions answered. 566 problems, mostly answered. 36 pages of useful constants, formulae for ready reference. Index. v + 431pp. 5⅜ x 8.
T370 Paperbound **$2.00**

MONOGRAPHS ON TOPICS OF MODERN MATHEMATICS, edited by **J. W. A. Young.** Advanced mathematics for persons who haven't gone beyond or have forgotten high school algebra. 9 monographs on foundation of geometry, modern pure geometry, non-Euclidean geometry, fundamental propositions of algebra, algebraic equations, functions, calculus, theory of numbers, etc. Each monograph gives proofs of important results, and descriptions of leading methods, to provide wide coverage. New introduction by Prof. M. Kline, N. Y. University. 100 diagrams. xvi + 416pp. 6⅛ x 9¼.
S289 Paperbound **$2.00**

MATHEMATICS: INTERMEDIATE TO ADVANCED

INTRODUCTION TO THE THEORY OF FOURIER'S SERIES AND INTEGRALS, H. S. Carslaw. 3rd revised edition. This excellent introduction is an outgrowth of the author's courses at Cambridge. Historical introduction, rational and irrational numbers, infinite sequences and series, functions of a single variable, definite integral, Fourier series, Fourier integrals, and similar topics. Appendixes discuss practical harmonic analysis, periodogram analysis, Lebesgues theory. Indexes. 84 examples, bibliography. xiii + 368 pp. 5⅝ x 8.
S48 Paperbound **$2.00**

INTRODUCTION TO THE THEORY OF NUMBERS, L. E. Dickson. Thorough, comprehensive approach with adequate coverage of classical literature, an introductory volume beginners can follow. Chapters on divisibility, congruences, quadratic residues & reciprocity, Diophantine equations, etc. Full treatment of binary quadratic forms without usual restriction to integral coefficients. Covers infinitude of primes, least residues, Fermat's theorem, Euler's phi function, Legendre's symbol, Gauss's lemma, automorphs, reduced forms, recent theorems of Thue & Siegel, many more. Much material not readily available elsewhere. 239 problems. Index. 1 figure. viii + 183pp. 5⅜ x 8.
S342 Paperbound **$1.65**

MECHANICS VIA THE CALCULUS, P. W. Norris, W. S. Legge. Covers almost everything from linear motion to vector analysis: equations determining motion, linear methods, compounding of simple harmonic motions, Newton's laws of motion, Hooke's law, the simple pendulum, motion of a particle in 1 plane, centers of gravity, virtual work, friction, kinetic energy of rotating bodies, equilibrium of strings, hydrostatics, sheering stresses, elasticity, etc. 550 problems. 3rd revised edition. xii + 367pp.
S207 Clothbound **$3.95**

NON-EUCLIDEAN GEOMETRY, Roberto Bonola. The standard coverage of non-Euclidean geometry. It examines from both a historical and mathematical point of view the geometries which have arisen from a study of Euclid's 5th postulate upon parallel lines. Also included are complete texts, translated, of Bolyai's THEORY OF ABSOLUTE SPACE, Lobachevsky's THEORY OF PARALLELS. 180 diagrams. 431pp. 5⅜ x 8.
S27 Paperbound **$1.95**

ELEMENTS OF THE THEORY OF REAL FUNCTIONS, J. E. Littlewood. Based on lectures given at Trinity College, Cambridge, this book has proved to be extremely successful in introducing graduate students to the modern theory of functions. It offers a full and concise coverage of classes and cardinal numbers, well-ordered series, other types of series, and elements of the theory of sets of points. 3rd revised edition. vii + 71pp. 5⅜ x 8.
S171 Clothbound **$2.85**
S172 Paperbound **$1.25**

THE CONTINUUM AND OTHER TYPES OF SERIAL ORDER, E. V. Huntington. This famous book gives a systematic elementary account of the modern history of the continuum as a type of serial order. Based on the Cantor-Dedekind ordinal theory, which requires no technical knowledge of higher mathematics, it offers an easily followed analysis of ordered classes, discrete and dense series, continuous series, Cantor's transfinite numbers. 2nd edition. Index. viii + 82pp. 5⅜ x 8.
S129 Clothbound **$2.75**
S130 Paperbound **$1.00**

GEOMETRY OF FOUR DIMENSIONS, H. P. Manning. Unique in English as a clear, concise introduction. Treatment is synthetic, and mostly Euclidean, although in hyperplanes and hyperspheres at infinity, non-Euclidean geometry is used. Historical introduction. Foundations of 4-dimensional geometry. Perpendicularity, simple angles. Angles of planes, higher order. Symmetry, order, motion; hyperpyramids, hypercones, hyperspheres; figures with parallel elements; volume, hypervolume in space; regular polyhedroids. Glossary. 78 figures. ix + 348pp. 5⅜ x 8.
S181 Clothbound **$3.95**
S182 Paperbound **$1.95**

VECTOR AND TENSOR ANALYSIS, G. E. Hay. One of the clearest introductions to this increasingly important subject. Start with simple definitions, finish the book with a sure mastery of oriented Cartesian vectors, Christoffel symbols, solenoidal tensors, and their applications. Complete breakdown of plane, solid, analytical, differential geometry. Separate chapters on application. All fundamental formulae listed & demonstrated. 195 problems, 66 figures. viii + 193pp. 5⅜ x 8.
S109 Paperbound **$1.75**

INTRODUCTION TO THE DIFFERENTIAL EQUATIONS OF PHYSICS, L. Hopf. Especially valuable to the engineer with no math beyond elementary calculus. Emphasizing intuitive rather than formal aspects of concepts, the author covers an extensive territory. Partial contents: Law of causality, energy theorem, damped oscillations, coupling by friction, cylindrical and spherical coordinates, heat source, etc. Index. 48 figures. 160pp. 5⅜ x 8.
S120 Paperbound **$1.25**

INTRODUCTION TO THE THEORY OF GROUPS OF FINITE ORDER, R. Carmichael. Examines fundamental theorems and their application. Beginning with sets, systems, permutations, etc., it progresses in easy stages through important types of groups: Abelian, prime power, permutation, etc. Except 1 chapter where matrices are desirable, no higher math needed. 783 exercises, problems. Index. xvi + 447pp. 5⅜ x 8.
S299 Clothbound **$3.95**
S300 Paperbound **$2.00**

THEORY OF GROUPS OF FINITE ORDER, W. Burnside. First published some 40 years ago, this is still one of the clearest introductory texts. Partial contents: permutations, groups independent of representation, composition series of a group, isomorphism of a group with itself, Abelian groups, prime power groups, permutation groups, invariants of groups of linear substitution, graphical representation, etc. 45pp. of notes. Indexes. xxiv + 512pp. 5⅜ x 8.
S38 Paperbound **$2.45**

INFINITE SEQUENCES AND SERIES, Konrad Knopp. First publication in any language! Excellent introduction to 2 topics of modern mathematics, designed to give the student background to penetrate farther by himself. Sequences & sets, real & complex numbers, etc. Functions of a real & complex variable. Sequences & series. Infinite series. Convergent power series. Expansion of elementary functions. Numerical evaluation of series. Bibliography. v + 186pp. 5⅜ x 8.
S152 Clothbound **$3.50**
S153 Paperbound **$1.75**

THEORY OF SETS, E. Kamke. Clearest, amplest introduction in English, well suited for independent study. Subdivisions of main theory, such as theory of sets of points, are discussed, but emphasis is on general theory. Partial contents: rudiments of set theory, arbitrary sets and their cardinal numbers, ordered sets and their order types, well-ordered sets and their ordinal numbers. Bibliography. Key to symbols. Index. vii + 144pp. 5⅜ x 8.
S141 Paperbound **$1.35**

ELEMENTS OF NUMBER THEORY, I. M. Vinogradov. Detailed 1st course for persons without advanced mathematics; 95% of this book can be understood by readers who have gone no farther than high school algebra. Partial contents: divisibility theory, important number theoretical functions, congruences, primitive roots and indices, etc. Solutions to both problems and exercises. Tables of primes, indices, etc. Covers almost every essential formula in elementary number theory! 233 problems, 104 exercises. viii + 227pp. 5⅜ x 8.
S259 Paperbound **$1.60**

FIVE VOLUME "THEORY OF FUNCTIONS" SET BY KONRAD KNOPP. This five-volume set, prepared by Konrad Knopp, provides a complete and readily followed account of theory of functions. Proofs are given concisely, yet without sacrifice of completeness or rigor. These volumes are used as texts by such universities as M.I.T., University of Chicago, N. Y. City College, and many others. "Excellent introduction . . . remarkably readable, concise, clear, rigorous," JOURNAL OF THE AMERICAN STATISTICAL ASSOCIATION.

ELEMENTS OF THE THEORY OF FUNCTIONS, Konrad Knopp. This book provides the student with background for further volumes in this set, or texts on a similar level. Partial contents: Foundations, system of complex numbers and the Gaussian plane of numbers, Riemann sphere of numbers, mapping by linear functions, normal forms, the logarithm, the cyclometric functions and binomial series. "Not only for the young student, but also for the student who knows all about what is in it," MATHEMATICAL JOURNAL. Bibliography. Index. 140pp. 5⅜ x 8. S154 Paperbound **$1.35**

THEORY OF FUNCTIONS, PART I., Konrad Knopp. With volume II, this book provides coverage of basic concepts and theorems. Partial contents: numbers and points, functions of a complex variable, integral of a continuous function, Cauchy's integral theorem, Cauchy's integral formulae, series with variable terms, expansion of analytic functions in power series, analytic continuation and complete definition of analytic functions, entire transcendental functions, Laurent expansion, types of singularities. Bibliography. Index. vii + 146pp. 5⅜ x 8. S156 Paperbound **$1.35**

THEORY OF FUNCTIONS, PART II., Konrad Knopp. Application and further development of general theory, special topics. Single valued functions: entire, Weierstrass. Meromorphic functions: Mittag-Leffler. Periodic functions. Multiple-valued functions. Riemann surfaces. Algebraic functions. Analytical configuration, Riemann surface. Bibliography. Index. x + 150pp. 5⅜ x 8.
S157 Paperbound **$1.35**

PROBLEM BOOK IN THE THEORY OF FUNCTIONS, VOLUME 1., Konrad Knopp. Problems in elementary theory, for use with Knopp's THEORY OF FUNCTIONS, or any other text, arranged according to increasing difficulty. Fundamental concepts, sequences of numbers and infinite series, complex variable, integral theorems, development in series, conformal mapping. Answers. viii + 126pp. 5⅜ x 8. S158 Paperbound **$1.35**

PROBLEM BOOK IN THE THEORY OF FUNCTIONS, VOLUME 2, Konrad Knopp. Advanced theory of functions, to be used either with Knopp's THEORY OF FUNCTIONS, or any other comparable text. Singularities, entire & meromorphic functions, periodic, analytic, continuation, multiple-valued functions, Riemann surfaces, conformal mapping. Includes a section of additional elementary problems. "The difficult task of selecting from the immense material of the modern theory of functions the problems just within the reach of the beginner is here masterfully accomplished," AM. MATH. SOC. Answers. 138pp. 5⅜ x 8. S159 Paperbound **$1.35**

SYMBOLIC LOGIC

AN INTRODUCTION TO SYMBOLIC LOGIC, Susanne K. Langer. Probably the clearest book ever written on symbolic logic for the philosopher, general scientist and layman. It will be particularly appreciated by those who have been rebuffed by other introductory works because of insufficient mathematical training. No special knowledge of mathematics is required. Starting with the simplest symbols and conventions, you are led to a remarkable grasp of the Boole-Schroeder and Russell-Whitehead systems clearly and quickly. PARTIAL CONTENTS: Study of forms, Essentials of logical structure, Generalization, Classes, The deductive system of classes, The algebra of logic, Abstraction of interpretation, Calculus of propositions, Assumptions of PRINCIPIA MATHEMATICA, Logistics, Logic of the syllogism, Proofs of theorems. "One of the clearest and simplest introductions to a subject which is very much alive. The style is easy, symbolism is introduced gradually, and the intelligent non-mathematical should have no difficulty in following argument," MATHEMATICS GAZETTE. Revised, expanded second edition. Truth-value tables. 368pp. 5⅜ x 8.
S164 Paperbound **$1.75**

THE ELEMENTS OF MATHEMATICAL LOGIC, Paul Rosenbloom. FIRST PUBLICATION IN ANY LANGUAGE. This book is intended for readers who are mature mathematically, but have no previous training in symbolic logic. It does not limit itself to a single system, but covers the field as a whole. It is a development of lectures given at Lund University, Sweden in 1948. Partial contents: Logic of classes, fundamental theorems, Boolean algebra, logic of propositions, logic of propositional functions, expressive languages, combinatory logics, development of mathematics within an object language, paradoxes, theorems of Post and Goedel, Church's theorem, and similar topics. iv + 214pp. 5⅜ x 8. S277 Paperbound **$1.45**

THE LAWS OF THOUGHT, George Boole. This book founded symbolic logic some hundred years ago. It is the 1st significant attempt to apply logic to all aspects of human endeavour. Partial contents: derivation of laws, signs & laws, interpretations, eliminations, conditions of a perfect method, analysis, Aristotelian logic, probability, and similar topics. xviii + 424pp. 5⅜ x 8.
S28 Paperbound **$2.00**

ELEMENTARY MATHEMATICS FROM AN ADVANCED STANDPOINT, Felix Klein.

This classic text is an outgrowth of Klein's famous integration and survey course at Göttingen. Using one field of mathematics to interpret, adjust, illuminate another, it covers basic topics in each area, illustrating its discussion with extensive analysis. It is especially valuable in considering areas of modern mathematics. "Makes the reader feel the inspiration of . . . a great mathematician, inspiring teacher . . . with deep insight into the foundations and interrelations," BULLETIN, AMERICAN MATHEMATICAL SOCIETY.

Vol. 1. ARITHMETIC, ALGEBRA, ANALYSIS. Introducing the concept of function immediately, it enlivens abstract discussion with graphical and geometrically perceptual methods. Partial contents: natural numbers, extension of the notion of number, special properties, complex numbers. Real equations with real unknowns, complex quantities. Logarithmic, exponential functions, goniometric functions, infinitesimal calculus. Transcendence of e and pi, theory of assemblages. Index. 125 figures. ix + 247pp. 5⅜ x 8. S150 Paperbound **$1.75**

Vol. 2. GEOMETRY. A comprehensive view which accompanies the space perception inherent in geometry with analytic formulas which facilitate precise formulation. Partial contents: Simplest geometric manifolds: line segment, Grassmann determinant principles, classification of configurations of space, derivative manifolds. Geometric transformations: affine transformations, projective, higher point transformations, theory of the imaginary. Systematic discussion of geometry and its foundations. Indexes. 141 illustrations. ix + 214pp. 5⅜ x 8. S151 Paperbound **$1.75**

MATHEMATICS: ADVANCED

ALMOST PERIODIC FUNCTIONS, A. S. Besicovitch. This unique and important summary by well-known mathematician covers in detail the two stages of development in Bohr's theory almost periodic functions: (1) as a generalization of pure periodicity, with results and proc (2) the work done by Stepanoff, Wiener, Weyl, and Bohr in generalizing the theory. Bibliograph xi + 180pp. 5⅜ x 8.
S17 Clothbound $3.
S18 Paperbound $1.

LECTURES ON THE ICOSAHEDRON AND THE SOLUTION OF EQUATIONS OF THE FIFTH DEGRE Felix Klein. The solution of quintics in terms of rotations of a regular icosahedron around axes of symmetry. A classic & indispensable source for those interested in higher algebr geometry, crystallography. Considerable explanatory material included. 230 footnotes, mos bibliographic. 2nd edition, xvi + 289pp. 5⅜ x 8.
S314 Paperbound $1.

LINEAR INTEGRAL EQUATIONS, W. V. Lovitt. Systematic survey of general theory, with so application to differential equations, calculus of variations problems of math, physics. Part contents: integral equations of 2nd kind by successive substitutions; Fredholm's equation as ra of 2 integral series in lambda, applications of the Fredholm theory, Hilbert-Schmidt theory symmetric kernels, application, etc. Neumann, Dirichlet, vibratory problems. Index. ix + 253p 5⅜ x 8.
S175 Clothbound $3.
S176 Paperbound $1.

MATHEMATICAL FOUNDATIONS OF STATISTICAL MECHANICS, A. I. Khinchin. Offering a prec and rigorous formulation of problems, this book supplies a thorough and up-to-date expositi It provides analytical tools needed to replace cumbersome concepts, and furnishes for the f time a logical step-by-step introduction to the subject. Partial contents: geometry & kinemat of the phase space, ergodic problem, reduction to theory of probability, application of cen limit problem, ideal monatomic gas, foundation of thermodynamics, dispersion and distributic of sum functions. Key to notations. Index. xiii + 179pp. 5⅜ x 8.
S146 Clothbound $2.
S147 Paperbound $1.

ORDINARY DIFFERENTIAL EQUATIONS, E. L. Ince. A most compendious analysis in real c complex domains. Existence and nature of solutions, continuous transformation groups, soluti in an infinite form, definite integrals, algebraic theory, Sturmian theory, boundary probler existence theorems, 1st order, higher order, etc. "Deserves the highest praise, a notable addit to mathematical literature," BULLETIN, AM. MATH. SOC. Historical appendix. Bibliograph 18 figures. viii + 558pp. 5⅜ x 8.
S349 Paperbound $2.

TRIGONOMETRICAL SERIES, Antoni Zygmund. Unique in any language on modern advanced lev Contains carefully organized analyses of trigonometric, orthogonal, Fourier systems of functio with clear adequate descriptions of summability of Fourier series, proximation theory, conjug series, convergence, divergence of Fourier series. Especially valuable for Russian, Eastern Europe coverage. Bibliography. 329pp. 5⅝ x 8.
S290 Paperbound $1.

FOUNDATIONS OF POTENTIAL THEORY, O. D. Kellogg. Based on courses given at Harvard i is suitable for both advanced and beginning mathematicians. Proofs are rigorous, and m material not generally available elsewhere is included. Partial contents: forces of gravity, fie of force, divergence theorem, properties of Newtonian potentials at points of free space, potenti as solutions of Laplace's equations, harmonic functions, electrostatics, electric images, logarithr potential, etc. ix + 384pp. 5⅜ x 8.
S144 Paperbound $1

LECTURES ON CAUCHY'S PROBLEMS, J. Hadamard. Based on lectures given at Columbia c Rome, this discusses work of Riemann, Kirchhoff, Volterra, and the author's own research on hyperbolic case in linear partial differential equations. It extends spherical and cylindrical wa to apply to all (normal) hyperbolic equations. Partial contents: Cauchy's problem, fundamer formula, equations with odd number, with even number of independent variables; method descent. 32 figures. Index. iii + 361pp. 5⅜ x 8.
S105 Paperbound $1

MATHEMATICAL PHYSICS, STATISTICS

THE MATHEMATICAL THEORY OF ELASTICITY, A. E. H. Love. A wealth of practical illustrat combined with thorough discussion of fundamentals—theory, application, special problems c solutions. Partial contents: Analysis of Strain & Stress, Elasticity of Solid Bodies, Isotropic Ela Solids, Equilibrium of Aeolotropic Elastic Solids, Elasticity of Crystals, Vibration of Spher Cylinders, Propagation of Waves in Elastic Solid Media, Torsion, Theory of Continuous Bea Plates. Rigorous treatment of Volterra's theory of dislocations, 2-dimensional elastic systems, ot topics of modern interest. "For years the standard treatise on elasticity," AMERICAN MATH MATICAL MONTHLY. 4th revised edition. Index. 76 figures. xviii + 643pp. 6⅛ x 9¼.
S174 Paperbound $2

TABLES OF FUNCTIONS WITH FORMULAE AND CURVES, E. Jahnke & F. Emde. The world's m comprehensive 1-volume English-text collection of tables, formulae, curves of transcendent functio 4th corrected edition, new 76-page section giving tables, formulae for elementary functions— in other English editions. Partial contents: sine, cosine, logarithmic integral; factorial functi error integral; theta functions; elliptic integrals, functions; Legendre, Bessel, Riemann, Mathi hypergeometric functions, etc. Supplementary books. Bibliography. Indexed. "Out of the w functions for which we know no other source," SCIENTIFIC COMPUTING SERVICE, Ltd. 212 figur 400pp. 5⅜ x 8.
S133 Paperbound $2

PRACTICAL ANALYSIS, GRAPHICAL AND NUMERICAL METHODS, F. A. Willers. Translated by R. T. Beyer. Immensely practical handbook for engineers, showing how to interpolate, use various methods of numerical differentiation and integration, determine the roots of a single algebraic equation, system of linear equations, use empirical formulas, integrate differential equations, etc. Hundreds of shortcuts for arriving at numerical solutions. Special section on American calculating machines, by T. W. Simpson. 132 illustrations. 422pp. 5⅜ x 8. S273 Paperbound **$2.00**

DICTIONARY OF CONFORMAL REPRESENTATIONS, H. Kober. Laplace's equation in 2 dimensions solved in this unique book developed by the British Admiralty. Scores of geometrical forms & their transformations for electrical engineers, Joukowski aerofoil for aerodynamists, Schwartz-Christoffel transformations for hydrodynamics, transcendental functions. Contents classified—according to analytical functions describing transformation. Twin diagrams show curves of most transformations with corresponding regions. Glossary. Topological index. 447 diagrams. 244pp. 6⅛ x 9¼. S160 Paperbound **$2.00**

FREQUENCY CURVES AND CORRELATION, W. P. Elderton. 4th revised edition of a standard work covering classical statistics. It is practical in approach, and one of the books most frequently referred to for clear presentation of basic material. Partial contents. Frequency distributions. Method of moment. Pearson's frequency curves. Correlation. Theoretical distributions, spurious correlation. Correlation of characters not quantitatively measurable. Standard errors. Test of goodness of fit. The correlation ratio—contingency. Partial correlation. Corrections for moments, beta and gamma functions, etc. Key to terms, symbols. Bibliography. 25 examples in text. 40 useful tables. 16 figures. xi + 272pp. 5½ x 8½. Clothbound **$1.49**

HYDRODYNAMICS, H. Dryden, F. Murnaghan, Harry Bateman. Published by the National Research Council in 1932 this enormous volume offers a complete coverage of classical hydrodynamics. Encyclopedic in quality. Partial contents: physics of fluids, motion, turbulent flow, compressible fluids, motion in 1, 2, 3 dimensions; viscous fluids rotating, laminar motion, resistance of motion through viscous fluid, eddy viscosity, hydraulic flow in channels of various shapes, discharge of gases, flow past obstacles, etc. Bibliography of over 2,900 items. Indexes. 23 figures. 634pp. 5⅜ x 8. S303 Paperbound **$2.75**

HYDRODYNAMICS, A STUDY OF LOGIC, FACT, AND SIMILITUDE, Garrett Birkhoff. A stimulating application of pure mathematics to an applied problem. Emphasis is placed upon correlation of theory and deduction with experiment. It examines carefully recently discovered paradoxes, theory of modelling and dimensional analysis, paradox & error in flows and free boundary theory. The author derives the classical theory of virtual mass from homogeneous spaces, and applies group theory to fluid mechanics. Index. Bibliography. 20 figures, 3 plates. xiii + 186pp. 5⅜ x 8. S21 Clothbound **$3.50** S22 Paperbound **$1.85**

HYDRODYNAMICS, Horace Lamb. Internationally famous complete coverage of standard reference work on dynamics of liquids & gases. Fundamental theorems, equations, methods, solutions, background, for classical hydrodynamics. Chapters include Equations of Motion, Integration of Equations in Special Gases, Irrotational Motion, Motion of Liquid in 2 Dimensions, Motion of Solids through Liquid—Dynamical Theory, Vortex Motion, Tidal Waves, Surface Waves, Waves of Expansion, Viscosity, Rotating Masses of Liquids. Excellently planned, arranged; clear, lucid presentation. 6th enlarged, revised edition. Index. Over 900 footnotes, mostly bibliographical. 119 figures. xv + 738pp. 6⅛ x 9¼. S256 Paperbound **$2.95**

INTRODUCTION TO RELAXATION METHODS, F. S. Shaw. Fluid mechanics, design of electrical networks, forces in structural frameworks, stress distribution, buckling, etc. Solve linear simultaneous equations, linear ordinary differential equations, partial differential equations, Eigenvalue problems by relaxation methods. Detailed examples throughout. Special tables for dealing with awkwardly-shaped boundaries. Indexes. 253 diagrams. 72 tables. 400pp. 5⅜ x 8. S244 Paperbound **$2.45**

PARTIAL DIFFERENTIAL EQUATIONS OF MATHEMATICAL PHYSICS, A. G. Webster. A keystone work in the library of every mature physicist, engineer, researcher. Valuable sections on elasticity, compression theory, potential theory, theory of sound, heat conduction, wave propagation, vibration theory. Contents include: deduction of differential equations, vibrations, normal functions, Fourier's series, Cauchy's method, boundary problems, method of Riemann-Volterra. Spherical, cylindrical, ellipsoidal harmonics, applications, etc. 97 figures. vii + 440pp. 5⅜ x 8. S263 Paperbound **$1.98**

THE THEORY OF GROUPS AND QUANTUM MECHANICS, H. Weyl. Discussions of Schroedinger's wave equation, de Broglie's waves of a particle, Jordon-Hoelder theorem, Lie's continuous groups of transformations, Pauli exclusion principle, quantization of Maxwell-Dirac field equations, etc. symmetry permutation group, algebra of symmetric transformation, etc. 2nd revised edition. Unitary geometry, quantum theory, groups, application of groups to quantum mechanics, symmetry permutation group, algebra of symmetric transformation, etc. 2nd revised edition. Bibliography. Index. xxii + 422pp. 5⅜ x 8. S268 Clothbound **$4.50** S269 Paperbound **$1.95**

PARTIAL DIFFERENTIAL EQUATIONS OF MATHEMATICAL PHYSICS, Harry Bateman. Solution of boundary value problems by means of definite analytical expressions, with wide range of representative problems, full reference to contemporary literature, and new material by the author. Partial contents: classical equations, integral theorems of Green, Stokes; 2-dimensional problems; conformal representation; equations in 3 variables; polar coordinates; cylindrical, ellipsoidal, paraboloid, toroidal coordinates; non-linear equations, etc. "Must be in the hands of everyone interested in boundary value problems," BULLETIN, AM. MATH. SOC. Indexes. 450 bibliographic footnotes. 175 examples. 29 illustrations. xxii + 552pp. 6 x 9. S15 Clothbound **$4.95**

NUMERICAL SOLUTIONS OF DIFFERENTIAL EQUATIONS, H. Levy & E. A. Baggott. Comprehensive collection of methods for solving ordinary differential equations of first and higher order. All must pass 2 requirements: easy to grasp and practical, more rapid than school methods. Partial contents: graphical integration of differential equations, graphical methods for detailed solution. Numerical solution. Simultaneous equations and equations of 2nd and higher orders. "Should be in the hands of all in research in applied mathematics, teaching," NATURE. 21 figures. viii + 238pp. 5⅜ x 8. S168 Paperbound **$1.75**

ASYMPTOTIC EXPANSIONS, A. Erdélyi. The only modern work available in English, this is an unabridged reproduction of a monograph prepared for the Office of Naval Research. It discusses various procedures for asymptotic evaluation of integrals containing a large parameter and solutions of ordinary linear differential equations. Bibliography of 71 items. vi + 108pp. 5⅜ x 8. S318 Paperbound **$1.35**

THE FOURIER INTEGRAL AND CERTAIN OF ITS APPLICATIONS, Norbert Wiener. The only book length study of the Fourier integral as link between pure and applied math. An expansion of lectures given at Cambridge. Partial contents: Plancherel's theorem, general Tauberian theorem special Tauberian theorms, generalized harmonic analysis. Bibliography. viii + 201pp. 5⅜ x 8. S272 Clothbound **$3.95**

THE THEORY OF SOUND, Lord Rayleigh. Most vibrating systems likely to be encountered in practice can be tackled successfully by the methods set forth by the great Noble laureate, Lord Rayleigh. Complete coverage of experimental, mathematical aspects of sound theory. Partial contents Harmonic motions, vibrating systems in general, lateral vibrations of bars, curved plates or shells applications of Laplace's functions to acoustical problems, fluid friction, plane vortex-sheet vibrations of solid bodies, etc. This is the first inexpensive edition of this great reference and study work. Bibliography. Historical introduction by R. B. Lindsay. Total of 1040pp. 97 figures. 5⅜ x 8. S292, S293, Two volume set, paperbound **$4.00**

ANALYSIS & DESIGN OF EXPERIMENTS, H. B. Mann. Offers a method for grasping the analysis of variance and variance design within a short time. Partial contents: Chi-square distribution and analysis of variance distribution, matrices, quadratic forms, likelihood ratio tests and tests of linear hypotheses, power of analysis, Galois fields, non-orthogonal data, interblock estimates etc. 15pp. of useful tables. x + 195pp. 5 x 7⅜. S180 Paperbound **$1.45**

MATHEMATICAL ANALYSIS OF ELECTRICAL AND OPTICAL WAVE-MOTION, Harry Bateman. Written by one of this century's most distinguished mathematical physicists, this is a practical introduction to those developments of Maxwell's electromagnetic theory which are directly connected with the solution of the partial differential equation of wave motion. Methods of solving wave-equations, polar-cylindrical coordinates, diffraction, transformation of coordinates, homogeneous solutions electromagnetic fields with moving singularities, etc. Index. 168pp. 5⅜ x 8. S14 Paperbound **$1.60**

PHYSICAL PRINCIPLES OF THE QUANTUM THEORY, Werner Heisenberg. A Nobel laureate discusses quantum theory; Heisenberg's own work, Compton, Schroedinger, Wilson, Einstein, many others. Written for physicists, chemists who are not specialists in quantum theory, only elementary formulae are considered in the text; there is a mathematical appendix for specialists. Profound without sacrifice of clarity. Translated by C. Eckart, F. Hoyt. 18 figures. 192pp. 5⅜ x 8. S113 Paperbound **$1.25**

FOUNDATIONS OF NUCLEAR PHYSICS, edited by **R. T. Beyer.** 13 of the most important papers on nuclear physics reproduced in facsimile in the original languages of their authors: the papers most often cited in footnotes, bibliographies. Anderson, Curie, Joliot, Chadwick, Fermi, Lawrence Cockcroft, Hahn, Yukawa. Unparalleled Bibliography: 122 double-columned pages, over 4,000 articles, books, classified. 57 figures. 288pp. 6⅛ x 9¼. S19 Paperbound **$1.7**

SELECTED PAPERS ON NOISE AND STOCHASTIC PROCESS, edited by **Prof. Nelson Wax,** U. of Illinois. 6 basic papers for newcomers in the field, for those whose work involves noise characteristics. Chandrasekhar, Uhlenbeck & Ornstein, Uhlenbeck & Ming, Rice, Doob. Included is Kac' Chauvenet-Prize winning Random Walk. Extensive bibliography lists 200 articles; up through 1953 21 figures. 337pp. 6⅛ x 9¼. S262 Paperbound **$2.2**

THERMODYNAMICS, Enrico Fermi. Unabridged reproduction of 1937 edition. Elementary in treatment; remarkable for clarity, organization. Requires no knowledge of advanced math beyond calculus, only familiarity with fundamentals of thermometry, calorimetry. Partial Contents Thermodynamic systems; First & Second laws of thermodynamics; Entropy; Thermodynamic potentials: phase rule, reversible electric cell; Gaseous reactions: Van't Hoff reaction box, principle of LeChatelier; Thermodynamics of dilute solutions:: osmotic & vapor pressure, boiling & freezing points; Entropy constant. Index. 25 problems. 24 illustrations. x + 160pp. 5⅜ x 8. S361 Paperbound **$1.7**

AN INTRODUCTION TO THE STUDY OF STELLAR STRUCTURE, Subrahmanyan Chandrasekhar. Outstanding treatise on stellar dynamics by one of world's greatest astrophysicists. Uses classical & modern math methods to examine relationship between loss of energy, the mass, and radius of stars in a steady state. Discusses thermodynamic laws from Caratheodory's axiomatic standpoint; adiabatic, polytropic laws; work of Ritter, Emden, Kelvin, others; Stroemgren envelopes as starter for theory of gaseous stars; Gibbs statistical mechanics (quantum, degenerate stellar configurations & theory of white dwarfs, etc. "Highest level of scientific merit," BULLETIN, AMER. MATH. SOC. Bibliography. Appendixes. Index. 33 figures. 509pp. 5⅜ x 8. S413 Paperbound **$2.7**

APPLIED OPTICS AND OPTICAL DESIGN, A. E. Conrady. Thorough, systematic presentation of physical & mathematical aspects, limited mostly to "real optics." Stresses practical problem of maximum aberration permissible without affecting performance. All ordinary ray tracing methods; complete theory primary aberrations, enough higher aberration to design telescopes, low-powered microscopes, photographic equipment. Covers fundamental equations, extra-axial image points, transverse chromatic aberration, angular magnification, aplanatic optical systems, bending of lenses, oblique pencils, tolerances, secondary spectrum, spherical aberration (angular, longitudinal, transverse, zonal), thin lenses, dozens of similar topics. Index. Tables of functions of N. Over 150 diagrams. x + 518pp. 6⅛ x 9¼. S366 Paperbound **$2.95**

SPACE-TIME-MATTER, Hermann Weyl. "The standard treatise on the general theory of relativity," Nature), written by a world-renowned scientists, provides a deep clear discussion of the logical coherence of the general theory, with introduction to all the mathematical tools needed: Maxwell, analytical geometry, non-Euclidean geometry, tensor calculus, etc. Basis is classical space-time, before absorption of relativity. Partial contents: Euclidean space, mathematical form, metrical continuum, relativity of time and space, general theory. 15 diagrams. Bibliography. New preface for this edition. xviii + 330pp. 5⅜ x 8. S267 Paperbound **$1.75**

RAYLEIGH'S PRINCIPLE AND ITS APPLICATION TO ENGINEERING, G. Temple & W. Bickley. Rayleigh's principle developed to provide upper and lower estimates of true value of fundamental period of a vibrating system, or condition of stability of elastic systems. Illustrative examples; rigorous proofs in special chapters. Partial contents: Energy method of discussing vibrations, stability. Perturbation theory, whirling of uniform shafts. Criteria of elastic stability. Application of energy method. Vibrating system. Proof, accuracy, successive approximations, application of Rayleigh's principle. Synthetic theorems. Numerical, graphical methods. Equilibrium configurations, Ritz's method. Bibliography. Index. 22 figures. ix + 156pp. 5⅜ x8. S307 Paperbound **$1.50**

PHYSICS, ENGINEERING

THEORY OF VIBRATIONS, N. W. McLachlan. Based on an exceptionally successful graduate course given at Brown University, this discusses linear systems having 1 degree of freedom, forced vibrations of simple linear systems, vibration of flexible strings, transverse vibrations of bars and tubes, transverse vibration of circular plate, sound waves of finite amplitude, etc. Index. 99 diagrams. 160pp. 5⅜ x 8. S190 Paperbound **$1.35**

WAVE PROPAGATION IN PERIODIC STRUCTURES, L. Brillouin. A general method and application to different problems: pure physics, such as scattering of X-rays of crystals, thermal vibration in crystal lattices, electronic motion in metals; and also problems of electrical engineering. Partial contents: elastic waves in 1-dimensional lattices of point masses. Propagation of waves along 1-dimensional lattices. Energy flow. 2 dimensional, 3 dimensional lattices. Mathieu's equation. Matrices and propagation of waves along an electric line. Continuous electric lines. 131 illustrations. Bibliography. Index. xii + 253pp. 5⅜ x 8. S34 Paperbound **$1.85**

THE ELECTROMAGNETIC FIELD, Max Mason & Warren Weaver. Used constantly by graduate engineers. Vector methods exclusively: detailed treatment of electrostatics, expansion methods, with tables converting any quantity into absolute electromagnetic, absolute electrostatic, practical units. Discrete charges, ponderable bodies, Maxwell field equations, etc. Introduction. Indexes. 416pp. 5⅜ x 8. S185 Paperbound **$2.00**

APPLIED HYDRO- AND AEROMECHANICS by L. Prandtl and O. G. Tietjens. Presents, for the most part, methods which will be valuable to engineers. Covers flow in pipes, boundary layers, airfoil theory, entry conditions, turbulent flow in pipes and the boundary layer, determining drag from measurements of pressure and velocity, etc. "Will be welcomed by all students of aerodynamics," NATURE. Unabridged, unaltered. Index. 226 figures. 28 photographic plates illustrating flow patterns. xvi + 311pp. 5⅜ x 8. S375 Paperbound **$1.85**

FUNDAMENTALS OF HYDRO- AND AEROMECHANICS by L. Prandtl and O. G. Tietjens. The well-known standard work based upon Prandtl's unique insights and including original contributions of Tietjens. Wherever possible, hydrodynamic theory is referred to practical considerations in hydraulics with the view of unifying theory and experience through fundamental laws. Presentation is exceedingly clear and, though primarily physical, proofs are rigorous and use vector analysis to a considerable extent. Translated by L. Rosenhead. 186 figures. Index. xvi + 270pp. 5⅜ x 8. S374 Paperbound **$1.85**

DYNAMICS OF A SYSTEM OF RIGID BODIES (Advanced Section), E. J. Routh. Revised 6th edition of a classic reference aid. Much of its material remains unique. Partial contents: moving axes, relative motion, oscillations about equilibrium, motion. Motion of a body under no forces, many forces. Nature of motion given by linear equations and conditions of stability. Free, forced vibrations, constants of integration, calculus of finite differences, variations, procession and nutation, motion of the moon, motion of string, chain, membranes. 64 figures. 498pp. 5⅜ x 8. S229 Paperbound **$2.35**

MECHANICS OF THE GYROSCOPE, THE DYNAMICS OF ROTATION, R. F. Deimel, Professor of Mechanical Engineering at Stevens Institute of Technology. Elementary general treatment of dynamics of rotation, with special application of gyroscopic phenomena. No knowledge of vectors needed. Velocity of a moving curve, acceleration to a point, general equations of motion, gyroscopic horizon, free gyro, motion of discs, the dammed gyro, 103 similar topics. Exercises. 75 figures. 208pp. 5⅜ x 8. S66 Paperbound **$1.65**

TABLES FOR THE DESIGN OF FACTORIAL EXPERIMENTS, Tosio Kitagawa and Michiwo Mitome. An invaluable aid for all applied mathematicians, physicists, chemists and biologists, this book contains tables for the design of factorial experiments. It covers Latin squares and cubes, factorial design, fractional replication in factorial design, factorial designs with split-plot confounding, factorial designs confounded in quasi-Latin squares, lattice designs, balanced incomplete block designs, and Youden's squares. New revised corrected edition, with explanatory notes. vii + 253pp. 7⅛ x 10. **S437 Clothbound $8.00**

NUMERICAL INTEGRATION OF DIFFERENTIAL EQUATIONS, Bennett, Milne & Bateman. Unabridged republication of original monograph prepared for National Research Council. New methods of integration of differential equations developed by 3 leading mathematicians: THE INTERPOLATIONAL POLYNOMIAL and SUCCESSIVE APPROXIMATIONS by A. A. Bennett; STEP-BY-STEP METHODS OF INTEGRATION by W. W. Milne; METHODS FOR PARTIAL DIFFERENTIAL EQUATIONS by H. Bateman. Methods for partial differential equations, transition from difference equations to differential equations, solution of differential equations to non-integral values of a parameter will interest mathematicians and physicists. 288 footnotes, mostly bibliographic; 235-item classified bibliography. 108pp. 5⅜ x 8. **S305 Paperbound $1.35**

DESIGN AND USE OF INSTRUMENTS AND ACCURATE MECHANISM, T. N. Whitehead. For the instrument designer, engineer; how to combine necessary mathematical abstractions with independent observation of actual facts. Partial contents: instruments & their parts, theory of errors, systematic errors, probability, short period errors, erratic errors, design precision, kinematic semikinematic design, stiffness, planning of an instrument, human factor, etc. Index. 85 photos, diagrams. xii + 288pp. 5⅜ x 8. **S270 Paperbound $1.95**

CHEMISTRY AND PHYSICAL CHEMISTRY

KINETIC THEORY OF LIQUIDS, J. Frenkel. Regarding the kinetic theory of liquids as a generalization and extension of the theory of solid bodies, this volume covers all types of arrangements of solids, thermal displacements of atoms, interstitial atoms and ions, orientational and rotational motion of molecules, and transition between states of matter. Mathematical theory is developed close to the physical subject matter. 216 bibliographical footnotes. 55 figures. xi + 485pp. 5⅜ x 8.
S94 Clothbound $3.95
S95 Paperbound $2.45

THE PHASE RULE AND ITS APPLICATION, Alexander Findlay. Covering chemical phenomena of 1, 2, 3, 4, and multiple component systems, this "standard work on the subject" (NATURE, London), has been completely revised and brought up to date by A. N. Campbell and N. O. Smith. Brand new material has been added on such matters as binary, tertiary liquid equilibria, solid solutions in ternary systems, quinary systems of salts and water. Completely revised to triangular coordinates in ternary systems, clarified graphic representation, solid models, etc. 9th revised edition. Author, subject indexes. 236 figures. 506 footnotes, mostly bibliographic. xii + 494pp. 5⅜ x 8. **S92 Paperbound $2.45**

DYNAMICAL THEORY OF GASES, James Jeans. Divided into mathematical and physical chapters for the convenience of those not expert in mathematics, this volume discusses the mathematical theory of gas in a steady state, thermodynamics, Boltzmann and Maxwell, kinetic theory, quantum theory, exponentials, etc. 4th enlarged edition, with new material on quantum theory, quantum dynamics, etc. Indexes. 28 figures. 444pp. 6⅛ x 9¼. **S136 Paperbound $2.45**

POLAR MOLECULES, Pieter Debye. This work by Nobel laureate Debye offers a complete guide to fundamental electrostatic field relations, polarizability, molecular structure. Partial contents: electric intensity, displacement and force, polarization by orientation, molar polarization and molar refraction, halogen-hydrides, polar liquids, ionic saturation, dielectric constant, etc. Special chapter considers quantum theory. Indexed. 172pp. 5⅜ x 8. **S63 Clothbound $3.50**
S64 Paperbound $1.50

TREATISE ON THERMODYNAMICS, Max Planck. Based on Planck's original papers this offers a uniform point of view for the entire field and has been used as an introduction for students who have studied elementary chemistry, physics, and calculus. Rejecting the earlier approaches of Helmholtz and Maxwell, the author makes no assumptions regarding the nature of heat, but begins with a few empirical facts, and from these deduces new physical and chemical laws. 3rd English edition of this standard text by a Nobel laureate. xvi + 297pp. 5⅜ x 8.
S219 Paperbound $1.75

ATOMIC SPECTRA AND ATOMIC STRUCTURE, G. Herzberg. Excellent general survey for chemists, physicists specializing in other fields. Partial contents: simplest line spectra and elements of atomic theory, multiple structure of line spectra and electron spin, building-up principle and periodic system of elements, finer details of atomic spectra, hyperfine structure of spectral lines, some experimental results and applications. Bibliography of 159 items. 80 figures. 20 tables. Index. xiii + 257pp. 5⅜ x 8. **S115 Paperbound $1.95**

EARTH SCIENCES

THE EVOLUTION OF THE IGNEOUS ROCKS, N. L. Bowen. Invaluable serious introduction applies techniques of physics and chemistry to explain igneous rocks diversity in terms of chemical composition and fractional crystallization. Discusses liquid immiscibility in silicate magmas, crystal sorting, liquid lines of descent, fractional resorption of complex minerals, petrogenesis, etc. Of prime importance to geologists & mining engineers, also to physicists, chemists working with high temperatures and pressures. "Most important," TIMES, London. 3 indexes. 263 bibliographic notes. 82 figures. xviii + 334pp. 5⅜ x 8. **S311 Paperbound $1.85**

EOGRAPHICAL ESSAYS, William Morris Davis. Modern geography & geomorphology rests on e fundamental work of this scientist. 26 famous essays presenting most important theories, eld researches. Partial contents: Geographical Cycle, Plains of Marine and Subaerial Denuda- on, The Peneplain, Rivers and Valleys of Pennsylvania, Outline of Cape Cod, Sculpture of ountains by Glaciers, etc. "Long the leader and guide," ECONOMIC GEOGRAPHY. "Part of e very texture of geography . . . models of clear thought," GEOGRAPHIC REVIEW. Index. 0 figures. vi + 777pp. 5⅜ x 8. S383 Paperbound **$2.95**

TERNAL CONSTITUTION OF THE EARTH, edited by **Beno Gutenberg.** Completely revised, ought up-to-date, reset. Prepared for the National Research Council this is a complete & orough coverage of such topics as earth origins, continent formation, nature & behavior of e earth's core, petrology of the crust, cooling forces in the core, seismic & earthquake material, avity, elastic constants, strain characteristics and similar topics. "One is filled with admira- on . . . a high standard . . . there is no reader who will not learn something from this ook," London, Edinburgh, Dublin, Philosophic Magazine. Largest bibliography in print: 1127 assified items. Indexes. Tables of constants. 43 diagrams. 439pp. 6⅛ x 9¼. S414 Paperbound **$2.45**

IE BIRTH AND DEVELOPMENT OF THE GEOLOGICAL SCIENCES, F. D. Adams. Most thorough story of the earth sciences ever written. Geological thought from earliest times to the end the 19th century, covering over 300 early thinkers & systems: fossils & their explanation, lcanists vs. neptunists, figured stones & paleontology, generation of stones, dozens of similar pics. 91 illustrations, including medieval, renaissance woodcuts, etc. Index. 632 footnotes, ostly bibliographical. 511pp. 5⅜ x 8. T5 Paperbound **$2.00**

'DROLOGY, edited by **Oscar E. Meinzer.** Prepared for the National Research Council. Detailed mplete reference library on precipitation, evaporation, snow, snow surveying, glaciers, lakes, filtration, soil moisture, ground water, runoff, drought, physical changes produced by water, drology of limestone terranes, etc. Practical in application, especially valuable for engineers. experts have created "the most up-to-date, most complete treatment of the subject," AM. SSOC. OF PETROLEUM GEOLOGISTS. Bibliography. Index. 165 illustrations. xi + 712pp. ⅛ x 9¼ S191 Paperbound **$2.95**

E RE METALLICA, Georgius Agricola. 400-year old classic translated, annotated by former esident Herbert Hoover. The first scientific study of mineralogy and mining, for over 200 ars after its appearance in 1556, it was the standard treatise. 12 books, exhaustively anno- ted, discuss the history of mining, selection of sites, types of deposits, making pits, shafts, ntilating, pumps, crushing machinery; assaying, smelting, refining metals; also salt, alum, re, glass making. Definitive edition, with all 289 16th century woodcuts of the original. oliographical, historical introductions, bibliography, survey of ancient authors. Indexes. A scinating book for anyone interested in art, history of science, geology, etc. DELUXE EDITION. 9 illustrations. 672pp. 6¾ x 10¾. Library cloth. S6 Clothbound **$10.00**

ANIUM PROSPECTING, H. L. Barnes. For immediate practical use, professional geologists nsiders uranium ores, geological occurrences, field conditions, all aspects of highly profitable cupation. Index. Bibliography. x +117pp. 5⅜ x 8. T309 Paperbound **$1.00**

BIOLOGICAL SCIENCES

IE BIOLOGY OF THE AMPHIBIA, G. K. Noble, Late Curator of Herpetology at the Am. Mus. Nat. Hist. Probably the most used text on amphibia, unmatched in comprehensiveness, arity, detail. 19 chapters plus 85-page supplement cover development; heredity; life history; aptation; sex, integument, respiratory, circulatory, digestive, muscular, nervous systems; stinct, intelligence habits environment economic value, relationships, classification, etc. "Nothing mparable to it," C. H. Pope, Curator of Amphibia, Chicago Mus. of Nat. Hist. 1047 biblio- aphic references. 174 illustrations. 600pp. 5⅜ x 8. S206 Paperbound **$2.98**

IE BIOLOGY OF THE LABORATORY MOUSE, edited by **G. D. Snell.** 1st prepared in 1941 by e staff of the Roscoe B. Jackson Memorial laboratory, this is still the standard treatise on the ouse, assembling an enormous amount of material for which otherwise you would spend hours research. Embryology, reproduction, histology, spontaneous neoplasms, gene & chromosomes utations, genetics of spontaneous tumor formation, genetics of tumor formation, inbred, hybrid imals, parasites, infectious diseases, care & recording. Classified bibliography of 1122 items. '2 figures, including 128 photos. ix + 497pp. 6⅛ x 9¼. S248 Clothbound **$6.00**

HAVIOR AND SOCIAL LIFE OF THE HONEYBEE, Ronald Ribbands. Oustanding scientific study; compendium of practically everything known about social life of the honeybee. Stresses be- vior of individual bees in field, hive. Extends von Frisch's experiments on communication nong bees. Covers perception of temperature, gravity, distance, vibration; sound production; ands; structural differences; wax production, temperature regulation; recognition communication; ifting, mating behavior, other highly interesting topics. Bibliography of 690 references. Indexes. 7 diagrams, graphs, sections of bee anatomy, fine photographs. 352pp. S410 Clothbound **$4.50**

EMENTS OF MATHEMATICAL BIOLOGY, A. J. Lotka. A pioneer classic, the first major attempt apply modern mathematical techniques on a large scale to phenomena of biology, biochem- ry, psychology, ecology, similar life sciences. Partial Contents: Statistical meaning of irre- rsibility; Evolution as redistribution; Equations of kinetics of evolving systems; Chemical, inter- ecies equilibrium; parameters of state; Energy transformers of nature, etc. Can be read with ofit even by those having no advanced math; unsurpassed as study-reference. Formerly titled EMENTS OF PHYSICAL BIOLOGY. 72 figures. xxx + 460pp. 5⅜ x 8. S346 Paperbound **$2.45**

THE ORIGIN OF LIFE, A. I. Oparin. A classic of biology. This is the first modern statement of the theory of gradual evolution of life from nitrocarbon compounds. A brand-new evaluation of Oparin's theory in light of later research, by Dr. S. Margulis, University of Nebraska. xxv + 270pp. 5⅜ x 8.   S213 Paperbound **$1.75**

THE TRAVELS OF WILLIAM BARTRAM, edited by **Mark Van Doren.** This famous source-book of American anthropology, natural history, geography is the record kept by Bartram in the 1770's on travels through the wilderness of Florida, Georgia, the Carolinas. Containing accurate and beautiful descriptions of Indians, settlers, fauna, flora, it is one of the finest pieces of Americana ever written. Introduction by Mark Van Doren. 13 original illustrations. Index. 448pp. 5⅜ x 8.   T13 Paperbound **$2.00**

A SHORT HISTORY OF ANATOMY AND PHYSIOLOGY FROM THE GREEKS TO HARVEY, Charles Singer. Corrected edition of THE EVOLUTION OF ANATOMY, classic work tracing evolution of anatomy and physiology from prescientific times through Greek & Roman periods, Dark Ages, Renaissance, to age of Harvey and beginning of modern concepts. Centered on individuals, movements, periods that definitely advanced anatomical knowledge: Plato, Diocles, Aristotle, Theophrastus, Herophilus, Erasistratus, the Alexandrians, Galen, Mondino, da Vinci, Linacre, Harvey, others. Special section on Vesalius; Vesalian atlas of nudes, skeletons, muscle tabulae. Index of names. 20 plates, 270 extremely interesting illustrations of ancient, medieval, renaissance, oriental origin. xii + 209pp. 5⅜ x 8.   T389 Paperbound **$1.75**

NEW BOOKS

LES MÉTHODES NOUVELLES DE LA MÉCANIQUE CÉLESTE by H. Poincaré. Complete text (in French) of one of Poincaré's most important works. Revolutionized celestial mechanics: first use of integral invariants, first major application of linear differential equations, study of periodic orbits, lunar motion and Jupiter's satellites, three body problem, and many other important topics. "Started a new era . . . so extremely modern that even today few have mastered his weapons," E. T. Bell. Three volumes; 1282pp. 6⅛ x 9¼.

Vol. 1. S401 Paperbound **$2.75**
Vol. 2. S402 Paperbound **$2.75**
Vol. 3. S403 Paperbound **$2.75**

APPLICATIONS OF TENSOR ANALYSIS by A. J. McConnell. (Formerly, APPLICATIONS OF THE ABSOLUTE DIFFERENTIAL CALCULUS). An excellent text for understanding the application of tensor methods to familiar subjects such as: dynamics, electricity, elasticity, and hydrodynamics. It explains the fundamental ideas and notation of tensor theory, the geometrical treatment of tensor algebra, the theory of differentiation of tensors, and includes a wealth of practice material. Bibliography. Index. 43 illustrations. 685 problems. xii + 381pp.

S373 Paperbound **$1.85**

BRIDGES AND THEIR BUILDERS, David B. Steinman and Sara Ruth Watson. Engineers, historians and everyone who has ever been fascinated by great spans will find this book an endless source of information and interest. Dr. Steinman, the recent recipient of the Louis Levy Medal, is one of the great bridge architects and engineers of all time, and his analysis of the great bridges of all history is both authoritative and easily followed. Greek and Roman bridges, medieval bridges, oriental bridges, modern works such as the Brooklyn Bridge and the Golden Gate Bridge (and many others) are described in terms of history, constructional principles, artistry and function. All in all this book is the most comprehensive and accurate semipopular history of bridges in print in English. New greatly revised enlarged edition. 23 photographs, 26 line drawings. Index. xvii + 401pp. 5⅜ x 8.   T431 Paperbound **$1.95**

MATHEMATICS IN ACTION, O. G. Sutton. Excellent middle-level exposition of application of advanced mathematics to the study of the universe. The author demonstrates how mathematic is applied in ballistics, theory of computing machines, waves and wavelike phenomena, theory of fluid flow, meterological problems, statistics, flight, and similar phenomena. No knowledge of advanced mathematics is necessary to follow the author's presentation. Differential equations, Fourier series, group concepts, eigen functions, Planck's constant, airfoil theory and similar topics are explained so clearly in everyday language that almost anyone can derive benefit from reading this book. 2nd edition. Index. 88 figures. viii + 236pp. 5⅜ x 8.

T450 Clothbound **$3.50**

MATHEMATICAL FOUNDATIONS OF INFORMATION THEORY by A. I. Khinchin. For the first time, mathematicians, statisticians, physicists, cyberneticists and communications engineers are offered a complete and exact introduction to this relatively young field. Entropy as a measure of a finite "scheme," applications to coding theory, study of sources, channels and codes, detailed proofs of both Shannon theorems for any ergodic source and any stationary channel with finite memory, and much more is covered. Bibliography. vii + 120pp. 5⅜ x 8.

S434 Paperbound **$1.35**